CHAUCER

THE PROLOGUE, THE KNIGHTES TALE
THE NONNE PREESTES TALE

MORRIS

CHAUCER

THE PROLOGUE, THE KNIGHTES TALE
THE NONNE PREESTES TALE

FROM

THE CANTERBURY TALES

EDITED BY

REV. RICHARD MORRIS, LL.D.

Author of 'Historical Outlines of English Accidence'
Editor of Hampole's 'Pricke of Conscience,' 'Early English Alliterative Poems'
'The Story of Genesis and Exodus,' 'The Ayenbite of Inwyt,' 'Old English Homilies,' &c.
Member of the Council of the Philological Society

A NEW EDITION

WITH COLLATIONS AND ADDITIONAL NOTES

BY THE

REV. WALTER W. SKEAT, Litt.D.

'O maister dere and fader reverent,
  My maister Chaucers, flour of eloquence!'
        HOCCLEVE, *De Regim. Princ.* st. 281.

OXFORD
AT THE CLARENDON PRESS

Oxford University Press, Amen House, London E.C.4.

GLASGOW NEW YORK TORONTO MELBOURNE WELLINGTON
BOMBAY CALCUTTA MADRAS CAPE TOWN

Geoffrey Cumberlege, Publisher to the University

IMPRESSION OF 1949
FIRST EDITION 1867

PRINTED IN GREAT BRITAIN

INTRODUCTION.

CHAUCER was, like Spenser, Ben Jonson, Milton, etc., a Londoner born and bred[a]. In his Release of his right to his father's former house in Thames-street, London, to one Henry Herbury, the poet describes himself as son of John Chaucer, citizen and vintner of London (City Hustings Roll, 110, 5 Ric. II, membrane 2). His mother was no doubt Agnes Chaucer, who is described in another Roll as the wife of John Chaucer in 1349. Chaucer's grandfather was Robert Chaucer, of Ipswich and London, who married a widow, Maria Heyroun, with a son Thomas Heyroun. (Her third husband was Richard Chaucer, a London vintner.) This Thomas Heyroun left his land to be sold by his brother (that is, brother of the half-blood) John Chaucer, the poet's father. As John Chaucer's house in Thames-street was by Walbrook—a stream flowing from Finsbury Moor—it must have been near the spot where the South Eastern Railway (from Cannonstreet) now crosses Thames-street. There, on Thames bank, the poet spent his earliest days; there for twelve and a half years later, 1374–1386, he did his daily work in the Custom House, after his marriage and settling down in his rooms at Aldgate. Near there he must have gone to school. Out of school and after play, the boy would probably sometimes help his father in his wineshop and cellar, and fill citizens' pots with the wine they required.

Young men in Chaucer's time finished their education either at the University, or in some nobleman's house as pages. Chaucer's father (John) was in attendance on Edward III and his queen Philippa in their expedition to Flanders and Cologne in 1338 (Rymer, v. 51) ; and to the father's connection with the court, the son no doubt owed his training and first appointment.

The first records of the name of Geoffrey Chaucer are on two parchment leaves, fragments of a Household Account,

---

[a] The Testament of Love, which names London as the birthplace of its writer, contains internal evidence that it was not the poet's work.

for the years 1356 to 1359, of Elizabeth, wife of Prince Lionel, third son of Edward III ; and they contain, besides other things, entries of —(1) in April 1357, 'An entire suit of clothes, consisting of a paltock' (or short cloak), 'a pair of red and black breeches, with shoes, provided for Geoffrey Chaucer [b] ;' (2) on May 20, 1357, an article of dress, of which the name is lost by a defect in the leaf, purchased for Geoffrey Chaucer in London ; (3) in December of the same year, a donation of 2s. 6d. to Geoffrey Chaucer, for 'necessaries.' That this Geoffrey Chaucer was the poet is almost certain. But the next and very important record as to Chaucer is quite certain. It heads his own statement, in a deposition made by him at Westminster in October 1386, at the famous trial between Richard Lord Scrope and Sir Robert Grosvenor. The Council-clerk then entered Chaucer— no doubt by the poet's own authority—as forty years of age and upwards, and as having borne arms for twenty-seven years.

If then we take Chaucer's 'forty years and upwards' as forty-six, we fix the date of his birth at 1340 ; and this would make him seventeen years old when he was in Prince Lionel's household, probably as a page, as the sums paid for his dress, and given to him, are a good deal lower than those allotted to other members of the household. This date would also make Chaucer nineteen when, doubtless in the retinue of Prince Lionel, he joined Edward the Third's army, which invaded France in the autumn of 1359, and was taken prisoner in that country, as he himself informs us. (Against this date of 1340 as that of the poet's birth used to be set the traditional date of 1328. But the Petition of Geffrey Stace in 1328—see *Rolls of Parliament*, ii. 14—expressly states that John Chaucer (the poet's father, whom Stace and his confederates had forcibly carried off from London in December 1324) was then still unmarried, '*unkore dismarie*,' and living with his mother Maria, and his stepfather Richard Chaucer. Moreover, the Coram-Rege Roll of Trinity Term, 5 Edward III, A.D. 1331, shows no plea by Geffrey Stace that John Chaucer

---

[b] At a cost of 7s. (of which the paltock was 4s.), equal to about 5l. of our present money.

had then married the Joan de Esthalle whom they tried to marry him to in 1324.) Chaucer's position in Prince Lionel's household would, says Mr. Bond, have given him 'the benefit of society of the highest refinement, in personal attendance on a young and spirited prince of the blood. He would have had his imagination fed by scenes of the most brilliant court festivities [c], rendered more imposing by the splendid triumphs with which they were connected; and he would have had the advantage of royal patrons in the early exercise of his genius.' He would have been helped in 'perfecting that gift which so transcendently distinguishes him from the versifiers of his time—refinement of expression in his own language'—a gift which his first poems show as well as his last. It is quite certain that Chaucer was a diligent student and a man of the most extensive learning. 'The acquaintance he possessed with the classics, with divinity, with astronomy, with so much as was then known of chemistry, and indeed with every other branch of the scholastic learning of the age, proves that his education had been particularly attended to [d].'

Chaucer's military career commenced, as we have seen, in the year 1359, at which time he must have joined Edward the Third's army, which invaded France in the beginning of November of that year. After ineffectually besieging Rheims the English army laid siege to Paris (1360), when at length, suffering from famine and fatigue, Edward made peace at Bretigny near Chartres. This treaty, called the 'Great Peace,' was ratified in the following October, and King John was set at liberty. In this expedition Chaucer was made prisoner, and on March 1, 1360, Edward III paid 16*l.* towards Chaucer's ransom; 13*s.* 4*d.* less than he gave another man for a horse.

---

[c] That most splendid entertainment given by Edward III (in 1358) to the royal personages then in England—including the King of France, the Queen of Scotland, the King of Cyprus, and the sister of the captive King of France, and Edward's own mother, the almost forgotten Queen Isabella —at what was ever after called 'the Great Feast of St. George.' Chaucer was probably also present, with Prince Lionel, at the wedding of John of Gaunt and Lady Blanche of Lancaster, at Reading, and at the famous joustings subsequently held at London in honour of the event.

[d] Life of Chaucer by Sir H. Nicolas; see Chaucer, ed. Morris, i. 4.

We have no means of ascertaining how he spent the next six years of his life, except from hints in our official records[e] and the poet's own works. In 1367 the first notice of the poet occurs on the Issue Rolls of the Exchequer, when a pension of 20 marks[f] for life was granted by the king to Chaucer as one of the 'valets of the king's chamber'—or, as the office was sometimes called, 'valet of the king's household'—in consideration of former and future services. This pension for 'former' services as well as future, leaves little doubt that Chaucer entered the king's household soon after his return to England. In this service the poet, then probably twenty-one, seems to have fallen desperately and hopelessly in love, probably with a lady above him in rank, who rejected him. His earliest original poem, his Compleynte to Pite (pity), which may have been written about 1367, after his rejection by his lady-love, tells us that for many years he dared not speak his feelings towards her, and when at last he did so, he found Pity dead in her heart; but still he pleads pathetically with her for her love, and declares that, though she still refuses it, and he desires only death, he will love her alone till that death comes[g]. See also his *Minor Poems*, ed. Skeat, pp. 213-7.

---

[e] Issue Rolls of the Exchequer and the Tower Rolls. The details here are from Sir H. Nicolas' Life of Chaucer, prefixed to Chaucer's poetical works in the Aldine series of the Poets.

[f] A mark was 13s. 4d. of our money, but the buying power of money was at least ten times greater than at present. In 1350 the average price of a horse was 18s. 4d.; of an ox 1l. 4s. 6d.; of a cow 17s. 2d.; of a sheep 2s. 6d.; of a goose 9d.; of a hen 2d.; of a day's labour in husbandry 3d. In Oxford, in 1310, wheat was 10s. a quarter; in December 7s. 8d.; and in October, 1311, 4s. 10d.

[g] The old supposition that the 'Philippa' whom Chaucer married was the daughter of Sir Paon de Roet (a native of Hainault and King of Arms of Guienne) and sister to Katherine, widow of Sir Hugh Swynford, successively governess, mistress, and wife to John of Gaunt, Duke of Lancaster, was founded on heraldic grounds. The Roet arms were adopted by Thomas Chaucer. Then Thomas Chaucer was made (without the slightest evidence) Geoffrey's son, and Philippa Roet was then made Geoffrey's wife. Chaucer's wife Philippa was one of the ladies in attendance on Queen Philippa, and in 1366 a pension of 10 marks was granted to her. After the death of the queen she appears to have been attached to the court of Constance of Castile, second wife of John of Gaunt.

During the years 1368 and 1369, Chaucer was in London, and received his pension in person.

In 1369 (Aug. 15) the death of Queen Philippa took place, and in less than a month later, Blanche, the wife of John of Gaunt, died, at the age of twenty-nine. Chaucer did honour to the memory of his patron's wife in a funeral poem entitled 'The Deth of Blaunche the Duchesse [h].' And in this poem he tells us, though sadly, that his own hopeless eight years' love is cured, 'what will not be, must needs be left;' or, as he says in Troilus,

> 'Criseyde loveth the sone of Tydeus,
> And Troilus mot wepe in cares colde.
> Swich is this world, whoso kan it biholde!
> In ech estat is litil hertes reste!
> God leve [i] us for to take it for the beste!'
>
>   (Bk. V. st. ccli. ll. 1760–4.)

Chaucer's lines in the Blaunche (35–42) about his hopeless love, which are referred to above, are in answer to the question why he cannot sleep at night.

> 'Trewely, as I gesse,
> I holde hit [moot] be a siknesse
> That I have suffred this eight yere;
> And yet my boote is never the nere;
> For there is phisicien but oon
> That may me hele. But that is doon.
> Passe we over until eft;
> That wil not be, moot nede be left.'

It was no good crying for the moon ; and although the early shadow of disappointed love was still thrown over Chaucer's life, and made him tell of Troilus' sorrow, and sing the Complaint of Mars for his lost Venus, yet our poet was henceforth to work himself out into the freshness and brightness that still draw men to him as to spring sunshine.

---

[h]   'And goodë fairë whyte she heet (was called),
            That was my lady namë right.
            She was bothë fair and bright,
            She haddë not hir namë wrong.'
                    (Deth of Blaunche the Duchesse, ll. 948–951.)

[i] = allow, grant.

In the course of the next ten years (1370–1380) the poet was attached to the court, and employed in no less than seven diplomatic services. In 1370 he was abroad in the king's service, and received letters of protection, to be in force from June till Michaelmas. Two years after this (Nov. 12, 1372) Chaucer was joined in a commission with two citizens of Genoa to treat with the doge, citizens, and merchants of Genoa, for the choice of an English port where the Genoese might form a commercial establishment. He appears to have left England before the end of the year, having on the 1st of December received the sum of 66l. 13s. 4d. in aid of his expenses. He remained in Italy nearly twelve months, and went on the king's service to Florence as well as to Genoa. His return to England must have taken place before the 22nd of Nov. 1373, as on this day he received his pension in person[k].

This was Chaucer's first important mission. It was no doubt skilfully executed, and gave entire satisfaction to the king, who on the 23rd of April, 1374, on the celebration of the feast of St. George, at Windsor, made him a grant of a pitcher of wine daily, to be received in the Port of London from the hands of the king's butler[l]. On the 10th of May the Corporation of London granted Chaucer a lease for his life of the dwelling-house above the gate of Aldgate, with the rooms built over, and a certain cellar beneath, on condition that he kept these buildings in good

---

[k] In this embassy Chaucer is supposed to have made acquaintanceship with Petrarch, who was at Arqua, two miles from Padua, in 1373, from January till September, and to have learned from him the tale of the patient Griselda. But it is not certain that the old biographers of Chaucer are to be trusted in this matter. If the date of the later editions of Petrarch's version can be trusted (there is no date in Ulrich Tell's first edition), Petrarch did not translate this tale from Boccaccio's Decameron into Latin until the end of Sept. 1373, after Chaucer's return [but some copies give the date June 8, 1373]. And though it is the Clerk of Oxenford, and not Chaucer, that asserts that he learned the tale of 'a worthy clerk' at Padua, 'Fraunces Petrarch, the laureate poete,' yet there can be no question that Chaucer's Clerk's Tale is an enlarged and adorned translation of Petrarch's Latin version of Boccaccio's Italian story.

[l] This was commuted in 1378 for a yearly payment of 20 marks.

repair. About four weeks later, on the 8th of June, he was appointed Comptroller of the Customs and Subsidy of Wools, Skins, and Leather, in the Port of London [m], and on the 13th of the same month he received a pension of 10*l.* for life from the Duke of Lancaster for the good service rendered by him and his wife Philippa to the said Duke, to his Consort, and to his mother the Queen. This is the first mention of Philippa Chaucer as Geoffrey's wife, though a Philippa Chaucer is named as one of the Ladies of the Chamber to Queen Philippa on Sept. 12, 1366, and subsequently. It is possible that Philippa Chaucer was a relative or namesake of Geoffrey, and that he married her in the spring or early summer of 1374; if not, he must have married her before Sept. 12, 1366.

Chaucer's Italian journey, and his study of Italian literature in consequence of it, exercised a marked influence on his writings, and opened the second period of his development, in which his Lyf of Seynt Cecile, Parlement of Foules, Compleynt of Mars, Anelida and Arcite, Boece, Former Age, Troilus, and House of Fame, were probably composed.

In 1375 Chaucer's income was augmented by receiving from the crown (Nov. 8) the custody of the lands and person of Edmond Staplegate of Kent, which he retained for three years, during which time he received as wardship and marriage fee the sum of 104*l.*; and (on Dec. 28) the custody of five 'solidates' of rent [n] in Soles in Kent. Toward the end of 1376 Sir John Burley and Chaucer were employed in some secret service, the nature of which is not known. On the 23rd of the same month the poet received 6*l.* 13*s.* 4*d.*, and Burley twice that sum, for the work upon which they had been employed.

In February 1377, the last year of Edward's reign, the poet was associated with Sir Thomas Percy (afterward Earl of Worcester)

---

[m] In July 1376, Chaucer, as Comptroller of Wool Customs, received from the king the sum of 71*l.* 4*s.* 6*d.*, being the fine paid by John Kent of London for shipping wool to Dordrecht without having paid the duty thereon.

[n] A *solidate* of land was as much land (probably an acre) as was worth a shilling.

in a secret mission to Flanders⁰, and was shortly afterwards
(April) probably joined with Sir Guichard d'Angle (afterwards
Earl of Huntingdon) and Sir Richard Sturry to treat of peace
with Charles V, King of Franceᵖ.   In 1377 Richard II succeeded
to the throne, and Chaucer appears to have been reappointed one
of the king's esquires.   In January, 1378, he was probably
sent with the Earl of Huntingdon to France to treat for a
marriage of Richard with the daughter of the king of France.
On his return he was employed in a new mission to Lombardy,
along with Sir Edward Berkeley, to treat with Bernard Visconti,
Lord of Milan (whose death Chaucer afterwards brought into
his Monk's Tale) and Sir John Hawkwood, 'on certain affairs
touching the expediting the king's warᑫ.'   When Chaucer set
out on this embassy he appointed Gower as one of his trustees
to appear for him in the courts in case of any legal proceed-
ings being instituted against him during his absenceʳ.

By deed of May 1, 1380, Cecilia Chaumpayne released Chaucer
from his *raptus* of her.   On the 8th of May, 1382, he was made
Comptroller of the Petty Customs, retaining at the same time his
office of Comptroller of the Wool Customs.   These emoluments he
continued to hold till Dec. 1, 1386, and in Feb. 1385 was allowed the
privilege of nominating a deputy, so that he had perhaps now, or
perhaps soon after the loss of his office, leisure to devote himself to
his great work, the Canterbury Tales, which, though never completed, was written at different times of his life, from 1373 to

---

⁰ Chaucer received for this service 10*l*. on Feb. 17, and 20*l*. on April 11.

ᵖ Chaucer received 26*l*. 13*s*. 4*d*. on April 30, as part payment for this
service, and in 1381 (March) he was paid an additional sum of 22*l*.

ᑫ Chaucer was absent on this service from May 28 to Sept. 19, but
was not paid till 1380, when he received 56*l*. 13*s*. 4*d*.

ʳ This circumstance proves the existence of an intimate friendship
between the two poets.   Chaucer dedicated his Troilus and Criseyde to
Gower; and the latter poet, in the Confessio Amantis (Book viii.), makes
Venus speak of Chaucer as follows :—

 'And grete wel Chaucer, whan ye mete,
  As my disciple and my poete,
  For in the floures of his youthe,
  In sondry wyse, as he wel couthe,

1400, and prefaced by a Prologue, written on or about a journey in 1388. To this, the third period of his poetical life, also belong The Legende of Good Women (written about 1385), and Truth. (The 'Moder of God' formerly attributed to him is Hoccleve's.)

In 1386 Chaucer was elected a knight of the shire for Kent, in the Parliament held at Westminster. John of Gaunt was abroad at this time; and the Duke of Gloucester, at the head of the government, was most likely not well disposed towards the *protégé* of his brother, with whom he was now on ill terms. On the 1st of December, Chaucer was dismissed from his offices of Comptroller of Wool, Woolfells, and Leather, and of Comptroller of Petty Customs, and others were appointed in his place[s]. The loss of his emoluments reduced the poet from affluence to poverty—his beautiful 'balade of Truth' ('Flee fro the prees') probably speaks his own feelings in this time of his distress—and we find him raising money upon his two pensions of 20 marks, which on the 1st of May, 1388, were cancelled and assigned to John Scalby. To add to his trouble, his wife died in 1387: yet in 1388 he made his merry Canterbury pilgrimage. Richard, in 1389, dismissed his council, and took the reins of government into his own hands; the Lancastrian party were restored to power, and Chaucer was appointed Clerk of the King's Works at West-minster, at a salary of 2s. a-day, about 1l. of our money. The

Of dytees and of songes glade,
The whiche he for my sake made,
The land fulfilled is over al;
Whereof to him in special
Above alle other, I am most holde (beholden).
Forthy now in his dayes olde
Thou shalt him telle this message,
That he upon his latter age,
To sette an end of al his werke,
As he, whiche is myn owne clerke,
Do make his Testament of Love,
As thou hast doon thy shrift above,
So that my court it may recorde.'

[s] The Parliament of 1386 compelled Richard to appoint a commission to enquire into the state of the subsidies and customs. The commissioners began their duties in November, and the removal of certain officers may be attributed to their investigations.

next year (1390) he was also appointed Clerk of the Works at St. George's Chapel, Windsor, and made one of a Commission to repair the Thames Banks between Woolwich and Greenwich, but was superseded in 1391. In 14 Rich. II (June, 1390–1), he was appointed joint Forester, with Rd. Brittle, of North Petherton Park in Somerset, by the Earl of March. He had besides, 10*l.* yearly from the Duke of Lancaster, and 40*s.* as the king's esquire. In a writ, dated July 1, 1390, Chaucer is allowed the costs of putting up scaffolds in Smithfield for the King and Queen to see the jousts which took place in May, 1390. Compare this with Kn. Tale, 1023–1034. In Sept., 1390, he was robbed, at Westminster, of 10*l.* of the King's money, and of 9*l.* 3*s.* 8*d.* near the 'foule ok' (foul oak) at Hatcham, Surrey; but the repayment of it was forgiven him. In 1391 Chaucer translated and compiled his Treatise on the Astrolabe, for his 'little son' Lewis. This was probably followed by his Fortune, Gentilesse, Lak of Stedfast-nesse, his Envoys to Skogan and Bukton, the Compleynt of Venus, and his Compleynt to his Purse (in Sept. 1399).

On the 28th of Feb., 1394, Chaucer obtained a grant from the king of 20*l.* a-year for life, payable half-yearly at Easter and Michaelmas; but at this time the poet appears to have been in very distressed circumstances, for we find him making application for advances from the Exchequer on account of his annuity, and as these were not always made to him personally during the next few years, he was probably ill. In 21 Rich. II (June, 1397–8), Alianor, Countess of March, made him sole Forester of North Petherton in Somerset.

In Easter Term, 1398, Isabella Buckholt sued Chaucer for 14*l.* 1*s.* 11*d.* The sheriff twice returned the poet as *non inventus*, though in 1398 (May 4) letters of protection were issued to Chaucer forbidding any one, for the term of two years, to sue or arrest him on any plea except it were connected with land. Five months later (Oct. 15) the king made him a grant of a tun of wine a-year for life. Next year Henry Bolingbroke, son of John of Gaunt, supplanted his cousin Richard, and within four days after he came to the throne Chaucer's pension of 20 marks was doubled—in addition to the annuity of 20*l*. which had been given him by Richard II—doubtless in answer to the poet's Compleynt of his poverty[t], which was addressed to Henry IV, and hailed him as 'verray King by lyne and free eleccioun.'

On Christmas Eve, 1399, the poet covenanted for the lease for fifty-three years (a long agreement for a man in his fifty-ninth year to make), of a house in the garden of the Chapel of St. Mary, Westminster, where it is probable that he ended his days. The date (Oct. 25, 1400) assigned to his death by Nicholas Brigham is corroborated by the entries in the Issue Rolls, no note of payment being found after June 5th, 1400.

Thus on the bank of the noble river by which he was born and bred, on which for years his daily life was spent, our great early poet passed away. As he was at least sixty when he died, he was justly entitled to the epithets *old* and *reverent*, applied to him by his contemporaries Gower and Hoccleve[u].

Chaucer had one son, Lewis, who probably died young, to

---

[t] 'To yow, my Purse, and to non other wight,
  Compleyne I, for ye be my lady dere;
  I am so sory now that ye be light,
  For, certes, but ye make me hevy chere,
  Me were as leef be leyd upon my bere.
  For whiche unto your mercy thus I crye,
  Beth hevy ageyn, or elles mot I dye!
    Now voucheth sauf this day, or hit be night,
  That I of yow the blisful soun may here,
  Or see your colour lyk the sonne bright,
  That [as] of yelownesse hadde never pere;
  Ye be my lyf, ye be myn hertes stere,
  Quene of comfort and of good companye;
  Beth hevy ageyn, or elles mot I dye.
    Now Purs, that art to me my lyves light,
  And saveour, as doun in this worlde here,
  Out of this toune help me thurgh your might,
  Sin that ye wole nat ben my tresorere;
  For I am shave as nye as any frere.
  But yit I pray unto your curtesye,
  Beth hevy ageyn, or elles mot I dye.'
                        (Chaucer's Minor Poems, ed. Skeat, p. 210.)
[u] Leland says that Chaucer 'lived to the period of grey hairs, and at length found old age his greatest disease.' In Hoccleve's portrait of the poet he is represented with grey hair and beard.

whom he addressed his treatise on the Astrolabe in 1391. There is no evidence whatever that Thomas Chaucer, who attained to immense wealth, and whose great-grandson, John de la Pole (Earl of Lincoln), was declared by Richard III heir-apparent to the throne, was Chaucer's son, though he may have been a relative.

In the Prologue to The Rime of Sir Thopas[x], we have probably a faithful picture of Chaucer's personal appearance in 1388, agreeing in some points with his later portrait by Hoccleve[a]. In person he was corpulent, and, like his host of the Tabard, 'a large man,' and no 'poppet' to embrace; but his face was small, fair, and intelligent, his eye downcast and meditative, but dazed by age and study. Altogether, he had an 'elvish' or weird[b] expression of countenance, which attracted the attention of those who came into contact with him for the first time, and with whom he seems to have been reserved and reticent. His extensive acquirements and voluminous writings show that he was a hard-working student; from incidental allusions in The House of Fame, we learn that when his labours and 'reckonings' at the Custom House were over, and he returned home, instead of rest and novelties he sat and pored over his books until his eyes were 'dased' and dull; and often at night an aching head followed the making of 'books, songs, and ditties.' So absorbed was he in

---

[x]
    'Our hoste iapen tho began,
  And than at erst he loked upon me,
  And seydë thus, "What man artow?" quod he;
  "Thou lokest as thou woldest fynde an hare,
  For ever upon the ground I se thee stare;
   Approchë neer, and loke up merily.
  Now war you, sirs, and lat this man have place;
  He in the waast is shape as wel as I;
  This were a popet in an arm tenbrace
  For any womman, smal and fair of face.
  He semeth elvish by his contenance,
  For unto no wight doth he daliaunce."'

[a] This is a coloured portrait found in the margin of Hoccleve's work 'De Regimine Principum' in Harl. MS. 4866. Other MSS. contain other paintings of Chaucer; but the care bestowed on the Harleian one, which really looks like a portrait, has made critics believe it a genuine likeness.

[b] Tyrwhitt renders *elvish* by 'shy.'

hís studies, that for the time neither foreign affairs, his neigh-bours' gossip, 'nor anything else that God had made,' had any interest for him. Hermit-like though he lived, Chaucer was not naturally a recluse, and still less an ascetic: given more to observe than to talk, he loved good and pleasant society, and to sit at the festive board; for, as he himself tells us, 'his absti-nence was but little.'

Though an essentially dramatic spirit pervades nearly the whole of his works, yet Chaucer is above all things a narrator, and we must reckon him among the objective and not the subjective poets; among the epic, of Goethe's threefold division of all poets into epic, dramatic, and lyrical. Yet he is subjective, lyrical, too. Chaucer himself is in all his original works: hopeless and sad in his early poems, bright and humourful in his later ones, poor and suppliant in his last. Among his chief characteristics are his delightful freshness and simplicity, his roguish genial humour—he was full of quaint fun—his heartfelt love of nature, his tender pathos, his knowledge of women—the naughty he quizzed in most happy style, and the good he honoured and praised with all his might—his love of his dear old books, his power of lifelike portraiture, his admirable story-telling, and the perfection of his verse. 'His best tales run on like one of our inland rivers, sometimes hastening a little and turning upon themselves in eddies that dimple without retarding the current; sometimes loitering smoothly, while here and there a quiet thought, a tender feeling, a pleasant image, a golden-hearted verse, opens quietly as a water-lily, to float on the surface without breaking it into ripple[c].' Chaucer's ardent love of Nature, finely apostrophised by the poet as 'the vicar of the Almighty Lord,' is everywhere apparent. What is more spon-taneous and characteristic of the poet than such joyous outbursts as the following?—

> 'Herkneth thise blisful briddës how they singe,
> And see the fresshë floures how they springe;
> Ful is myn hert of revel and solas.'
>
> (Nonne Prestes Tale, ll. 381–383.)

---

[c] Prof. J. R. Lowell's essay, in his 'My Study Windows,' p. 87,—a book that every Chaucer student should buy and read.

Even his love and reverence for books gave way before an eager desire to enjoy the beauties of nature in that season of the year when all around him was manifesting life and loveliness[d].

Not less evident is Chaucer's high estimation of women, and his 'perception of a sacred bond, spiritual and indestructible, in true marriage between man and woman[e].' Of all the flowers in the mead, the daisy, 'the emperice and flour of floures alle,' was Chaucer's favourite, because to him it was the fit representative of the 'trouthe of womanhede'; Good Wom. 185, 297.

---

[d]   'And as for me, thogh that I can but lyte (little),
       On bokes for to rede I me delyte,
       And to hem yeve (give) I feyth and ful credence,
       And in myn herte have hem in reverence
       So hertely that there is game noon,
       That fro my bokes maketh me to goon,
       But hit be seldom, on the holy day,
       Save, certeynly, whan that the month of May
       Is comen, and that I here the foules singe,
       And that the floures ginnen for to springe,
       Farwel my book, and my devocioun!'
                (Legend of Good Women, ed. Skeat, p. 3, ll. 29-39.)

[e]   'For who can be so buxom as a wyf?
       Who is so trewe and eek so ententyf,
       To kepe him, seek and hool, as is his make?
       For wele or woo sche wol him not forsake.
       Sche is not wery him to love and serve,
       Theigh that he lay bedred til that he sterve.
         .   .   .   .   .   .
       A wyf is Goddes yifte verrayly;
         .   .   .   .   .   .
       Mariage is a ful gret sacrament;
         .   .   .   .   .   .
       Her may ye see, and here may ye prove,
       That wyf is mannes help and his comfort,
       His paradis terrestre and his desport.
       So buxom and so vertuous is sche,
       Thay mosten neede lyve in unité;
       O fleisch thay ben, and on blood, as I gesse,
       Have but oon herte in wele and in distresse.
       A wyf? a! Seinte Mary, *benedicite*,
       How mighte a man have eny adversité
       That hath a wyf? certes I can not saye.'
                    The Marchaundes Tale; 41, 67, 75, 86.
  See Morley's English Writers, vol. ii. pp. 135, 256, 286.

As Mr. Morley has well remarked, 'Ditties in praise of the Marguerite, or daisy, were popular with the French fashionable poets; but none of them, like Chaucer, among all their allegorical dreamings, ever dreamed of celebrating in that flower an emblem of womanly truth and purity, wearing its crown as a gentle, innocent, devoted wife.'

Though Chaucer was so intimately connected with the court, and enjoyed no small share of courtly favours, he protested nobly and fearlessly against the popular opinion that churls or villains (in the legal sense of the term, that is, persons of plebeian rank) were necessarily prone to be guilty of base and unworthy actions; and at the present day we can hardly appreciate the boldness which made him assert more than once that the true test of gentility is nobleness of life and courtesy of manners, and not mere ancestral rank [f], and which made him in the Persones Tale denounce the oppression of thralls or 'villeins' by their lords. (See Persones Tale, ed. Morris, iii. pp. 301, 332–334.)

As we have already said, Chaucer's great work, the Canterbury Tales, was not put together till after the year 1386. His earlier literary productions were mostly translations, or imitations from foreign sources, Latin, French, and Italian, and have therefore but little claim to originality, except so far as he altered or added to his originals; but even in these efforts there are many excellences and traces of the poet's genius, especially of his great power over language, which made his ability as a translator known and highly appreciated by his literary contemporaries. Francis Eustace Deschamps, in a 'Ballade à Geoffroi Chaucer,' speaks of him in the warmest terms of praise as 'grand translateur, noble Geoffroy Chaucier!' But it is to the Canterbury Tales that Chaucer owes his fame and rank as the

---

[f]   'Lok who that is most vertuous alway,
            Privé and pert (open), and most entendith aye
            To do the gentil dedes that he can,
            Tak him for the grettest gentilman.
            Crist wol we clayme of him oure gentilesse,
            Nought of oure eldres for her olde richesse.'
                              The Wife of Bath's Tale, ll. 257–262.

first poet of modern English literature, and in this work—the result of years of labour and study—the genius and power of the poet are most strongly expressed g.

The Canterbury Tales are a collection of stories related by certain pilgrims who rode together in true English fellowship to worship and pay their vows at the shrine of the 'holy and blisful (blessed) martyr' Thomas à Becket.

The first hint of thus joining together a number of stories by one common bond was probably borrowed from Boccaccio's Decameron h; 'but Chaucer's plan was better than that of the Decameron, and looked to a much greater result. . . . Boccaccio, who died twenty-five years before Chaucer, placed the scene of his Decameron in a garden, to which seven fashionable ladies had retired with three fashionable gentlemen, during the plague that devastated Florence in 1348. The persons were all of the same class, young and rich, with no concern in life beyond the bandying of compliments. They shut themselves up in a delicious

---

g The chief minor works of Chaucer are :—The Romaunt of the Rose (a translation, *now lost*, of a portion of the Roman de la Rose, a work in two parts, the first part, of 4,070 lines, by Guillaume de Lorris (1200–1230), and the Sequel, of 18,002 lines, by Jean de Meung, written nearly half a century later) ; The Assembly of Fowls, or the Parliament of Birds (? 1382); Chaucer's A B C, translated out of Guillaume de Guilevile's 'Pelerinage de l'Homme,' written about 1330; The Book of the Duchesse (1369); Troylus and Criseyde, an enlarged version of Boccaccio's Filostrato (? written 1380–83); The Complaint of Mars (? 1374); The Complaint of Venus (translated from Gransson); The House of Fame (? 1384); The Legend of Good Women (about 1385); Anelida and Arcite; and a prose Treatise on the Astrolabe (1391).

The Court of Love, Lydgate's Complaint of the Black Knight, The Cuckoo and the Nightingale, The Isle of Ladies or Chaucer's Dream, The Flower and the Leaf, the *extant* Romaunt of the Rose, are also usually ascribed to Chaucer, but Mr. Bradshaw holds that they bear internal evidence of not being the production of the author of the Canterbury Tales—for 'all these poems contravene the laws of rhyme observed by Chaucer in the works, both of youth and old age, that are certainly his.' (See Temporary Preface to the Six-Text Edition of Chaucer's Canterbury Tales, ed. Furnivall, p. 108.) Hertzberg, Mr. Bradshaw, &c., have adduced good reasons for excluding The Testament of Love from the list of Chaucer's works.

h Mr. Wright thinks that the widespread Romance of the 'Seven Sages,' of which there are several English versions, gave Chaucer the idea of his plot.

garden of the sort common in courtly inventions of the middle ages, and were occupied in sitting about idly, telling stories to each other. The tales were usually dissolute, often witty, sometimes exquisitely poetical, and always told in simple charming prose. The purpose of the story-tellers was to help each other to forget the duties on which they had turned their backs, and stifle any sympathies they might have had for the terrible griefs of their friends and neighbours who were dying a few miles away. Chaucer substituted for the courtly Italian ladies and gentlemen who withdrew from fellowship with the world, as large a group as he could form of English people, of rank widely differing, in hearty human fellowship together. Instead of setting them down to lounge in a garden, he mounted them on horseback, set them on the high road, and gave them somewhere to go and something to do. The bond of fellowship was not fashionable acquaintance and a common selfishness. It was religion ; not indeed in a form so solemn as to make laughter and jest unseemly, yet according to the custom of his day, a popular form of religion, the pilgrimage to the shrine of Thomas à Becket, into which men entered with much heartiness. It happened to be a custom which had one of the best uses of religion, in serving as a bond of fellowship in which conventional divisions of rank were for a time disregarded ; partly because of the sense, more or less joined to religious exercise of any sort, that men are equal before God, and also, in no slight degree, because men of all ranks trotting upon the high road with chance companions, whom they might never see again, have been in all generations disposed to put off restraint, and enjoy such intercourse as might relieve the tediousness of travel [i].'

It would take up too much space to enter upon any analysis of the several stories which make up this wonderful collection. It will suffice to consider briefly such portions of the Canterbury Tales as are included in this volume of Selections ; and first in order and importance comes the **Prologue**, in which we have

---

[i] Morley's English Writers, from Chaucer to Dunbar, vol. ii. pp. 287, 288.

laid before us the general plan, and the several characters of the whole work.

In the pleasant season of April [j], as Chaucer lay at the Tabard, one of the chief houses of public entertainment, situated in the High-street of Southwark, nine-and-twenty pilgrims on their way to Canterbury arrived at the 'hostelry.' The poet, being on the same errand as themselves, joined them, and in a short time was on intimate and friendly terms with each member of the company. The host of the inn, ' Harry Bailly,' made one more, and presided over this ' merry company ' during their journey to and from Canterbury. At his suggestion it was agreed that each pilgrim should tell two tales on their road to Becket's shrine, and two other tales on their way home ; but as the number of the pilgrims was thirty-two [k], and there are only twenty-four stories, it is clear that four-fifths of the tales are wanting, which may be accounted for by supposing that Chaucer died before the completion of his work, or even before he had settled upon the exact arrangement of the several tales, though the order of those he has left, and the probable stages of the journey to Canterbury, have been made out by Mr. Bradshaw and Mr. Furnivall in the latter's Temporary Preface to the Six-Text Edition of Chaucer, Part i.

' After a brief introduction, filled with the most cheerful images of spring, the season of the pilgrimage, the poet commences the narrative with a description of the person and the character of each member of the party. This description extends to about seven hundred lines, and of course affords space for a very spirited and graphic portrayal of the physical aspect, and an outline of the moral features of each. This latter part of the description is generally more rapidly sketched, because it was a part of the author's plan to allow his personages to bring out their special traits of character, and thus to depict and individualise them-

---

[j] Elsewhere a date is given, the 18th of April, being, probably, the second day of the pilgrimage ; see Introd. to Prior. Tale, p. xi.

[k] The canon and his yeoman joined them at Boughton-under-Blean, seven miles on the London side of Canterbury ; but the master's doings being exposed by his servant, he was glad to ride away ' for very sorrow and shame.'

selves, in the interludes between the tales. The selection of
the pilgrims is evidently made with reference to this object of
development in action, and therefore constitutes an essential
feature of the plot. We have persons of all the ranks not too
far removed from each other by artificial distinctions to be
supposed capable of associating upon that footing of temporary
equality which is the law of good fellowship, among travellers
bound on the same journey and accidentally brought together.
All the great classes of English humanity are thus represented,
and opportunity is given for the display of the harmonies and
the jealousies which now united, now divided, the interests of
different orders and different vocations in the commonwealth.
The clerical pilgrims, it will be observed, are proportionately
very numerous. The exposure of the corruptions of the Church
was doubtless a leading aim with the poet ; and if the whole
series, which was designed to extend to at least 58 [128] tales,
had been completed, the criminations and recriminations of
the jealous ecclesiastics would have exhibited the whole profession in an unenviable light.

'But Chaucer could be just as well as severe. His portrait
of the prioress, though it does not spare the affectations of the
lady, is complimentary; and his "good man of religion," the
"pore Persoun of a toun," of whom it is said that—

> "Cristes lore, and his apostles twelve,
>   He taughte, but first he folwed it himselve,"

has been hundreds of times quoted as one of the most beautiful
pictures of charity, humility, and generous, conscientious, intelligent devotion to the duties of the clerical calling, which can be
found in the whole range of English literature.

'None of these sketches, I believe, has ever been traced to
a foreign source ; and they are so thoroughly national, that it is
hardly possible to suppose that any imagination but that of an
Englishman could have conceived them. In the first introduction of the individuals described in the prologues to the several
stories, and in the dialogues which occur at the pauses between

the tales, wherever, in short, the narrators appear in their own persons, the characters are as well marked and discriminated, and as harmonious and consistent in action, as in the best comedies of modern times[1]. Although, therefore, there is in the plan of the composition nothing of technical dramatic form or incident, yet the admirable conception of character, the consummate skill with which each is sustained and developed, and the nature, life, and spirit of the dialogue, abundantly prove that if the drama had been known in Chaucer's time as a branch of living literature, he might have attained to as high excellence in comedy as any English or continental writer. The story of a comedy is but a contrivance to bring the characters into contact and relation with each other, and the invention of a suitable plot is a matter altogether too simple to have created the slightest difficulty to a mind like Chaucer's. He is essentially a dramatist; and if his great work does not appear in the conventional dramatic form, it is an accident of the time, and by no means proves a want of power of original conception or of artistic skill in the author.

' This is a point of interest in the history of modern literature, because it is probably the first instance of the exhibition of unquestionable dramatic genius in either the Gothic or the Romance languages. I do not mean that there had previously existed in modern Europe nothing like histrionic representation of real or imaginary events ; but neither the Decameron of Boccaccio, to which the Canterbury Tales have been compared, nor any of the Mysteries and Moralities, or other imaginative works of the middle ages, in which several personages are introduced, show any such power of conceiving and sustaining individual character as to prove that its author could have furnished the *personnel* of a respectable play. Chaucer therefore may fairly be said to be not only the earliest dramatic genius of modern Europe, but to

---

[1] ' I see all the pilgrims in the *Canterbury Tales*, their humours, their features, and the very dress, as distinctly as if I had supped with them at the Tabard in Southwark.' (Dryden, Preface to *The Fables*.)

have been a dramatist before that which is technically known as the existing drama was invented [m].'

'**The Knightes Tale**, or at least a poem. upon the same subject, was originally composed by Chaucer as a separate work. As such, it is mentioned by him, among some of his other works, in the Legende of Goode Women (ll. 420, 1), under the title of "Al the love of Palamon and Arcyte Of Thebes, thogh the storye ys knowen lyte;" and the last words [copied from Boccaccio] seem to imply that it [the old story] had not made itself very popular. It is not impossible that at first it was a mere translation of the Teseide of Boccaccio, and that its present form was given it when Chaucer determined to assign it the first place among his Canterbury Tales [n].

' It may not be unpleasing to the reader to see a short summary of it, which will show with what skill Chaucer has proceeded in reducing a poem of about ten thousand lines to a little more than two thousand without omitting any material circumstance.

' The Teseide is distributed into twelve Books or Cantos.

' Bk. i. Contains the war of Theseus with the Amazons, their submission to him, and his marriage with Hippolyta.

' Bk. ii. Theseus, having spent two years in Scythia, is reproached by Perithous in a vision, and immediately returns to

---

[m] Marsh, Origin and History of the English Language, pp. 417–419.

[n] 'The Knight's Tale is an abridged translation of a part of Boccaccio's Teseide, but with considerable change in the plan, which is, perhaps, not much improved, and with important additions in the descriptive and the more imaginative portions of the story. These additions are not inferior to the finest parts of Boccaccio's work ; and one of them, the description of the Temple of Mars, is particularly interesting, as proving that Chaucer possessed a power of treating the grand and terrible, of which no modern poet but Dante had yet given an example.' (Marsh, Origin and History of the English Language, pp. 423, 424.) 'Out of 2,250 of Chaucer's lines, he has only translated 270 (less than one-eighth) from Boccaccio ; only 374 more lines bear a general likeness to Boccaccio; and only 132 more a slight likeness.' (Furnivall, Temporary Preface to Six-Text Edition of Chaucer.) 'Several parallel lines between Chaucer's Troilus and the Knightes Tale show that Troilus and the original draught of the Knightes Tale, to which Chaucer himself gives the name of "Palemon," were in hand at about the same time.' (Skeat, in Notes and Queries, Fourth Series, iv. 292.)

Athens with Hippolyta and her sister Emilia. He enters the city in triumph; finds the Grecian ladies in the temple of Clemenzia; marches to Thebes; kills Creon, &c., and brings home Palemone and Arcita who are "Damnati—ad eterna presone."

'Bk. iii. Emilia, walking in a garden and singing, is heard and seen first by Arcita[o], who calls Palemone. They are both equally enamoured of her, but without any jealousy or rivalship. Emilia is supposed to see them at the window, and to be not displeased with their admiration. Arcita is released at the request of Perithous; takes his leave of Palemone, with embraces, &c.

'Bk. iv. Arcita, having changed his name to *Pentheo*, goes into the service of Menelaus at Mycenae, and afterwards of Peleus at Aegina. From thence he returns to Athens and becomes a favourite servant of Theseus, being known to Emilia, though to nobody else; till after some time he is overheard making his complaint in a wood, to which he usually resorted for that purpose, by Pamphilo, a servant of Palemone.

'Bk. v. Upon the report of Pamphilo, Palemone *begins* to be jealous of Arcita, and is desirous to get out of prison in order to fight with him. This he accomplishes with the assistance of Pamphilo, by changing clothes with Alimeto, a physician. He goes armed to the wood in quest of Arcita, whom he finds sleeping. At first, they are very civil and friendly to each other. Then Palemone calls upon Arcita to renounce his pretensions to Emilia, or to fight with him. After many long expostulations on the part of Arcita, they fight, and are discovered first by Emilia, who sends for Theseus. When he finds who they are, and the

---

[o] 'In describing the commencement of this amour, which is to be the subject of the remainder of the poem, Chaucer has entirely departed from his author in three principal circumstances, and, I think, in each with very good reason: (1) By supposing Emilia to be seen first by Palamon, he gives him an advantage over his rival which makes the catastrophe more consonant to poetical justice; (2) The picture which Boccaccio has exhibited of two young princes violently enamoured of the same object, without jealousy or rivalship, if not absolutely unnatural, is certainly very insipid and unpoetical; (3) As no consequence is to follow from their being seen by Emilia at this time, it is better, I think, to suppose, as Chaucer has done, that they are not seen by her.'—Tyrwhitt.

cause of their difference, he forgives them, and proposes the method of deciding their claim to Emilia by a combat of a hundred on each side, to which they gladly agree.

'Bk. vi. Palemone and Arcita live splendidly at Athens, and send out messengers to summon their friends, who arrive; and the principal of them are severally described, viz. Lycurgus, Peleus, Phocus, Telamon, &c.; Agamemnon, Menelaus, Castor and Pollux, &c.; Nestor, Evander, Perithous, Ulysses, Diomedes, &c.; with a great display of ancient history and mythology.

'Bk. vii. Theseus declares the laws of the combat, and the two parties of a hundred on each side are formed. The day before the combat, Arcita, after having visited the temples of all the gods, makes a formal prayer to Mars. The prayer, *being personified*, is said to go and find Mars in his Temple in Thrace, which is described; and Mars, upon understanding the message, causes favourable signs to be given to Arcita. In the same manner Palemone closes his religious observances with a prayer to Venus. His prayer *being also personified*, sets out for the temple of Venus on Mount Citherone, which is also described; and the petition is granted. Then the sacrifice of Emilia to Diana is described, her prayer, the appearance of the goddess, and the signs of the two fires. In the morning they proceed to the theatre with their respective troops, and prepare for the action. Arcita puts up a private prayer to Emilia, and harangues his troop publicly, and Palemone does the same.

'Bk. viii. Contains a description of the battle, in which Palemone is taken prisoner.

'Bk. ix. The horse of Arcita, being frighted by a Fury, sent from Hell at the desire of Venus, throws him. However, he is carried to Athens in a triumphal chariot with Emilia by his side; is put to bed dangerously ill; and there by his own desire espouses Emilia.

'Bk. x. The funeral of the persons killed in the combat. Arcita, being given over by his physicians, makes his will, in discourse with Theseus, and desires that Palemone may inherit all his possessions and also Emilia. He then takes leave of Palemone and

Emilia, to whom he repeats the same request. Their lamentations. Arcita orders a sacrifice to Mercury, which Palemone performs for him, and dies.

'Bk. xi. Opens with the passage of Arcita's soul to heaven, imitated from the Ninth Book of Lucan. The funeral of Arcita. Description of the wood felled takes up six stanzas. Palemone builds a temple in honour of him, in which his whole history is painted. The description of this painting is an abridgment of the preceding part of the poem.

'Bk. xii. Theseus proposes to carry into execution Arcita's will by the marriage of Palemone and Emilia. This they both decline for some time in formal speeches, but at last are persuaded and married. The kings, &c. take their leave, and Palemone remains—in gioia e in diporto con la sua dona nobile e cortese [P].'

The Nonne Prestes Tale is so characteristic of Chaucer's genius, that Dryden, who modernised it as the fable of the ' Cock and Fox,' thought it to be of the poet's own invention ; but it is no doubt taken from a fable of about forty lines, ' Dou Coc et dou Werpil,' in the poems of Marie of France, which is amplified in the fifth chapter of the old French metrical Roman de Renart, entitled 'Si comme Renart prist Chantecler le Coc.' See p. liii.

Chaucer's English, like that of the present day, is an uninflected or analytic language, and in this respect it differed from the language of many earlier authors, and especially from that oldest form of English usually termed Anglo-Saxon, which was originally inflected or synthetic, that is to say, it expressed grammatical relation by a change in the *form* of words, instead of employing auxiliary words. The circumstances which led to this conversion are well known, forming as they do a part of the history of the English people. The first in order of time is the invasion, settlement, and conquest of the country by the Danes, extending over a period of nearly a century and a half (A.D. 867–1013). The Danish influence upon the language seems to have affected

---

[P] Tyrwhitt, Introductory Discourse to the Canterbury Tales.

chiefly the dialects of the north and east parts of the island, in consequence of which their inflexions and syntactical structure were much simplified, and they assumed a more modern appearance than the speech prevailing in other districts. Doubtless it caused the language generally to be in a very unsettled state, and the revolution thus commenced was accelerated by the Norman Conquest, which followed in the year 1066. Norman rule introduced a new civilization of a far higher order than had ever before existed in England, and of this the Normans were fully sensible, and utterly despised both the language and literature of the Saxons as only fit for churls and villains. In a certain sense English ceased to be the language of literature [q], and for about two hundred years Norman-French was the language of the Court, the Church, the Courts of Law, and of the upper and middle classes of society, and divided literature with the Latin tongue. But though the English were thus made to feel their position as a subject people, they clung most pertinaciously to the speech of their forefathers, and after a long and continuous struggle English regained its supremacy as the language of literature and the common tongue of all who claimed the name of Englishmen, while Norman-French was reduced to a mere provincial dialect. This was brought about by the fusion of the Saxon and Norman races, about the time of Henry II; by the severance of Normandy from England and its annexation to France, in the time of John; by the wars of Edward III, which did much to promote religious and political liberty, and by the adoption of English as the household speech by that part of the nation that had previously spoken French, which happened about the middle of the fourteenth century.

The Norman Conquest wrought a twofold revolution in the language: the first, which extended over nearly the whole of

---

[q] It is altogether erroneous to suppose that immediately after the Norman Conquest English ceased to be written, for from Ælfric to Chaucer we have an almost unbroken series of vernacular literature by which we are able to determine with tolerable exactness the various changes in grammar and vocabulary which occurred during this interval.

the twelfth century, affected the grammatical forms of the language; final vowels were changed, some consonants became softened, and many of the older inflexions of nouns, adjectives and verbs went out of use, their place being supplied by prepositions and auxiliary words. This was a period of great grammatical confusion, but the vocabulary remained unchanged. At the beginning of the thirteenth century, we find the grammatical forms more settled; but many provincial elements unknown to the oldest English had crept in, and about the middle of this period we have to note a further change in the *substance* of the language, caused by the infusion of the Norman-French element. The additions to the vocabulary were at first small, but they gradually increased, and about the middle of the fourteenth century they formed no inconsiderable part of the *written* language. In Chaucer's works these loans are so numerous that he has been accused of corrupting the English language by a large and unnecessary admixture of Norman-French terms. But Chaucer, with few exceptions, employed only such terms as were in use in the *spoken* language, and stamped them with the impress of his genius, so that they became current coin of the literary realm.

The period in which Chaucer lived was one of great literary activity, and such names as Richard Rolle of Hampole, Minot, Mandeville, Langland, Wicliffe, and Gower, prove that the English language was in a healthy and vigorous condition, and really deserving of the importance into which it was rising. But as yet there was no *national language*, and consequently no *national literature*; the English of the twelfth, thirteenth, and fourteenth centuries diverged into many dialects, each having its own literature intelligible only to a comparatively small circle of readers, and no one form of English can be considered as the type of the language of the period. Of these dialects the East Midland, spoken, with some variation, from the Humber to the Thames, was perhaps the simplest in its grammatical structure, the most free from those broad provincialisms which particularised the speech of other districts, and presented the nearest approach in form and substance to the language of the present day as spoken and written by educated Englishmen. In the works of Ormin and Robert of Brunne we have evidence of its great capacity for literary purposes. Wicliffe and Gower added considerably to its importance, but in the hands of Chaucer it attained to the dignity of a national language [r]. He represented, and identified himself with, that new life which the English people at this time were just commencing, and his works reflect not only his own inimitable genius, but the spirit, tastes, and feelings of his age. It was this, combined with his thorough mastery over the English language, that caused Chaucer to become to others (what no one had been before) a standard of literary excellence; and for two hundred years after he had no equal, but was regarded as the father of English poetry, the Homer[s] of his country, and the well of English undefiled.

With the Canterbury Tales commences the modern period of English literature. Our earlier authors are usually studied for their philological importance, and most of them require the aid of a grammar and a glossary, but Chaucer is as easily understood as Spenser and Shakespeare. Not many of his terms are wholly obsolete, and but few of his inflections have gone wholly out of use. But as some special acquaintance with Chaucer's English will be of great service in mastering the poet's system of versification, an outline of his grammatical forms (for the most part taken from Prof. F. J. Child's Essay on Chaucer) is here subjoined, which will be found useful should

---

[r] 'From this Babylonish confusion of speech [i.e. the numerous local dialects of the English language in the fourteenth century] the influence and example of Chaucer did more to rescue his native tongue than any other single cause; and if we compare his dialect with that of any writer of an earlier date, we shall find that in compass, flexibility, expressiveness, grace, and all the higher qualities of poetical diction, he gave it at once the utmost perfection which the materials at his hand would admit of.' (Marsh, Origin and History of the English Language, p. 381.)

[s] 'In the first place, as he (Chaucer) is the father of English poetry, so I hold him in the same degree of veneration as the Grecians held Homer, or the Romans Virgil.' (Dryden's Preface to *The Fables.*)

the young student feel disposed to make himself acquainted with the works of earlier English writers.

NOUNS.

Number.—The plural for the most part terminates in *-ës* :—

> 'And with his *stremës* dryeth in the *grevës*
> The silver *dropës* hanging on the *levës*.'
>
> (Knightes Tale, ll. 637–8.)

1. *-s* is frequently added, (*a*) to nouns terminating in a liquid or dental, as *bargayns, naciouns, palmers, pilgryms*, &c.; (*b*) to most words of more than one syllable.

In some MSS. we find *-is, -us*, for *-es*—as *bestis*, beasts; *leggus*, legs; *othus*, oaths—which seem to be dialectical varieties, and probably due to the scribes who copied the MSS.

2. Some few nouns (originally forming the plural in *-an*) have *-en, -n*; as *asschen*, ashes; *assen*, asses; *been*, bees; *eyen, yen*, eyes; *fleen*, fleas; *flon*, arrows; *oxen*; *ton, toon*, toes; *schoon, shoon*, shoes.

The following have *-n*, which has been added to older forms— (*a*) in *-e* (originally in *-u*); (*b*) in *-y*.

(*a*) *Brethren* (A. S. *bróthru*, O. E. *brothre, brethre*), brothers.
Doughtren (A. S. *dohtru*, O. E. *dohtre*), daughters.
Sistren, sustren (A. S. *sweostru*, O. E. *swustre*), sisters.
Children (A. S. *cildru*, O. E. *childre*), children[t].

(*b*) *Kyn* (A. S. *cý*), kine[u]. Add *fon, foon* (A. S. *fán*), foes.

3. The following nouns, originally neuter, have no termination in the plural :—*deer, folk, good, hors, neet, scheep, swin, thing, yer, yeer*; as in the older stages of the language *night, winter, freond* (A. S. *frýnd*) are used as plurals.

4. *Feet, gees, men, teeth*, are examples of the plural by vowel-change.

---

[t] In some of the O.E. Northern and Midland dialects we find *brether* (brothers), *childer* (children), *deghter* (daughters).

[u] In some of the Northern and Midland dialects we find *kye* (cows).

Case.—The genitive case singular ends in *-ës*; as—

'Ful worthy was he in his *lordës* werre.' (Prol. l. 47.)

1. In Anglo-Saxon, *fæder, bróthor, dohtor,* took no inflexion in the genitive singular: this explains such phrases as '*fader* day,' '*fader* soule,' '*brother* sone,' '*doughter* name.'

2. The following phrases contain remnants of feminine nouns which originally formed the genitive in *-an* (first declension of A. S. nouns) :—'*Lady* (=*ladyë*) grace ;' '*lady* veyl ;' '*cherchë* blood ;' '*hertë* blood ;' '*widow* (= *widewë*) sone ;' '*sonnë* upriste' (uprising).

3. The dative case singular occasionally occurs and terminates in *-e*; as *beddë, holtë,* &c.

4. The genitive plural is much the same as in modern English; as '*foxës* tales ;' '*mennës* wittes.' Forms in *-en* (= *-ene*) are not common in Chaucer's works : 'his *eyghen* (of eyes) sight' occurs in Canterbury Tales, l. 10134 (Wright's Text).

ADJECTIVES.

Adjectives, like the modern German, have two forms—Definite and Indefinite. The definite form is preceded by the definite article, a demonstrative adjective, or a possessive pronoun, and terminates in *-ë* in all cases of the singular ; as 'the *yong-e* sone,' 'his *half-e* cours.' Words of more than one syllable nearly always omit the final *-e*.

The vocative case of the adjective takes this *-e*; as '*lev-e* brother' (l. 326, p. 42) ; 'O *strong-e* God' (l. 1515, p. 81).

Degrees of Comparison.—The Comparative degree is formed by adding *-er* (*-rë*) to the Positive ; as *lever, gretter*[x].

We find some few forms in *-re* remaining ; as *derre* (dearer) ; *more* (*mare*) ; *ferre* (further) ; *herre* (higher) ; *nerre, ner* (nearer) ; *sorre* (sorer).

Leng, lenger (*lengrë*), = longer ; *strenger,* = stronger, are

---

[x] Occasionally the definite form of the comparative seems to end in *-ere* (*-rë*), to distinguish it from the indefinite form in *-er* ; but no positive rule can be laid down, as *-er* and *-re* are easily interchanged.

examples of vowel-change; as seen in the modern English *elder*, the comparative of *old*.

Bet (*bettre*) and *mo* are contracted forms.

The Superlative degree terminates in *-este* (*-est*)[y]: *nest* or *next*, and *hext* (highest) are abbreviated forms.

Number.—The plural of adjectives is denoted by the final *-e*:—

> 'And *smalë* fowles maken melodye.' (Prol. l. 9.)

Adjectives of more than one syllable, and adjectives used predicatively, mostly drop the *-e* in the plural. Some few adjectives of Romance origin form the plural in *-es*; as '*places delitables.*'

DEMONSTRATIVES.

1. The old plural *tho* (A. S. *thá*) of the definite article is still used by Chaucer, but the uninflected *the* is more frequently used.

In the phrases '*that* oon,' '*that* other'—which in some dialects became *the toon* (*ton*), *the tother*—*that* is the old form of the neuter article; but Chaucer never uses *that* except as a demonstrative adjective, as in the present stage of the language.

2. *Atte*=at the (A.S. *æt thám*; O.E. *at than, attan, atta*, masc. and neut.); the feminine would be *atter* (O. E.), *æt þǽre* (A.S.).

3. *Tho* must be rendered *those*, as well as *the*; as '*tho* wordes,' 'and *tho* were bent.' It is occasionally used pronominally, as 'oon of *tho* that,' one of those that.

4. *This* has for its plural *thise, thes, these* (A.S. *thás, thǽs*). In some MSS. *this* occurs for *thise*.

5. *Thilkë* (A.S. *thyllic, thylc*=the like; O. E. *thellich*, pl. *thelliche*), the like, that.

6. *That ilkë*, that same (A. S. *ylc*, same; *y* is a remnant of an old demonstrative base; *-lc*=*lic*=like).

7. *Som . . . som*=one . . . another.

> 'He moot ben deed, the king as shal a page;
> *Som* in his bed, *som* in the depë see,
> *Som* in the largë feeld, as men may se.'
> (Knightes Tale, ll. 2172-4.)

---

[y] The superlatives of adverbs always seem to end in *-est*, and not in *-este*; cp. p. 76, ll. 1340, 1349, with ll. 1342, 1343, 1344, 1345.

PRONOUNS.

	SINGULAR.			PLURAL.
Nom.	I, Ich, Ik,			we.
Gen.	min (myn), mi (my),			our, oure.
Dat. } Acc. }	me,			us.
Nom.	thou, thow,			ye.
Gen.	thin (thyn), thi (thy),			your, youre.
Dat. } Acc. }	the, thee,			yow, you.

	Masc.	*Fem.*	*Neut.*	
Nom.	he,	she,	hit, it,	thei, they.
Gen.	his,	hire, hir,	his,	here (her, her, hir).
Dat. } Acc. }	him,	{ hir, hire, } { here, }	hit, it,	hem.

1. The Independent forms of the pronouns, which are also used predicatively, are *min* (pl. *mine*); *oure, oures,* ours; *thin* (pl. *thine*); *youre, youres,* yours; *hire, heres,* hers; *here, heres,* theirs.

2. The Midland dialect seems to have borrowed the forms *oures, youres,* &c., from the Northern dialect, in which *oure, youre,* &c., are not used.

3. The dative cases of the pronouns are used after *wel, wo, loth, leef* (lief); with impersonal verbs, as '*me* mette,' '*him* thoughte'; and with some verbs of motion, as 'goth *him*,' 'he rydeth *him*.'

4. The pronoun *thow* is sometimes joined to the verb, as *schaltow, wiltow.*

5. The Interrogative pronouns are *who* (gen. *whos*; dat. and acc. *whom*), *which* and *what.*

(a) *Which* has often the sense of *what, what sort of*:—

'*Which* a miracle ther bifel anoon.'
(Knightes Tale, 1817 ; see Prol. l. 40.)

It is not used exactly as a relative, as in modern English, but is joined with *that*; as 'Hem *whiche that* wepith;' 'His love *the which that* he oweth.'

(b) *What* is occasionally used for *why* (cp. Lat. *quid*, Ger. *was*) :—

> '*What* sholde he studie and make himselven wood?'
> (Prol. l. 184.)
> '*What* sholde I alday of his wo endyte?'
> (Knightes Tale, l. 522.)

6. *That* is a relative pronoun, but it is often used with the personal pronouns, in the following manner :—

(a) *That he* = who.

> 'A knight ther was, and that a worthy man,
> *That* fro the tymë that he first began
> To ryden out, *he* loved chivalrye.'   (Prol. ll. 43–45.)

(b) *That his* = whose.

> 'Al were they sore y-hurt, and namely oon,
> *That* with a spere was thirled *his* brest-boon.'
> (Knightes Tale, ll. 1851–52.)

(c) *That him* = whom.

> 'I saugh to-day a corps yborn to chirche
> *That* now on Monday last I saugh *him* wirche.'
> (Milleres Tale, l. 243.)

This construction occurs in A.S. writers. Cp. *Þæt næs ná eówres þances ac thurh God, þe ic þurh* HIS *willan hider ásend wæs* = that was not of your own accord but through God, through whose will I was sent hither. (Gen. xlv. 8.)

7. The words *who* and *who so* are used indefinitely; as, 'As who seith' = as *one* says; 'Who so that can him rede' (Prol. l. 741) = if that *any one* can read him.

8. *Me* and *men* are used like the French *on*, English *one*.

Me, which must be distinguished from the dative *me*, was in use as an indefinite pronoun much later than is usually considered by English grammarians :—

> 'And stop *me* (= let any one stop) his dice, you are a villaine.'
> (Lodge, 'Wits Miserie.')

VERBS.

I. WEAK VERBS.

INDICATIVE MOOD.

Present Tense.

	Singular.	Plural.
1.	I lov-ë,	We lov-en, lov-ë.
2.	Thou lov-est,	Ye lov-en, lov-ë.
3.	He lov-eth,	They lov-en, lov-ë.

Past Tense.

	Singular.	Plural.
1.	I lov-ede [z],	We lov-eden, lov-ede.
2.	Thou lov-edest,	Ye lov-eden, lov-ede.
3.	He lov-ede,	They lov-eden, lov-ede.

1. In some manuscripts the *t* of the 2nd person sing. present tense is sometimes dropped, as in the Harl. MS. *dos* = dost, *has* = hast. This has been considered by some as a mere clerical error; but in the East Midland dialects, there was a tendency to drop the *t*, probably arising from the circumstance of the 2nd person of the verb in the Northumbrian dialects terminating always in *-es*.

2. Verbs of Saxon origin, which have *d* or *t* for the last letter of the root (and one or two that have *s*), sometimes keep the contracted form in the 3rd sing. as *sit* = sitteth, sits; *writ* = writeth, writes; *fint* = findeth, finds; *halt* = holdeth, holds; *rist* = riseth, rises; *stont* = *stondeth* = stands.

3. We often find *-th* instead of *-eth*, as *spekth* = speaketh [a].

4. In some MSS. of the Cant. Tales, the plural of the present indicative occasionally ends in *-eth* (*-th*), which was the

---

[z] In this edition I have often given the full form of the preterite in *-ede*, although the MSS. mostly write *-ed*; but in the best MS. of Chaucer's *prose* translation of Boethius the preterite ends in *ede* (*-ed*, *-te*), very seldom in *-ed* (*-d*, *-t*). Either the medial or the final *e* was frequently dropped.

[a] This contraction occasionally takes place in the imperative plural. See Nonne Prestes Tale, l. 620, where read *Tak'th*.

ordinary inflexion for all persons in the Old English Southern dialects.

> 'And over his heed ther *schyneth* two figures.'
>
> (Knightes Tale, l. 1185, Harl. MS.)

5. There are two other classes of the weak conjugation which form the past tense by *-dë* or *-të*. To the first class belong—

PRES.	PAST.
Heren, to hear,	herde.
Hiden, to hide,	hidde.
Kepen, to keep,	kepte.

Some few verbs have a change of vowel in the past tense ; as—

PRES.	PAST.
Delen, to deal,	dalte.
Leden, to lead,	ladde.
Leven, to leave,	lafte.

If the root ends in *d* or *t*, preceded by another consonant, *ë* only is added, as—

PRES.	PAST.
Wenden, to turn,	wende (= wend-de).
Sterten, to start,	sterte (=stert-te).
Letten, to hinder,	lette (=let-te).

To the second class belong—

PRES.	PAST.
Tellen, to tell,	tolde.
Sellen, to sell,	solde.
Sechen, to seek,	soughte.

II. STRONG VERBS.

1. These verbs have a change of vowel in the past tense, and the past participle ends in *-en* or *-ë*; as *sterven*, to die; pret. *starf*; p.p. *storven* or *storve*. (See Participles, p. xxxix. 3.)

2. Some few strong verbs take the inflexions of the weak verbs, so that we have double forms for the past tense, as—

> Slepen, sleep, slep, and slep-te.
> Crepen, creep, crep, and crep-te.
> Wepen, weep, wep, and wep-te.

3. The 1st and 3rd persons of the past indicative of strong verbs do *not* take an *-e* in the singular number ; the addition of this syllable turns them into plurals.   **Cf. 6 (below.)**

4. The East Midland dialect, in the Early English period, dropped the *-e* in the 2nd person past indicative ; and we find in Chaucer 'thou *bar*,' 'thou *spak*,' 'thou *dronk*' (O. E. thou *ber-e*, thou *spek-e*, thou *drunk-e*),=thou barest, thou spakest, thou drankest.   But these forms may be due merely to the scribes.

Occasionally we find *-est*, as in modern English ; as *bygonnest*, *knewest*, &c.

5. The plural indicative ends in *-en* or *-e*.

6. Some few verbs, as in the older stages of the language, have a change of vowel in the past tense plural, as—

INFINITIVE.	PRET. SING.	PAST PL.
Ryden, to ride,	rood, rod,	riden (rĭden).
Smyten, to smite,	smoot, smot,	smiten (smĭten).
Sterven, to die,	starf,	storven.

SUBJUNCTIVE MOOD.

1. The present subjunctive, singular number, terminates in *-e*, the plural in *-en* ; the past (of weak verbs) in *-ede, -de, -te*, the plural in *-eden, -den, -ten*, through all persons.

2. Such forms as *speke we, go we*,=let us speak, let us go.

IMPERATIVE MOOD.

1. Verbs conjugated like *loven* and *tellen* have the 2nd person sing. imperative in *-e* ; as *love* thou, *telle* thou.   All other verbs have properly no final *e*, as ' *her* thou '=hear thou, ' *ches* thou' =choose thou.

2. The plural terminates usually in *-eth*, but sometimes the *-th* is dropped.

INFINITIVE MOOD.

The infinitive ends in *-en* or *-e* ; as *speken, speke*, to speak.   The *-n* was dropped at a very early period in the Southern English dialect of the fourteenth century, and *-e* is preferred to *-en*.

The gerundial infinitive, or dative case of the infinitive (preceded by *to*), occasionally occurs, as *to doon-e* (=*to don-ne*), to *sen-e* (=*to sen-ne*), to do, to see. (See Kn. Ta. 177.)

PARTICIPLES.

1. The present participle ends usually in *-ing*. The A. S. suffix was *-ende*, which is used by Gower; but in the Southern dialect of Early English we find *-inde*[b], which has evidently given rise to *-inge*, of which *-ing* is a shorter form; but the longer *-inge* is occasionally employed by Chaucer, to rhyme with an infinitive verb in *-e*.

The suffix *-ing*, of nouns like *morning*, was *-ung* in the older stages of the language.

2. The past participle of weak verbs terminates in *-ed, -d*, and occasionally in *-et, -t*; that of strong verbs in *-en* or *-e*.

3. The prefix *y-* or *i-* (A.S. *ge-*) occurs frequently before the past participle, as *y-ronne* (run), *i-falle* (fallen), &c.

ANOMALOUS VERBS.

1. *Ben, been,* to be :—1st sing. pres. indic. *am*; 2nd *art*; 3rd *beth, is*; pl. *been, ben, aren, are*; past, 1st and 3rd *was*; 2nd *were*. Imperative pl. *beth*; p.p. *been, ben*.

2. *Conne,* to know, be able :—pres. indic., 1st and 3rd *can*; 2nd *can, canst*; pl. *connen, conne*; past, 1st and 3rd *couthe, cowthe, cowde*; p.p. *couth, coud*.

3. *Daren, dare* :—pres. indic. sing., 1st and 3rd *dar*; 2nd *darst*; pl. *dar, dorre*; past *dorste, durste*.

4. *May* :—pres. indic. sing., 1st and 3rd *mow, may*; 2nd *mayst, maist, might*; pl. *mowe, mowen*; pres. subjunctive *mowe*; past tense, 1st and 3rd *mighte, moghte*, 2nd *mightest* (Kn. Ta. 797).

5. *Mot,* must, may :—indic. pres. sing., 1st and 3rd *mot, moot*; 2nd *must, moot*; pl. *mooten, moote*; past *moste*.

---

[b] The Northern form of the participle was *-ande, -and*, which occasionally occurs in the Romaunt of the Rose, as *lepand*, leaping. The East Midland dialect had the double forms *-end* and *-and*.

6. *Owen,* to owe (debeo):—pres. *oweth*; past *oghte, oughte, aughte*; pl. *oghten, oughten, oughte.*

7. *Shal, schal,* shall:—pres. indic. sing., 1st and 3rd *shal*; 2nd *shalt*; pl. *shullen, shuln, shul*; past *shulde, sholde.* (Also *schal,* &c.)

8. *Thar,* need:—pres. indic. sing., 1st and 3rd *thar*; past *thurte*; subjunctive 3rd *ther.*

9. *Witen,* to know:—pres. indic. sing., 1st and 3rd *woot, wat, wot*; 2nd *wost*; pl. *witen, wite, woote*; past *wiste.*

10. *Wil,* will:—pres. indic. sing., 1st *wil, wol=wille, wolle*; 2nd *wilt, wolt*; 3rd *wile, wole, wol*; pl. *woln, wille, willen*; past *wolde.*

NEGATIVE VERBS.

Nam, nis, = am not, is not; *nas, nere,* = was not, were not; *nath* = hath not; *nadde, nad,* = had not; *nille, nil* = will not; *nolde* = would not; *nat, not, noot* = knows not; *nost* = knowest not; *niste, nisten,* = knew not.

ADVERBS.

1. Adverbs are formed from adjectives by adding *-e* to the positive degree; as *brighte,* brightly; *deepe,* deeply; *lowe,* lowly.

2. Some few adverbs have *e* before *ly,* as *boldely, needely, softely, semely, trewely.*

3. Adverbs in *-en* and *-e*:—*abouen, aboue*; *abouten, aboute*; *biforn, bifore*; *siththen, siththe* (since); *withouten, withoute.* Many have dropped the form in *-n*; as *asondre, behynde, bynethe, bytwene, biyonde*; *henne* (hence), *thenne* (thence).

4. Adverbs in *-e*:—*ofte, selde* (seldom), *sone, soone* (soon), *twie* (twice), *thrie* (thrice).

5. Adverbs in *-es*:—*needes* (A. S. *néade*), needs; *ones* (A. S. *ǽne*), once; *twies* (A. S. *twíwa*), twice; *thries* (A. S. *thríwa*), thrice.

    (*a*) *-es* for *-e, -an* or *-a*:—*unnethes* (A. S. *unéathe*), scarcely; *whiles* (A. S. *hwíle*), whilst; *bysides* (A. S. *besídan*); *togideres* (A. S. *to-gædere*).

   (*b*) *-es* for *-e* or *-en* :—*hennes* (A. S. *heonan*) ; *thennes*
     (A.S. *thanon*) ; *whennes* (A.S. *hwanon*) ; hence, thence,
     whence.

   (*c*) *-es* = -st :—*agaynes*, *ayens* (A. S. *ongéan*), against ;
     amonges (A. S. *gemang*), amongst ; *amyddes* (A. S.
     on middan, ámiddan), amidst.

6. *Of-newe*, newly (cp. of yore, of late), recently ; *as-now*, at
present ; *on slepe*, asleep (cp. *on honting, a hunting*, &c.).

7. Negative Adverbs. Two or more negatives (more common
than one in Chaucer) do *not* make an affirmative.

> 'He *nevere* yet *no* vileinye *ne* sayde,
> In al his lyf, unto no maner wight.' (Prol. ll. 70, 71.)

But (only) takes a negative *before* it ; as, 'I *nam but* deed.'
(Knightes Tale, l. 416.)

8. *As*, used before *in*, *to*, *for*, *by*, *of*,=considering, with respect to, so far as concerns. See Prol. l. 87.

As is used before the imperative mood in supplicatory phrases.
See Knightes Tale, ll. 1444, 1459.

9. *Ther*, *tho*, occasionally signify *where*, *when*.

PREPOSITIONS.

Occasionally *til*=to, *unto*=until, *up*=upon, *up-on*=on.

CONJUNCTIONS.

Ne ... *ne*=neither ... nor ; *other*=or ; *other* ... *other* = either
... or ; *what* ... *and*=both ... and ᶜ.

METRE AND VERSIFICATION.

1. Except the Tale of Melibeus and the Persones Tale,
the Canterbury Tales are written in rhyming verse ; but this
system of versification did not come into general use in England
until after the Norman Conquest. The poetry of the Anglo-
Saxons, like that of the Scandinavian and old Germanic races,

---

   ᶜ For a more detailed account of Chaucer's grammar, see Professor
Child's Essay on Chaucer, from which I have derived much assistance.

was rhythmical and alliterative. Their poems are written in couplets, in such a manner that in each couplet there are three (or two) emphatic syllables, two (or one) in the first line and one in the second, commencing with the same letter; and this letter is also the initial of the chief emphatic syllable in the second line.

> ' Ge*l*ic wæs he tham *l*eohtum steorrum,
>> *l*of sceolde he drihtnes wyrcean,
> *d*yran sceolde he his *d*reamas on heofonum,
>> and sceolde his *d*rihtne thancian
> thæs *l*eanes the he him on tham *l*eohte gescerede,
>> thonne *l*ete he his hine *l*ange wealdan :
> ac he a*w*ende hit him to *w*yrsan thinge,
>> ongan him *w*inn up-ahebban
> with thone *h*ehstan *h*eofnes wealdend,
>> the siteth on tham *h*algan stole[d].'
>> (Cædmon, ed. Thorpe, p. 17, ll. 7–16.)

Langland's Vision of Piers Ploughman, partly written in 1362, presents all the peculiarities of this form of verse :—

> ' I was *w*eori of *w*andringe,
>> And *w*ente me to reste
> Undur a *b*rod *b*anke
>> Bi a *b*ourne syde ;
> And as I *l*ay and *l*eonede
>> And *l*okede on the watres,
> I *s*lumberde in a *s*lepyng,
>> Hit *s*ownede so murie.' (ll. 7–10, A-text.)

In the North and West of England alliteration was employed as late as the end of the fifteenth century, but it appears to have gone out of use in the Southern and Eastern parts of the country, which early in the thirteenth century adopted the classical and Romance forms of versification.

---

[d] *L*ike was he (Satan) to the *l*ight stars ;
> The *l*aud (praise) of the Ruler ought he to have wrought,
*D*ear should he hold his *d*elights (joys) in heaven,
> And thank should he his *D*irector (Lord)
For the *l*oan (gift) he had bestowed on him in that *l*ight (heaven),
> Then would he have *l*et him *l*ong possess it ;
But he did *w*end (turn) it for himself to a *w*orse purpose,
> Began, for his part, to raise up *w*ar
Against the *h*ighest Ruler of *h*eaven
> Who sitteth on the *h*oly stool (seat).

2. The greater part of the Canterbury Tales is written in heroic couplets, or lines containing five accents. In this metre we have ten syllables ; but we often find eleven, and occasionally nine. Of these variations the former is obtained by the addition of an unaccented syllable at the end of a line [e].

'Him wolde | he snib | ben sharp | ly for | the nones.
A bet | trë preest | I trowe | that no | wher non is.'
(Prol. ll. 523-4.)

'Th' answere | of this | I le | të to | divynis,
But wel | I woot | that in | this world | gret pyne is.'
(Knightes Tale, ll. 465-6.)

So in lines 1 and 2 of the Prologue :—

'Whan that | April | lë with | his shou | res sootë
The drogt' | of Marche | hath per | ced to | the rootë.'

In the second variation, the first foot consists of a single accented syllable. See Prol. 170, 247, 294, 371, 391 ; Kn. Ta. 156, 324, 368, 652, 677, 1072, 1073, 1171, 1172, 1269, 1631, 1653, 1855, 1979, 1996, 2094. E. g. :—

'*Now* | it shyneth, now it reyneth fastë.' (Knightes Tale, l. 677.)

3. Chaucer frequently contracts two syllables into one ; as *nam, nis, nath, nadde*=*ne am, ne is, ne hath, ne hadde*, am not, is not, hath not, had not ; *thasse, theffect, tabide*=the ass, the effect, to abide, &c. In Troilus and Criseyde we find *ny*=*ne I*, not I, nor I ; *mathinketh*=*me athinketh*, it seems to me. But this contraction is not always so expressed in writing, though observed in reading :—

'And cer | tes lord | *to aby* | *den* your | presencë.'
(Knightes Tale, l. 69.)

'*By eter* | *ne* word | to dy | en in | prisoun.' (Ib. l. 251.)

4. The syllables -*en*, -*er*, -*eth*, -*el*, -*ow* (-*we*, -*ewe*), are often said to be contracted, but properly speaking they are *slurred* over and nearly, but not quite, absorbed by the syllable preceding :—

---

[e] For fuller information the reader is referred to Prof. Child's exhaustive Essay on Chaucer, and to the Introd. to Chaucer's Prioresses Tale, &c., ed. Skeat ; also to Mr. A. J. Ellis' valuable work on Early English Pronunciation, with special reference to Chaucer and Shakespeare (Chaucer Soc.). For the pronunciation, see Introd. to Man of Lawes Tale.

'*Weren* of | his bit | tre sal | të te | res wetë.'
(Knightes Tale, l. 422; see l. 2034.)

'And though | that I | no *wepne* | have in | this place.' (Ib. l. 733.)

'Thou shol | dest *nevere* | out of | this gro | ve pace.' (Ib. l. 744.)

With these compare the following:—

'And forth | we *riden* | a li | tel more | than pas.' (Prol. l. 825.)

'And won | derly | *delivere,* | and greet | of strengthe.' (Ib. l. 84.)

'As a | ny ra | venes *fether* | it shoon | for-blak.' (Kn. Ta. l. 1286.)

'I noot | *whether*[f] she | be wom | man or | goddesse.' (Ib. l. 243.)

'And *thinketh* | heer *cometh* | my mor | tel e | nemy.' (Ib. l. 785.)

'She ga | *dereth* flou | res par | ty whyte | and rede.' (Ib. l. 195.)

'Thus hath | this *widwe* | hir li | tel sone | y-taught.'
(Prioresses Tale; Group B, l. 1699.)

'A man | to light | a *candel* | at his | lanterne.'
(Cant. Tales, l. 5916, Wright's edition.)

5. Many words of French origin ending in *-ance* (*-aunce, -ence*), *-oun, -ie* (*-ye*), *-er* (*-ere*), *-age, -une, -ure*, are often accented on the final syllable (not counting the final *-e*), but at other times the accent is thrown further back, as in modern English: e. g. *batáille* and *bátaille*; *fortúne* and *fórtune*, &c.

So also many nouns of A. S. origin, in *-ing* (*-inge, -ynge*[g]), as *húnting* and *hunting*. (See Knightes Tale, ll. 821, 1450.)

6. Many nouns (of French origin) ending in *-le, -re*, were written, and probably pronounced, as in modern French; e. g. *table, temple, miracle, obstacle, propre* = *tabl', templ', miracl',* &c.

7. Final *-es* is a distinct syllable in—

    (*a*) The genitive case singular of nouns; as '*sowës* eres' (Prol. l. 556); '*kingës* court' (Knightes Tale, l. 323).

    (*b*) The plural of nouns (see Prol. ll. 1, 7, 9, &c.).

    (*c*) Adverbs; as *nonës, ellës, twyës*.

---

[f] The spelling *wher* in the text represents *whether*; see footnote 3, p. 39.

[g] The forms of the present participle in M. E. ended in *-inde* (*-ende, -ande*), and many verbal nouns ended in *-ung*. These endings were gradually changed into the affix *-ing*, which represented both.

8. The -ed of past participles is generally sounded; as *percëd, entunëd, pinchëd* (Prol. ll. 2, 123, 151).

9. The past tense of weak verbs ends in -*dë* or -*të*; as *wentë, coudë, woldë, bleddë, feddë, haddë* (Prol. ll. 78, 94, 144, 145, 146, 163).

A fuller form of the suffix is -*ede*; shortened occasionally to -*de* or to -*ed*; as *lovede* = *lov'de* (Prol. l. 97); whilst in l. 133 of Prologue we have *wyped*. In Troilus and Criseyde we often find *shrightë* and *sightë* written for *shrikedë* and *sighedë*.

10. Final -*en* is for the most part a distinct syllable in—
   (a) The gerund or the infinitive mood; as *to sekën, to wendën, yevën, makën* (Prol. ll. 13, 21, 487, 775).
   (b) Past participles of strong verbs; as *holpen, spoken* (Prol. ll. 18, 31).
   (c) Present and past tenses plural of verbs; as *makën, slepën, longën, werën* (Prol. ll. 9, 10, 12, 29); *bisekën, makën, lostën* (Knightes Tale, ll. 60, 77, 78).
   (d) Adverbs, prepositions, or conjunctions (originally ending in -*on* or -*an*); as *withoutën, sithën* (Prol. 461, 538; Kn. Ta. 663).

11. Final -*e*. As the manuscripts of the Canterbury Tales are not always grammatically correct, an attention to the final *e* is of great importance. The following remarks will enable the reader to understand when and why it is employed.
   a. In nouns and adjectives (of A. S. origin) the final *e* represents one of the final vowels *a, u, e*; as *asse, bane, cuppe* = A.S. *assa, bana, cuppa*; *herte, mere* = A.S. *heorte, mere*; *bale, care, wode* = A.S. *bealu, caru, wudu*; *dere, drye* = A.S. *déore, drýge*, &c.

   b. The final *e* (unaccented) in words of French origin is sounded as in French verse (but it is also frequently silent); as—
      'Who springeth up for *Ioyë* but Arcite.'
                              (Knightes Tale, l. 1013.)
      'Ne wette hir fingres in hir *saucë* depe.' (Prol. l. 129.)

c. Final *-e* is a remnant of various grammatical inflexions :—

(1) It is a sign of the dative case in nouns; as *roote, reste* (Prol. ll. 2, 30).

f is often changed into *v* (written *u* in the MSS.) before *e*, as nom. *wyf, lyf*; dat. *wyve, lyve* (Kn. Ta. 1002).

bedde, brigge (bridge), &c., are the datives of *bed, brig*, &c.

(2) In adjectives it marks—

(*a*) The definite form of the adjective; as 'the *yongë* sonne' (Prol. l. 7).

(*b*) The plural of adjectives; as '*smalë* fowles' (Prol. l. 9).

(*c*) The vocative case of adjectives; as 'O *strongë* god' (Knightes Tale, l. 1515).

(3) In verbs the final *-e* is a sign—

(*a*) Of the infinitive mood; as, *rydë, wrytë* (Prol. ll. 27, 96).

(*b*) Of the gerundial infinitive. See Infinitive Mood, p. xxxix. See Kn. Ta. 177.

(*c*) Of the past participles of strong verbs; as *yronnë, yfallë* (Prol. ll. 8, 25); *dronkë, knowë* (Knightes Tale, ll. 404, 406, 1442).

(*d*) Of the past tense (attached to *-ed, -d*, or *-t*). See p. xlv, sect. 9.

(*e*) Of the subjunctive and optative moods. See Prol. ll. 131, 770.

(*f*) Of the imperative mood 3rd person (properly the 3rd person of the subjunctive mood). See Subjunctive Mood, p. xxxix, sect. 2.

(4) In adverbs the *e* is very common :—

(*a*) It represents an older vowel-ending; as, *sonë* (soon), *twyë, thryë* (A. S. *sóna, twíwa, thríwa*).

(*b*) It distinguishes adverbs from adjectives; as *fairë*, *rightë*=fairly, rightly (Prol. 94).

(*c*) It represents an *-en*; as *aboutë*, *abovë* = E. E. *abouten, aboven* = A. S. *abútan, abúfan.*

(*d*) *-e-* is a distinct syllable in adverbs ending in *-ëly*; as *lustëly, nedëly, semëly, trewëly* (Prol. 136).

On the other hand, the final *e* is often silent—

1. In the personal pronouns; as *oure, youre, hire, here.*

2. In many words of more than one syllable, and in words of Romance origin. Cf. p. xlv, § 6.

It is elided—

1. Before a word commencing with a vowel :

  ' For I mot wep*e* and weylë whyl I live.' (Knightes Tale, l. 437.)

  ' And in the grov*e* at tym*e* and plac*e* yset.' (Ib. l. 777.)

2. Often before some few words beginning with *h*; as *he, his, him, hem, hire, hath, hadde, have, how, her, heer* :

  ' Wel coud*e* he dress*e* his takel yemanly.' (Prol. l. 106.)

  ' Then wold*e* he wep*e*, he mightë nat be stent.'

                                        (Knightes Tale, l. 510.)

  ' That in that grov*e* he wold*e* him hyd*e* al day.' (Ib. l. 623.)

In all other cases *h* is regarded as a consonant; as 'to fernë halwes' (Prol. l. 14) ; ' of smalë houndes' (Ibid. l. 146) ; 'the fairë hardy queen' (Knightes Tale, l. 24).

The following metrical analysis of the opening lines of the Prologue will enable the reader to apply the rules already given. The mark ˘ represents an unaccented, and ˉ an accented syllable ; the italic *e* represents that *e* is elided.

  ' Whăn thāt | Ăprīl | lĕ wīth | hĭs shōu | rĕs soōtĕ
  Thĕ drōght*e* | ŏf Mārch*e* | hăth pēr | cĕd tō | thĕ roōtĕ,
  Ănd bā | thĕd ēv*e* | rў vēyn*e* | ĭn swīch | lĭcoūr,
  Ŏf whĭch | vĕrtū | ĕngēn | drĕd īs | thĕ flōur ;
  Whăn Zē | phĭrūs | ĕek wĭth | hĭs swē | tĕ breēth
  Ĭnspī | rĕd hāth | ĭn ēv*e* | rў hōlt | ănd heēth
  Thĕ tēn | drĕ crŏp | pĕs, ānd | thĕ yōn | gĕ sōnnĕ
  Hăth īn | thĕ Rām | hĭs hal | fĕ coūrs | ў-rōnnĕ,

Ănd smā | lĕ fōw | lĕs mā | kĕn mē | lŏdўë,
Thăt slē | pĕn āl | thĕ nīght | wĭth ō | pĕn yë,
Sŏ prī | kĕth hēm | nătūre | ĭn hīr | cŏrāgĕs :—
Thăn lōn | gĕn fōlk | tŏ gōon | ŏn pīl | grĭmāgĕs,
Ănd pāl | mĕrs fōr | tŏ sē | kĕn strāun | gĕ strōndĕs,
Tŏ fēr | nĕ hāl | wĕs, coūthe | ĭn sōn | drў lōndĕs ;
Ănd spē | ciăllў, | frŏm ēve | rў shī | rĕs ēndĕ
Ŏf Eñ | gĕlōnd, | tŏ Cāunt | tĕrbūrў | thĕy wēndĕ,
Thĕ hō | lў blīs | fŭl mār | tĭr fōr | tŏ sēkĕ,
Thăt hēm | hăth hōlp | ĕn whān | thăt thĕy | wĕre sēkĕ.'

1. The final *e* in *Aprille, melodye*, is sounded ; but is elided in *Marche, veyne, nature* ; because in these cases it is followed by a word commencing with a vowel or with the letter *h*.

2. The final *e* in *soote, smale, straunge, ferne, seke* (l. 18), is sounded, as the sign of the plural number.

3. The final *e* in *roote* is sounded, as the sign of the dative case.

4. The final *e* in *swete, yonge, halfe*, is sounded, as the sign of the definitive form of the adjective.

5. The final *e* in *sonne, y-e, ende*, is sounded, and represents an older A. S. vowel-ending (A. S. *sunne, éage, ende*).

6. The final *e* in *yronne* is sounded, as the sign of the past participle, *yronne* representing the older *yronnen* (A.S. *gerunnen*).

7. The final *e* in *to seke* is sounded, as the sign of the gerund representing the fuller form *to sekene* (A. S. *tó sécanne*).

8. The final *en* in *holpen* is sounded, as being the sign of the p.p. of a strong verb.

9. The final *en* is sounded in *maken, slepen, longen*, as the sign of the present plural indicative.

10. The final *en* is sounded in *to seken*, as the sign of the gerund ; see above.

11. The final *es* in *shoures, croppes, fowles, strondes, halwes, londes*, is sounded, as the inflexion of the plural number.

12. The final *es* is sounded in *shires*, as the inflexion of the genitive case.

13. *Licour, vertu, nature,* and *corages,* are accented on the second syllable, as in Old French.

I gladly take the present opportunity of thanking my kind friends the Rev. W. W. Skeat and Mr. Furnivall for many valuable notes and suggestions.

R. M.

KING'S COLLEGE, LONDON,
September, 1872.

POSTSCRIPT TO THE REVISED EDITION OF 1888.

(BY THE REV. PROFESSOR SKEAT.)

THE text of former editions of this selection from the Canterbury Tales was at first taken from the well-known MS. Harl. 7334 (in the British Museum), which, however, is by no means free from clerical errors. It was afterwards revised throughout by a careful collation with the Ellesmere, Hengwrt, and Corpus MSS. printed in Dr. Furnivall's Six-Text edition of Chaucer's Canterbury Tales [h]. The Cambridge, Lansdowne, and Petworth MSS. in the same edition were also consulted in cases of difficulty, but did not prove of much service in correcting the blunders of the Harleian MS.

The present text, as revised in 1888, is entirely new, having been reprinted throughout. The differences thus introduced, though extremely numerous, are almost all of a minute character, and may not appear, at first sight, of any particular value or importance. They are, in fact, due to taking the Ellesmere MS. as the basis of the text, instead of the Harleian MS. This produces very little change in the wording, but the result is more satisfactory from a phonetic point of view, as the spelling in the Ellesmere MS. is remarkable for clearness and intelligibility, and is fairly uniform in character. There is also a great ad-

---

[h] This work, which is itself a great tribute to the memory of Chaucer, should be in the hands of every Chaucerian scholar.

vantage in conforming the spelling in the present selection to
that in the other two books of selections published in the same
series[i]; for in both of these books the Ellesmere MS. was taken
as the chief authority for the text.

A few modifications have been made in the spelling in order to
render the text more exactly phonetic. Of these, one is a more
regular use of *i* and *y*, symbols which are needlessly confused in
the MS. The short vowel is here usually printed as *i*, as in the
words *his, swich, is, Zephirus,* &c.; whilst the long vowel is
usually denoted by *y*, as *melodye, nyne, ryde, wyde.* This distinction is frequently made in the MS., and occurs in all the words
here cited. The MS. is also followed in words like *inspired,
shires,* where there can hardly be any mistake; the modern
sound is here a sure guide to the length of the vowel, though we
now substitute the sound of the *ei* in *height* for the Chaucerian *i*
(as in Mod. E. *machine*). It must suffice to say that the text is
now much more exactly phonetic than before, whilst at the same
time the readings of the Ellesmere MS. are usually better than
those of any other MS. The student who wishes to understand
the *pronunciation* of Chaucer's English, which is a very important
matter, is referred to the clear and full account of it by Mr. Ellis,
as printed in the Preface to The Tale of the Man of Lawe,
pp. ix–xix, where the spelling of the MS. is fully explained.

In the present edition, the opportunity has also been taken of
giving all the variations from the Ellesmere MS. that are of any
importance in the form of footnotes at the bottom of every page.
The abbreviations here used are the same as in the other
selections from Chaucer, and are there explained. Briefly, the
symbols, E., Hn., Cm., Cp., Pt., Ln., Hl., denote respectively the
Ellesmere MS., the Hengwrt MS., the Cambridge MS. (marked
Gg. 4. 27 in the Cambridge University Library), the MS. in
Corpus Christi College, Oxford, the Petworth MS. (belonging
to Lord Leconfield), the Lansdowne MS. 851 (in the British

---

[i] See 'The Prioresses Tale,' &c.; and 'The Tale of the Man of
Lawe,' &c.; edited by the Rev. W. W. Skeat.

Museum), and the Harleian MS. 7334 (in the same). The text
follows E., except where notice is given to the contrary.

The numbering of the lines in the Six-Text edition is noted
throughout. In the Prologue, there is no variation. In the
Knightes Tale, l. 2 corresponds to l. 860 of Group A in that
edition, which is denoted by printing (860) within marks of
parenthesis; and so on. In the Nonne Preestes Tale, l. 1
corresponds to l. 4011 of Group B in that edition, denoted by
printing (4011); and so on. In the Index of Proper Names, the
references are given to the Six-Text edition *only*; but can easily
be found by help of the numbers within marks of parenthesis.

The Introduction to The Prioresses Tale, &c., contains,
amongst other things; (1) the method of grouping the Tales,
according to the right dates; (2) remarks on Chaucer's varieties
of rhythm; (3) further remarks on grammatical forms; (4)
further remarks on metre and versification; (5) an analysis of
the metre of the Squire's Tale; (6) hints as to books useful for
understanding Chaucer; (7) a list of Chaucer's works, with
notes on some that have been falsely attributed to him; and
(8) a discussion of the Romaunt of the Rose. Some of this
information is almost indispensable, but is too full of detail to
be here repeated.

The Introduction to the Man of Lawes Tale, &c., contains
the account, by Mr. Ellis, of the pronunciation of Chaucer's
English, as already stated.

The Introduction to the Clarendon Press Edition of Chaucer's
Minor Poems discusses the genuineness of the numerous pieces
at various times attributed to Chaucer, and gives some account
of the editions of the poet's works. Some of the remarks upon
the poems of 'Anelida and Arcite' and 'The Parlement of
Foules' are so important for the right understanding of the
Knightes Tale that the substance of them is here repeated.

It appears, from internal evidence, that 'Anelida and Arcite'
was written *before* the Knightes Tale, and was never finished.
It is probable that Chaucer actually wrote an earlier draught of
the Knightes Tale, with the title of *Palamon and Arcite*, which

he afterwards partially rejected ; for he mentions ' The Love of
Palamon and Arcite' in the Prologue to the Legend of Good
Women as if it were an independent work. We must suppose
that Chaucer originally translated the *Teseide* of Boccaccio rather
closely, substituting a seven-line stanza for the *ottava rima* of
the Italian poet ; this formed the original ' Palamon and Arcite,'
a poem which was perhaps never finished. Not wishing, however, to abandon it altogether, Chaucer probably used some
of the lines over again in 'Anelida,' and introduced others into
the Parlement of Foules and elsewhere. At a later period, he
rewrote the whole story in rimed pairs of five-accent lines, which
is now known to us as The Knightes Tale. Whatever the right
explanation may be, we are at any rate certain that the *Teseide*
is the source of (1) sixteen stanzas in the Parlement of Foules [k];
(2) of part of the first ten stanzas of Anelida and Arcite [l]; (3)
of three stanzas near the end of Troilus and Creseida [m]; (4) of
the original Palamon and Arcite ; (5) of the Knightes Tale.

For further information, see Ten Brink, *Chaucer-Studien*,
Münster, 1870; and Essays on Chaucer, published by the Chaucer
Society. It must be added that Professor Ten Brink has written
another valuable work on Chaucer, entitled *Chaucers Sprache
und Verskunst*, Leipzig, 1884 ; from which much may be learnt.

With regard to the *Nonne Preestes Tale*, it has already been
remarked (at p. xxviii) that the germ of it is to be found in a
short fable by Marie de France, afterwards amplified in the old
French Roman du Renart. The fable by Marie de France
consists of 38 short lines, and is printed in Dr. Furnivall's
Originals and Analogues (Chaucer Society), p. 116, from MS.
Harl. 978, leaf 56 (formerly 76). The corresponding portion of
Le Roman du Rénart, as edited by Méon in 1826, vol. i. p. 49, is
also printed in the same, p. 117; it comprises 454 lines (ll. 1267–
1720). Professor Ten Brink shews that Marie's fable closely

---

[k] Ll. 183–294 ; from the *Teseide*, bk. vii. st. 51–66.
[l] From the *Teseide*, bk. i. st. 1–3 ; bk. ii. st. 10–12.
[m] Viz. st. 7, 8, 9 from the *end* of bk. v. ; translated from the *Teseide*,
xi. 1–3. Boccaccio here follows Lucan's *Pharsalia*, bk. ix.

resembles one found in a Latin collection of Æsopian fables in
a MS. at Göttingen, which he quotes in full (id. p. 114), and
refers us for it to Oesterley, *Romulus*, Berlin, 1870, p. 108.

A translation of Marie's fable, by myself, was printed in *The
Academy*, July 23, 1887 (p. 56); and is here reprinted for the
purpose of comparison with Chaucer's story.

THE COCK AND THE FOX.

A Cock our story tells of, who
High on a dunghill stood and crew.
A Fox, attracted, straight drew nigh,
And spake soft words of flattery.
 'Dear Sir!' said he, 'your look's divine;
I never saw a bird so fine!
I never heard a voice so clear
Except your father's—ah! poor dear!
His voice rang clearly, loudly—but
Most clearly, when his eyes were shut!'
 'The same with me!' the Cock replies,
And flaps his wings, and shuts his eyes.
Each note rings clearer than the last—
The Fox starts up, and holds him fast;
Towards the wood he hies apace.
 But as he crossed an open space,
The shepherds spy him; off they fly;
The dogs give chase with hue and cry.
The Fox still holds the Cock, though fear
Suggests his case is growing queer.—
'Tush!' cries the Cock, 'cry out, to grieve 'em,
"The cock is mine! I'll never leave him!"'
The Fox attempts, in scorn, to shout,
And opes his mouth; the Cock slips out,
And, in a trice, has gained a tree.
 Too late the Fox begins to see
How well the Cock his game has play'd;
For once his tricks have been repaid.
In angry language, uncontrolled,
He 'gins to curse the mouth that's bold
To speak, when it should silent be.
 'Well,' says the Cock, 'the same with me;
I curse the eyes that go to sleep
Just when they ought sharp watch to keep
Lest evil to their lord befal.'
 Thus fools contrariously do all:
They chatter when they should be dumb,
And, when they *ought* to speak, are mum.

The Notes have been carefully revised throughout, and the opportunity has been taken of verifying all the references, wherever practicable. Besides this, a considerable number of new Notes have been added (from my own stores), so that the additions amount to about a third of the whole.

The Glossarial Index has also been revised, because the numerous slight alterations in the spelling of the text rendered this absolutely necessary. For this purpose, every reference has been verified, and a few misprints in the numbers corrected. The etymologies have, in some cases, been reconsidered and altered.

The List of Proper Names, following the Glossarial Index, is a new addition. See p. lii.

We hope that the present reprint will be of increased service to all students and readers.

CAMBRIDGE,
July 9, 1888.

TABLE OF HISTORICAL EVENTS.

AT HOME.	A.D.	ABROAD.	A.D.
Edward III crowned . .	1327		
Death of Robert Bruce and accession of David II .	1328	Philip VI (Valois) King of France	1328
		Germany under Papal interdict	1330
		Order of Teutonic Knights settled in Prussia . .	1331
Edward Baliol crowned at Scone	1332		
Battle of Halidon Hill .	1333		
		Benedict XII . . .	1334
Freedom of trading guaranteed by the Legislature to foreign merchants . .	1335		
Exports of Wool prohibited; Foreign cloth-makers allowed to settle in England	1337	Sir John Froissart born .	1337
		Simon Boccanegra (first Doge of Genoa) . .	1339
? *Birth of Chaucer* . .	1340		
One weight and measure established for the whole kingdom (14 Edward III, c. 12)	,,		
Defeat of the French off Sluys	,,		
The Ayenbite of Inwyt, by Dan Michel of Northgate, Kent . . .	,,		
? Death of Robert of Brunne	,,		
		Petrarch crowned at Rome on Easter Day . .	1341
		Brittany the seat of civil war	,,

AT HOME.	A.D.	ABROAD.	A.D.
		Clement VI . . .	1342
		Boccaccio crowned in the Capitol by Robert the Good	,,
		Settlement of Turks in Europe	1343
		Jacob van Arteveldt (Edward the Third's partisan in Flanders) killed .	1345
Battle of Neville's Cross .	1346		
Battle of Creçy . . .	,,		
		Charles IV of Germany .	1347
		The Plague of Florence	1348-9
Death of Richard Rolle of Hampole, author of *The Pricke of Conscience* .	1349	The Black Death . .	1349
The First Great Pestilence	,,		
Order of the Garter instituted	,,		
		John II King of France .	1350
Papal Provisions forbidden	1351		
Poems on the Wars of Edward III, by Lawrence Minot	1352	Innocent VI . . .	1352
Polychronicon, by Ralph Higden	,,		
Sir John Mandeville . .	1354	Death of Rienzi . .	1354
The Scots surprise Berwick	1355		
Battle of Poictiers . .	1356		
Last Age of the Church (not by Wycliffe) . . .	,,		
Chaucer probably a Page to Prince Lionel's wife .	1357		
		La Jacquerie in France .	1358
Edward III invades France	1359	Charles the Bad claims the crown of France . .	1359
Chaucer commences his military career ; is taken prisoner by the French .	,,		
		Peace between the English and French at Bretigny .	1360

AT HOME.	A.D.	ABROAD.	A.D.
The Second Great Pestilence	1361		
Chaucer probably in Edward III's service . .	,,		
Law pleadings, &c. in English (36 Edward III, c. 15)	1362	Urban V	1362
The Vision of Piers Plowman (A-text), by Langland	,,	War between Florence and Pisa; English auxiliaries employed by the Pisans .	,,
Diet and apparel of each class of the community regulated by Statute .	1363		
		Charles V of France . .	1364
Chaucer receives an annual pension of 20 marks .	1367		
Chaucer's Compleynte to Pite (his love has rejected him) . . ?	1367–8		
The Third Great Pestilence	1369		
Chaucer's Deth of Blaunche the Duchesse . .	1369		
		War re-commenced between France and England .	1370
		Gregory XI . . .	,,
Robert II (the first of the Stuart family in Scotland)	1371		
Chaucer employed on a mission to Pisa and Genoa .	1372		
Death of Sir John Mandeville	,,		
Chaucer's Lyfe of St. Cecile	1373		
A pension of a pitcher of wine daily granted to Chaucer . . .	1374	Truce between England and France	1374
Chaucer appointed Comptroller of the Customs and Subsidy of Wools, &c. .	,,	Death of Petrarch . .	,,
? *Chaucer's Compleynt of Mars* . . .	,,		
The Bruce, by Barbour .	1375	Death of Boccaccio . .	1375
Death of Edward the Black Prince	1376		

AT HOME.	A.D.	ABROAD.	A.D.
Chaucer sent on a mission to France (Stowe, *Annals*).	1377	Gregory XI returns to Rome	1377
? *Chaucer's Boece*	,,		
Death of Edward III, and accession of Richard II .	,,		
The Vision of Piers Plowman (B-text) .	,,		
Wycliffe condemned by papal bull .	1378	Clement VII .	1378
Bible translated into English by Wycliffe . *about*	1380	Charles VI of France .	1380
(The work must have begun earlier, as it is alluded to in the B-text of *Piers Plowman*.)			
Poll-tax of 12 pence levied upon all persons above fifteen years of age .	,,		
Wat Tyler's Rebellion .	1381		
Chaucer is appointed Comptroller of the Petty Customs .	1382		
? *Chaucer's Troilus* .	,,		
Death of Wycliffe .	1384		
? *Chaucer's Hous of Fame* .	,,		
? *Chaucer's Legende of Good Women* .	1385	John I of Portugal .	1385
Chaucer dismissed from his offices of Comptroller of Wool and Petty Customs	1386		
? *Chaucer's Truth* .	,,		
The Polychronicon translated into English by John Trevisa .	1387	Conversion of the Lithuanians .	1387
Chaucer writes some of his Canterbury Tales .	,,		
Chaucer's wife dies .	,,		
Chaucer is appointed Clerk of the King's Works at Westminster .	1389	Victory of the Swiss over the Austrians at Näfels .	1389

AT HOME.	A.D.	ABROAD.	A.D.
		Ottoman victory over Christians at Kossova . .	1389
		Boniface IX . . .	,,
Chaucer has scaffolds put up in Smithfield for seeing the jousts there .	1390	Restoration of the Greek Language in Italy by Manuel Chrysolaras .	1390
Chaucer is appointed clerk of the works at Windsor.	,,		
Chaucer robbed of 20l. of the King's money . .	,,		
Robert III of Scotland .	,,		
Chaucer appointed joint Forester* of North Petherton, Somerset .	1390-1		
Chaucer's Astrolabe . .	1391		
Gower's *Confessio Amantis*	1393		
A pension of £20 a-year for life granted to Chaucer .	1394		
Persecution of Lollards .	1395	Benedict XIII . . .	1394
Death of Barbour . .	,,		
Some of Chaucer's Minor Poems . . .	1392-8		
Chaucer appointed sole Forester* of North Petherton, Somerset .	1397-8	Battle of Nicopolis . .	1396
Chaucer sued for £14 .	,,	Union of Calmar . .	1397
A grant of a tun of wine a-year made to Chaucer .	1398		
Henry IV becomes King .	1399		
Chaucer sends his Purse Poem to Henry IV .	,,		
Chaucer's Pension doubled .	,,		
Death of John of Gaunt .	,,		
Poem on '*Richard the Redeles* (probably by Langland)	,,		
Death of Chaucer . .	1400		

* See p. xiv. *Chaucer as Forester of North Petherton Park, Co. Somerset.* The Earls of March were Foresters of North Petherton under the King, and appointed substitutionary foresters. Among the appointments are these:

'10 Ric. II (June 1386-7).   Richard Brittle, by the appointment of the Earl of March.

'14 Ric. II (June 1390-1).   Richard Brittle and Gefferey Chaucer, by the appointment of the Earl of March (Roger, who died July 20, 1398).

'21 Ric. II (June 1397-8).   Gefferey Chaucer, by Alianor, Countess of March.'   Collinson, *Hist. and Antiq. of the Co. of Somerset*, iii. 62.

I take Chaucer's first appointment to be a joint one with Brittle, and suppose that this continued till Chaucer was made sole Forester by Lady March, probably while her husband was lying on his death-bed.   Mr. Floyd, however, who found the entries, and Mr. Walford D. Selby, who wrote on them in the *Athenæum*, Nov. 20, 1886, and *Life Records of Chaucer*, ii. p. 117 (Chaucer Soc. 1886), both better authorities than I, hold that as a joint appointment is most unusual, R. Brittle was Forester until 14 Ric. II; that in that year, that is, between June 22, 1390, and June 21, 1391, Chaucer succeeded him, and remained Forester till his own death in 1400.   Earl Roger died July 20, 1398, and soon after, his widow appointed Chaucer, that is, continued him in his office. Collinson should therefore read 22 Ric. II (June 1398-9), not 21. I doubt.—F. J. F.

CHAUCER.

THE PROLOGUE.

(Group A, ll. 1–858 in the Six-text edition.)

Whan that Aprille with his[1] shoures soote
The droghte of Marche hath perced to the roote,
And bathed every veyne in swich licour,
Of which vertu engendred is the flour;   *power*
Whan Zephirus eek with his swete breeth   5
Inspired hath in every holt and heeth   *wood*   *quickened*
The tendre croppes, and the yonge sonne
Hath in the Ram his halfe[2] cours y-ronne,
And smale fowles[3] maken melodye,
That slepen al the night with open yë[4],   10
(So priketh hem nature in hir corages):   *hearts*
Than[5] longen folk to goon on pilgrimages[6],
And palmers[7] for to seken straunge strondes,
To ferne halwes, couthe in sondry londes;   *distant shrines,*
And specially, from every shires ende   *well known.*   15
Of Engelond, to Caunterbury[8] they wende,

---

[1] E. hise; *rest* his.   [2] Hl. halfe; *rest* half.
[3] Pt. Ln. foules; E. Hn. foweles.   [4] Hl. yhe; Hn. Iye; E. eye.
[5] Pt. Ln. Than; E. Thanne.   [6] E. pilgrimage (*by mistake*).
[7] Pt. palmers; E. Palmeres.   [8] Hn. Caunter-; E. Cauntur-.

The holy blisful martir for to seke,
That hem hath holpen, whan that they were seke[1].
    Bifel[2] that, in that sesoun[3] on a day,
In Southwerk at the Tabard as I lay   20
Redy to wenden on my pilgrimage
To Caunterbury with ful devout corage,
At night was[4] come in-to that hostelrye
Wel nyne and twenty in a compaignye,
Of sondry folk, by aventure y-falle   25
In felawshipe[5], and pilgrims[6] were they alle,
That toward Caunterbury wolden ryde;
The chambres and the stables weren wyde,
And wel we weren esed atte beste.
And shortly, whan the sonne was to reste,   30
So hadde I spoken with hem everichon,
That I was of hir felawshipe[5] anon,
And made forward erly for to ryse,
To take our[7] wey, ther as I yow devyse.
    But natheles[8], whyl I have tyme and space,   35
Er that I ferther in this tale pace,
Me thinketh it acordaunt to resoun, *right*
To telle yow al the condicioun
Of ech of hem, so as it semed me,
And whiche they weren[9], and of what degree;   40
And eek in what array that they were inne:
And at a knight than wol I first biginne.
    A KNIGHT ther was, and that a worthy man, *distinguis*
That fro the tyme that he first bigan
To ryden out, he loved chivalrye, *knighthood*   45
Trouthe and honour, fredom and curteisye.

---

[1] E. seeke.   [2] Hn. Bifel; E. Bifil.   [3] E. seson.
[4] E. were; *rest* was.   [5] E. felaweshipe.
[6] Hl. pilgryms; E. pilgrimes.   [7] E. oure.   [8] E. nathelees.
[9] Hl. weren; *rest* were, weere.

Ful worthy was he in his lordes werre,
And therto hadde he riden (no man ferre)
As wel in cristendom as [1] hethenesse,
And evere honoured for his worthinesse.   *distinguished bearing* 50
At Alisaundre he was, whan it was wonne;
Ful ofte tyme he hadde the bord bigonne   *at the head of the table*
Aboven alle naciouns [2] in Pruce.
In Lettow hadde he reysed and in Ruce,   *raided* [Lithuania]
No cristen man so ofte of his degree.   55
In Gernade at the sege [3] eek hadde he be   *Granada*
Of Algezir, and riden in Belmarye.
At Lyeys was he, and at Satalye,
Whan they were wonne; and in the Grete See   *Mediterranean*
At many a noble aryve [4] hadde he be.   60 *arrival*
At mortal batailles hadde he been fiftene,
And foughten for our [5] feith at Tramissene
In listes thryes, and ay slayn his foo.   *ever*
This ilke worthy knight hadde been also
Somtyme with the lord of Palatye,   65
Ageyn another hethen in Turkye:
And everemore [6] he hadde a sovereyn prys.   *supreme praise*
And though that he were [7] worthy, he was wys,   *distinguished*
And of his port as meek as is a mayde.   *behaviour*
He nevere yet no vileinye ne sayde
In al his lyf, un-to no maner wight.   *sort of* 70
He was a verray parfit gentil knight.
But for to tellen yow of his array,
His hors were [8] goode, but he was [9] nat gay.   *the Kt*
Of fustian he wered a gipoun   *cassock* 75
Al bismotered with his habergeoun.   *hauberk*

---

[1] Hn. as; *rest* as in.   [2] E. nacions.   [3] E. seege.
[4] Hl. ariue; Cm. aryue; E. Hn. armee; Cp. Ln. arme.
[5] E. oure.   [6] E. -moore.   [7] *So* E. Hn. Cm.; *rest* was.
[8] E. weren; Hl. Ln. was; *rest* were.   [9] Hl. Hn. he ne was.

For he was late y-come from his viage,
And wente for to doon his pilgrimage.

　　With him ther was his sone, a yong SQUYER,
A lovyer, and a lusty bacheler,   *joyful* [s 207p] 80
With lokkes crulle, as they were leyd in presse.
Of twenty yeer of age he was, I gesse.
Of his stature he was of evene[1] lengthe,
And wonderly delivere, and greet of[2] strengthe. *active*
And he hadde[3] been somtyme in chivachye, *exped* 85 *ition*
In Flaundres, in Artoys, and Picardye,
And born him wel[4], as of so litel space,
In hope to stonden in his lady grace.
Embrouded was he, as it were a mede[5]
Al ful of fresshe floures, whyte and rede[5].   90
Singinge he was, or floytinge, al the day; *fluting*
He was as fresh[6] as is the month[7] of May.
Short was his goune, with sleves longe and wyde.
Wel coude he sitte on hors, and faire ryde.
He coude songes make and wel endyte, *relate* 95
Iuste and eek daunce, and wel[4] purtreye and wryte. *draw*
So hote he lovede, that by nightertale *nightime*
He sleep[8] namore[9] than doth[10] a nightingale.
Curteys he was, lowly[11], and servisable, *humble; helpful*
And carf biforn his fader at the table.   100

　　A YEMAN hadde he, and servaunts[12] namo
At that tyme, for him liste ryde so[13]; *it pleased him*
And he was clad in cote and hood of grene;
A sheef of pecok[14] arwes brighte[15] and kene *sharp*

---

[1] Ln. euen; *rest* euene.　　[2] E. Hn. of greet; Cm. of gret; *rest* gret of.
[3] Ln. had.　　[4] E. weel.　　[5] E. meede, reede.　　[6] E. fressh.
[7] E. Hn. Monthe; Cp. month; Hl. Pt. Ln. moneth.
[8] Hl. Cp. sleep; *rest* slepte.　　[9] E. -moore.　　[10] E. dooth.
[11] Hl. lowly; E. lowely.　　[12] E. seruantz.　　[13] E. soo.
[14] Hl. Cp. Pt. Ln. pocok.　　[15] E. bright.

Under his belt he bar ful thriftily,   *well*   105
(Wel coude he dresse his takel yemanly: *implements*
His [1] arwes drouped noght with fetheres lowe),
And in his hand he bar [2] a mighty bowe.
A not-heed hadde he, with a broun visage.
Of wode-craft wel coude he al the usage.   110
Upon his arm he bar [2] a gay bracer,   *archer's guard*
And by his syde a swerd and a bokeler,   *shield p 210*
And on that other [3] syde a gay daggere,
Harneised wel, and sharp as point of spere;
A Cristofre [4] on his brest of silver shene [5].   115
An horn he bar, the bawdrik was of grene;   *girdle*
A forster was he, soothly, as I gesse.   *truly*

   Ther was also a Nonne, a PRIORESSE,
That of hir smyling was ful simple and coy;   *quite   quiet*
Hir gretteste ooth was but by sëynt Loy;   120
And she was cleped madame Eglentyne.
Ful wel she song [6] the service divyne,
Entuned in hir nose ful semely;   *Intoned   comely*
And Frensh she spak ful faire and fetisly,   *neatly*
After the scole of Stratford atte Bowe,   125
For Frensh of Paris was to hir unknowe.
At mete wel y-taught was she with-alle;
She leet no morsel from hir lippes falle,
Ne wette hir fingres in hir sauce depe.
Wel coude she carie a morsel, and wel kepe,   130   *care*
That no drope ne fille up-on hir brest [7].
In curteisye was set ful moche [8] hir lest [9].   *pleasure*
Hir over lippe wyped she so clene,

---

[1] E. Hise.   [2] E. baar.   [3] E. oother.
[4] Hn. Cristofre; E. Cristophere.   [5] E. sheene.   [6] E. soong.
[7] Cm. brest; E. Hn. brist.
[8] Pt. moche; Cm. meche; E. Hn. muchel.
[9] Hl. lest; E. Hn. Cm. list.

That in hir coppe was [1] no ferthing sene   *dreg*
Of grece, whan she dronken hadde hir draughte.
Ful semely after hir mete she raughte,   *reached*   136
And sikerly she was of greet disport [2],   *diversion, solace*
And ful plesaunt, and amiable of port,   *behaviour*
And peyned hir to countrefete chere
Of court, and been [3] estatlich of manere,   *stately*   140
And to ben holden digne of reverence.
But, for to speken of hir conscience,   *feeling*
She was so charitable and so pitous,
She wolde wepe, if that she sawe [4] a mous
Caught in a trappe, if it were deed or bledde.   145
Of smale houndes had [5] she, that she fedde
With rosted flesh, or milk and wastel breed.   *bread cake*
But sore weep [6] she if oon [7] of hem were deed,
Or if men smoot it with a yerde smerte: *rod*
And al was conscience and tendre herte.   150
Ful semely [8] hir wimpel [9] pinched was;
Hir nose tretys; hir eyen greye as glas;   *well-proportioned*
Hir mouth ful smal, and ther-to softe and reed;
But sikerly she hadde a fair forheed.
It was almost a spanne brood, I trowe;   155
For, hardily, she was nat undergrowe.   *certainly*
Ful fetis was hir cloke, as I was war.   *neat*
Of smal coral aboute hir arm she bar
A peire of bedes, gauded al with grene;
And ther-on heng a broche of gold ful shene,   160
On which ther was first write a crowned A,
And after, *Amor vincit omnia.*

---

[1] Hl. was; *rest* ther was.   [2] E. Hn. desport; *rest* disport.
[3] E. to been; Hl. Hn. *omit* to.   [4] Hl. Hn. sawe; E. saugh.
[5] Pt. Ln. had; *rest* hadde.   [6] Ln. wepped; *rest* wepte; *read* weep.
[7] E. any; *rest* oon, on, one.   [8] E. semyly.
[9] E. wympul; Hn. wympel.

Another NONNE with hir hadde she,
That was hir chapeleyne, and PREESTES thre.   *fair one*
  A MONK ther was, a fair for the maistrye,   165   *skill*
An out-rydere, that lovede venerye;   *hunting*
A manly man, to been an abbot able.
Ful many a deyntee hors hadde he in stable: *valuable*
And, whan he rood, men mighte his brydel here
Ginglen in a whistling[1] wynd as[2] clere,   170
And eek as loude as doth the chapel-belle,
Ther as this lord was keper of the celle.
The reule of seint Maure or of seint Beneit,   *Maur. Benedict*
By-cause that it was old and som-del streit,
This ilke monk leet olde thinges pace,   *pass on* 175
And held[3] after the newe world the space.   *path?*
He yaf nat of that text a pulled hen,
That seith, that hunters been[4] nat holy men;
Ne that a monk, whan he is cloisterlees[5],
Is likned til a fish that is waterlees;   180
This is to seyn, a monk out of his cloistre.
But thilke text held[3] he nat worth an oistre.
And I seyde his opinioun was good.
What sholde he studie, and make him-selven wood,   *foolish*
Upon a book in cloistre alwey to poure,   185
Or swinken with his handes, and laboure,   *toil*
As Austin bit? How shal the world be served?   *commands*
Lat Austin have his[6] swink to him reserved.
Therfor he was a pricasour aright;   *hard rider*
Grehoundes he hadde, as swifte[7] as fowel in flight;
Of priking and of hunting for the hare   *riding* 191

---

[1] Cp. whistlyng; E. whistlynge.   [2] E. Cm. als; Hl. so; *rest* as.
[3] E. Hn. heeld; Cm. held.   [4] Hn. been; E. beth.
[5] Hl. cloysterles; E. Hn. recchelees; Cp. Pt. Ln. recheles; Cm.
rekeles (Ten Brink *proposes* recetlees).
[6] E. his owene; *rest om.* owene.   [7] Hl. swifte; *rest* swift.

Was al his lust, for no cost wolde he spare.
I seigh his sleves purfiled [1] at the hond   *embroidered, s*
With grys, and that the fyneste of a lond;
And, for to festne his hood under his chin,   195
He hadde of gold y-wroght a [2] curious pin :   *skilful*
A love-knot [2] in the gretter ende ther was.
His heed was balled, that shoon as any glas,
And eek his face, as he [3] hadde been anoint.
He was a lord ful fat and in good point ;   *ease*   200
His eyen stepe, and rollinge in his heed,   *glittering*
That stemed as a forneys of a leed ;   *gleamed. cauldron*
His botes souple, his hors in greet estat [4].   *condition*
Now certeinly he was a fair prelat [4] ;
He was nat pale as a for-pyned goost.   *tormented*   205
A fat swan loved he best of any roost.
His palfrey was as broun as is a berye.   *road-horse*
                                                    brisk
    A FRERE ther was, a wantown [5] and a merye,
A limitour, a ful solempne man.   *begging friar,*   *and pleasa*
                                                    important
In alle the ordres foure is noon that can   210
So moche [6] of daliaunce and fair langage.   *gossip*
He hadde maad ful many a mariage
Of yonge wommen, at his owne [7] cost.
Un-to his ordre he was a noble post.   *support*
Ful [8] wel biloved and famulier was he   215
With frankeleyns over-al in his contree,
And eek [9] with worthy wommen of the toun :
For he had power of confessioun,
As seyde him-self, more than a curat,
For of his ordre he was licentiat.   *see p 145*   220
Ful swetely herde he confessioun,

---

[1] Hl. Hn. purfiled ; E. ypurfiled.   [2] *All but* Hl. *ins.* ful.
[3] Cm. knot ; *rest* knotte.   [4] E. it ; *rest* he.   [5] E. estaat, prelaat.
[6] E. wantowne.   [7] Hl. moche ; E. muchel.   [8] Hl. owne ; E. owene.
[9] E. And ; *rest* Ful.   [10] Hl. Hn. eek ; *rest* omit.

And plesaunt was his absolucioun;
He was an esy man to yeve penaunce
Ther as he wiste to han[1] a good pitaunce;
For unto a povre ordre for to yive   225
Is signe that a man is wel y-shrive. *confessed*
For if he yaf, he dorste make avaunt, *dare, boast*
He wiste that a man was repentaunt.
For many a man so hard[2] is of his herte,
He may nat wepe al-thogh him sore smerte.   230
Therfore, in stede of weping[3] and preyeres,
Men moot[4] yeve silver to the povre freres.
His tipet was ay farsed ful of knyves *cowel, stuffed*
And pinnes, for to yeven faire[5] wyves.
And certeinly he hadde a mery[6] note;   235
Wel coude he singe and pleyen on a rote. *fiddle.*
Of yeddinges he bar[7] utterly[8] the prys. *popular songs*
His nekke whyt was as the flour-de-lys.
Ther-to he strong was as a champioun. *Besides*
He knew the tavernes wel in every[9] toun,   240
And everich hostiler and tappestere
Bet than a lazar or a beggestere; *leper*
For un-to swich a worthy man as he
Acorded nat, as by his facultee, *agreed*
To have with seke[10] lazars aqueyntaunce.   245
It is nat honest[11], it may nat avaunce
For to delen with no swich poraille, *poor*
But al with riche and sellers of vitaille. *victuals*
And over-al, ther as profit sholde aryse, *everywhere*
Curteys he was, and lowly[12] of servyse.   250

---

[1] Hl. Cm. han; E. haue.   [2] E. harde.   [3] E. wepynge.
[4] E. Hn. moote; *see note.*   [5] E. yonge; *rest* faire.
[6] Hl. mery; E. murye.   [7] E. baar.
[8] Pt. vttirly; Hl. utturly; E. Hn. outrely.
[9] E. al the; *rest* euery.   [10] E. Hn. Cm. sike; Pt. Ln. seke.
[11] Cm. honest; E. honeste.   [12] E. lowely.

Ther nas no man nowher so vertuous.
He was the beste beggere in his hous[1];
For thogh a widwe hadde noght a sho,
So plesaunt was his *In principio*,
Yet wolde he have a ferthing, er he wente.   *begging* 255
His purchas was wel bettre than his rente.   *income*
And rage he coude as it were right a whelpe.   *play*
In love-dayes ther coude he mochel[2] helpe.
For ther he was nat lyk a cloisterer[3],
With a thredbare cope, as is a povre scoler,   260
But he was lyk a maister or a pope.   *chief*
Of double worsted[4] was his semi-cope,   *priest's cloak*
That rounded as a belle out of the presse.
Somwhat he lipsed, for his wantownesse,   *capriciousness*
To make his English swete up-on his tonge;   265
And in his harping, whan that he had[5] songe,
His eyen twinkled in his heed aright,
As doon the sterres in the frosty night.
This worthy limitour was cleped Huberd.   *licensed Friar*

A MARCHANT was ther with a forked berd,   270
In mottelee[6], and hye on horse he sat,   *motley*
Up-on his heed a Flaundrish bever[7] hat;
His botes clasped[8] faire and fetisly.
His[9] resons he spak ful solempnely,   *opinions*
Sowninge alway thencrees of his winning.   *tending to profit* 275
He wolde the see were kept for any thing   *guarded for*
Bitwixe Middelburgh and Orewelle.   *fear of anything*
Wel coude he in eschaunge sheeldes selle.   *crowns*

---

[1] Hn. *alone inserts*—And yaf a certeyn ferme for the graunt
Noon of his bretheren cam ther in his haunt.
[2] E. muchel; Hl. mochîl.   [3] Hl. Cm. cloysterer; E. Cloystrer.
[4] *All* worstede (*badly*).   [5] Pt. Ln. had; *rest* hadde.
[6] Ln. motteley; Hl. motteleye; E. Hn. motlee.   [7] E. beuere.
[8] Cp. Pt. clapsed; Hl. clapsud.   [9] E. Hise.

This worthy man ful wel his wit bisette; *knowledge employed*
Ther wiste no wight that he was in dette,   280
So estatly [1] was he of his governaunce, *dignified, management*
With his bargaynes, and with his chevisaunce. *profit*
For sothe he was a worthy man with-alle,
But sooth to seyn, I noot how men him calle.

A CLERK ther was of Oxenford also,   285
That un-to logik hadde longe y-go.
As [2] lene was his hors as is a rake,
And he nas nat right fat, I undertake;
But loked holwe, and ther-to soberly [3].
Ful thredbar [4] was his overest [5] courtepy; *upermost* 290 *cloak*
For he had [6] geten him yet no benefice,
Ne was so worldly for to have office.
For him was levere have at his beddes heed
Twenty bokes, clad in blak or reed
Of Aristotle and his philosophye,   295
Than robes riche, or fithele, or gay sautrye. *fiddle, harp*
But al be that he was a philosophre,
Yet hadde he but litel gold in cofre;
But al that he mighte of his frendes hente, *obtain*
On bokes and on [7] lerninge he it spente,   300
And bisily gan for the soules preye
Of hem that yaf him wher-with to scoleye.
Of studie took he most cure and most hede.
Noght o word spak he more than was nede,
And that was seyd in forme and reverence,   305
And short and quik, and ful of hy sentence. *good meaning*
Sowninge in moral vertu was his speche,
And gladly wolde he lerne, and gladly teche.

---

[1] Cp. statly.   [2] E. And; Hl. Al so; *rest* As.   [3] E. sobrely.
[4] *All* -bare.   [5] Hl. ouerest; E. Hn. Cm. ouereste.
[6] Cp. Ln. had; *rest* hadde.   [7] E. Hl. his; *rest* on.

A Sergeant of the Lawe, war and wys,   *prudent*
That often hadde been at the parvys,   *portico*   310
Ther was also, ful riche of excellence.
Discreet he was, and of greet reverence :
He semed swich, his wordes weren so wyse,
Iustice he was ful often in assyse,
By patente, and by pleyn commissioun ;   *open*   315
For his science, and for his heigh renoun
Of fees and robes hadde he many oon.
So greet a purchasour was nowher noon.
Al was fee simple to him in effect,   *reward   see Note*
His purchasing mighte nat been infect.   *conveyancing* 320
Nowher so bisy a man as he ther nas,   *invalid*
And yet he semed bisier than he was.
In termes hadde he caas and domes alle,   *decisions*
That from the tyme of king William were falle[1].
Therto he coude endyte, and make a thing,   *relate* 325
Ther coude no wight pinche[2] at his wryting ;
And every statut coude he pleyn by rote.
He rood but hoomly in a medlee cote   *mixed colours*
Girt with a ceint of silk, with barres smale ;   *girdle*
Of his array telle I no lenger tale.   *ornament*
    330

A Frankeleyn was in his compaignye ;
Whyt was his berd[3], as is the[4] dayesye.
Of his complexioun he was sangwyn.
Wel loved he by the morwe a sop in wyn.
To liven in delyt was evere[5] his wone,   *custom*   335
For he was Epicurus owne[6] sone,
That heeld opinioun that pleyn delyt
Was verraily[7] felicitee parfyt.

---

[1] E. yfalle ; *rest* falle.   [2] E. Hn. pynchen ; *rest* pynche, pinche.
[3] E. heed ; *rest* berd, berde.   [4] E. a ; *rest* the.   [5] Hl. al.
[6] E. Hn. Cm. owene ; *rest* owne.
[7] Hl. verraily ; *rest* verray, verrey, uery.

An houshaldere, and that a greet, was he;
Seynt Iulian he was[1] in his contree.   340
His breed, his ale, was alwey[2] after oon;
A bettre envyned man was nevere[3] noon.   *stored*
With-oute bake mete was nevere his hous,
Of fish and flesh, and that so plentevous,
It snewed in his hous of mete and drinke,   345
Of alle deyntees that men coude thinke.
After the sondry sesons of the yeer,
So chaunged he his mete and his soper.
Ful many a fat partrich hadde he in mewe[4],   *coop*
And many a breem and many a luce in stewe[4]. 350   *pike*
Wo was his cook, but-if his sauce were
Poynaunt and sharp, and redy al his gere.   *apparel*
His table dormant in his halle alway
Stood redy covered al the longe day.
At sessiouns ther was he lord and sire.   355
Ful ofte tyme he was knight of the shire.
An anlas[5] and a gipser al of silk   *dagger, pouch*
Heng[6] at his girdel, whyt as morne milk.
A shirreve hadde he been, and a[7] countour;   *accountant*
Was nowher such a worthy vavasour.   *land owner* 360
   An HABERDASSHER and a CARPENTER,
A WEBBE, a DYERE[8], and a TAPICER,   *upholsterer*
And they were clothed alle in o liveree,
Of a solempne and[9] greet fraternitee.   *important*
Ful fresh and newe hir gere apyked was;   365 *trimmed*
Hir knyves were y-chaped[10] noght with bras,   *plated*

---

[1] E. was he; *rest* he was.
[2] Cm. Ln. alwey; Hl. alway; E. Hn. alweys.   [3] Hl. Pt. nowher.
[4] E. Hn. muwe, stuwe.
[5] E. Hn. anlaas; Cp. Pt. Ln. anelas; Hl. Cm. anlas.
[6] E. Hn. heeng.   [7] E. Hn. Cm. *om.* a.   [8] Hl. deyer.
[9] *All but* Hl. *insert* a.   [10] Hl. ichapud; Cm. chapid; *rest* chaped.

But al with silver wroght ful clene and weel,   *cleanly*
Hir girdles and hir pouches everydeel.
Wel semed ech of hem a fair burgeys,
To sitten in a yeldhalle[1] on a deys.   370
Everich, for the wisdom that he can,   *knew*
Was shaply for to been an alderman.   *purposed*
For catel hadde they ynogh and rente,   *revenue*
And eek hir wyves wolde it wel assente;
And elles certein were they to blame.   375
It is ful fair to been y-clept[2] *ma dame*,
And goon to vigilyes al bifore,   *festivals*
And have a mantel roialliche y-bore.

   A Cook they hadde with hem for the nones,
To boille[3] chiknes with the mary-bones,   380
And poudre-marchant tart, and galingale. *flavouring*
Wel coude he knowe a draughte of London ale. *boil*
He coude roste, and sethe, and broille[4], and frye, *boil*
Maken mortreux, and wel bake a pye.
But greet harm was it, as it thoughte me,   385
That on his shine a mormal hadde he;   *cancer*
For blankmanger, that made he with the beste. *cream sire*

   A Shipman was ther, woning fer by weste: *living*
For aught I woot, he was of Dertemouthe. *know*
He rood up-on a rouncy, as he couthe,   *hackney* 390
In a gowne of falding to the knee.   *cloth*
A daggere hanging on a laas hadde he
Aboute his nekke under his arm adoun.
The hote somer had maad his hewe al broun;
And, certeinly, he was a good felawe.   395

---

[1] E. yeldehalle.
[2] E. Hn. ycleped; Hl. clept; *rest* cleped, clepid.
[3] *All but* Hl. *insert* the.
[4] E. Hl. boille; Cm. boyle; *rest* broille, broile.

Ful many a draughte of wyn had he y-drawe[1]
From Burdeux-ward, whyl that the chapman sleep.   *merchant.*
Of nyce conscience took he no keep.
If that he faught, and hadde the hyer hond,
By water he sente hem hoom to every lond.   400
But of his craft to rekene wel his tydes,   *near him*
His stremes and his daungers him bisydes,   *harbour*
His herberwe and his mone, his lodemenage,   *pilotage*
Ther nas noon swich from Hulle to Cartage.
Hardy he was, and wys to undertake;   405
With many a tempest hadde his berd been shake.
He knew wel[2] alle the havenes, as they were,
From Gootlond to the cape of Finistere,
And every cryke in Britayne and in Spayne;
His barge y-cleped was the Maudelayne.   410

  With us ther was a DOCTOUR OF PHISYK,
In al this world ne was ther noon him lyk
To speke of phisik and of surgerye;
For he was grounded in astronomye.
He kepte his pacient a ful greet del[3]   *watched* 415
In houres, by his magik naturel[4].
Wel coude he fortunen the ascendent
Of his[5] images for his pacient.
He knew the cause of everich maladye,
Were it of hoot or cold, or moiste, or drye,   420
And where[6] engendred, and of what humour;
He was a verrey parfit practisour.
The cause y-knowe, and of his harm the rote,   *course it would take*
Anon he yaf the seke[7] man his bote.   *remedy*
Ful redy hadde he his[8] apothecaries,   425

---

[1] Cm. I-drawe; *rest* drawe.   [2] Hl. *ins.* wel; *rest om.*
[3] Hl. wondurly wel; *rest* a ful greet deel.   [4] E. Hn. natureel.
[5] E. Hn. hise; Cm. hese.   [6] E. Cm. Hl. *ins.* they; Hn. *ins.* it.
[7] Cm. Ln. seke; *rest* sike.   [8] E. hise.

To sende him drogges[1], and his letuaries,   *electuaries*
For ech of hem made other for to winne;
Hir frendschipe nas nat newe to biginne.
Wel knew he the olde Esculapius,
And Deiscorides, and eek Rufus[2];   430
Old Ypocras, Haly, and Galien;
Serapion, Razis, and Avicen;
Averrois, Damascien, and Constantyn;
Bernard, and Gatesden, and Gilbertyn.
Of his diete mesurable was he,   435
For it was of no superfluitee, [*seeing that l.443*]
But of greet norissing and digestible.   *nutriment*
His studie was but litel on the Bible.
In sangwin and in pers he clad was al,   *red & grey cloth*
Lyned with taffata and with sendal; *thin silk*   440
And yet he was but esy of dispence; *expenditure*
He kepte that he wan in pestilence.
For gold in phisik is a cordial,   *remedy*
Therfor he lovede gold in special.

  A good WYF was ther of bisyde BATHE,   445
But she was som-del deef, and that was scathe. *unfortunate*
Of cloth-making she hadde swiche an haunt, *skill*
She passed hem of Ypres and of Gaunt. *Ghent*
In al the parisshe wyf ne was ther noon
That to the offring bifore hir sholde goon; *see p450 158*
And if ther dide, certeyn, so wrooth was she,
That she was[3] out of alle charitee.
Hir coverchiefs ful fyne were[4] of ground;   *texture*
I dorste swere they weyeden ten pound
That on a Sonday were[4] upon hir heed.   455

---

[1] E. Hn. Cm. drogges ; Cp. Pt. Ln. drugges; Hl. dragges.
[2] Pt. Rufus ; Cm. Rufijs; Hn. Cp. Ln. Hl. Rusus; E. Risus.
[3] Hl. *inserts* thanne.   [4] E. weren.

Hir hosen weren of fyn scarlet reed,
Ful streite y-teyd, and shoos[1] ful moiste and newe. *soft*
Bold was hir face, and fair, and reed of hewe.
She was a worthy womman al hir lyve,
Housbondes at chirche-dore she hadde fyve,   460
Withouten other compaignye in youthe;
But therof nedeth nat to speke as nouthe. *at present*
And thryes hadde[2] she been at Ierusalem;
She hadde passed many a straunge streem;
At Rome she hadde been, and at Boloigne,   465
In Galice at seint Iame, and at Coloigne. *Galicia*
She coude moche[3] of wandring by the weye. *greatly* [talk]
Gat-tothed was she, soothly for to seye.
Up-on an amblere esily she sat,
Y-wimpled wel, and on hir heed an hat   470
As brood as is a bokeler or a targe;
A foot-mantel aboute hir hipes large, *riding petticoat*
And on hir feet a paire of spores sharpe.
In felaweschip wel coude she laughe and carpe. *talk*
Of remedies of love she knew per-chaunce,   475
For she coude of that art[4] the olde daunce. *game*

    A good man was ther of religioun,
And was a povre PERSOUN of a toun;
But riche he was of holy thoght and werk.
He was also a lerned man, a clerk,   480
That Cristes gospel trewely wolde preche;
His parisshens devoutly wolde he teche.
Benigne he was, and wonder diligent,
And in adversitee ful pacient;
And swich he was y-preved[5] ofte sythes. *times* 485

---

[1] Cp. Hl. schoos; E. shoes.   [2] Ln. had.
[3] Hl. Pt. Cp. moche; E. Hn. muchel.
[4] Hl. For of that art sche knew.
[5] Hl. i-proued; E. Cp. Pt. preued.

Ful looth were him to cursen for his[1] tythes,
But rather wolde he yeven, out of doute,   *without doubt*
Un-to his povre parisshens aboute
Of his offring, and eek of his substaunce.
He coude in litel thing han[2] suffisaunce.   490
Wyd was his parisshe, and houses fer a-sonder,
But he ne lafte nat, for reyn ne thonder,
In siknes[3] nor in meschief to visyte   *misfortune*
The ferreste in his parisshe, moche[4] and lyte,
Up-on his feet, and in his hand a staf.   495
This noble ensample to his sheep he yaf,
That first[5] he wroghte, and afterward[6] he taughte;
Out of the gospel he tho wordes caughte;
And this figure he added eek ther-to,
That if gold ruste, what shal yren do?   500
For if a preest be foul, on whom we truste,
No wonder is a lewed man to ruste;   *ignorant*
And shame it is, if[7] a preest take keep,   *care*
A [spotted] shepherde and a clene sheep.
Wel oghte a preest ensample for to yive[8],   505
By his clennesse, how that his sheep shold live.
He sette nat his benefice to hyre,
And leet his sheep encombred in the myre,
And ran to London, un-to sëynt[9] Poules,
To seken him a chaunterie[10] for soules,   *endowm 510 ent*
Or with a bretherhed to been withholde;   *maintained*
But dwelte[11] at hoom, and kepte[12] wel his folde,
So that the wolf ne made it nat miscarie;

---

[1] E. hise.   [2] Hl. Cm. Pt. han; E. Hn. Cp. haue.
[3] E. siknesse.   [4] Hl. Cp. moche; E. Hn. muche.
[5] E. firste.   [6] E. *ins.* that (*by mistake*).   [7] Tyrwhitt *ins.* that.
[8] Hl. ȝiue; E. yeue.   [9] Hl. Cp. seynte.
[10] Hl. chaunterie; E. chauntrie.   [11] E. dwelleth; *rest* dwelte.
[12] E. keepeth; Ln. keped; *rest* kepte.

He was a shepherde and no[1] mercenarie.

And though he holy were, and vertuous,   515

He was to sinful man nat[2] despitous,   *merciless*

Ne of his speche daungerous ne digne,   *difficult*

But in his teching discreet and benigne.   *kind*

To drawen folk to heven by fairnesse

By good ensample, this was his bisynesse :   520

But it were any persone obstinat,

What so he were, of heigh or lowe[3] estat,

Him wolde he snibben sharply for the nones[4].   *reprove*

A bettre preest, I trowe that nowher non is.

He wayted[5] after no pompe and reverence,   *looked* 525 *out for*

Ne maked him a spyced conscience,   *scrupulous sophisticated*

But Cristes lore, and his[6] apostles twelve,

He taughte, but first he folwed it him-selve.

   With him ther was a PLOWMAN, was his brother,   *carried*

That hadde y-lad of dong ful many a fother,   530 *load*

A trewe swinkere and a good was he,

Livinge in pees and parfit charitee.

God loved he best with al his hole herte

At alle tymes, thogh him[7] gamed or smerte,   *pleased*

And thanne his neighebour right as him-selve.   535

He wolde thresshe, and ther-to dyke and delve,

For Cristes sake, for[8] every povre wight,

Withouten hyre, if it lay in his might.

His tythes payed[9] he ful faire and wel,

Bothe of his propre[10] swink and his catel.   540

In a tabard he rood upon a mere.   *ploughman's frock*

---

[1] Hl. no ; *rest* not a.
[2] Hl. to senful man nought ; *rest* nat to sinful man.
[3] Hn. lowe ; E. lough.   [4] E. nonys.
[5] E. waiteth ; *rest* waited, wayted.   [6] E. hise.
[7] E. Pt. Ln. he ; *rest* him.   [8] Hn. Hl. with.
[9] Cp. Pt. payed ; Cm. Hl. payede ; E. Hn. payde.   [10] Hl. owne.

Ther was also a Reve and a Millere,
A Somnour and a Pardoner also,
A Maunciple, and my-self; ther were namo.
    The MILLER was a stout carl, for the nones,   545
Ful big he was of braun, and eek of bones; *muscle*
That proved wel, for over-al ther he cam,
At wrastling he wolde have alwey the ram.
He was short-sholdred, brood, a thikke knarre, *knotted*
Ther nas no dore that he nolde[1] heve of harre, 550 *Ring*
Or breke it, at a renning, with his heed.
His berd as any sowe or fox was reed,
And ther-to brood, as though it were a spade.
Up-on the cop right of his nose he hade *top*
A werte, and ther-on stood a tuft[2] of heres[3],   555
Reed as the bristles[4] of a sowes eres[3];
His nose-thirles blake were and wyde.
A swerd and[5] bokeler bar he by his syde;
His mouth as greet[6] was as a greet forneys.
He was a Ianglere and a goliardeys, *babbler,* *buf*560 *Fon*
And that was most of sinne and harlotryes.
Wel coude he stelen corn, and tollen thryes;
And yet he hadde a thombe of gold, pardee.
A whyt cote and a blew hood wered he.
A baggepype wel[7] coude he blowe and sowne, 565 *soun*
And therwithal he broghte us out of towne.
    A gentil MAUNCIPLE was ther of a temple,
Of which achatours mighte take exemple *caterers*
For to be wyse in bying of vitaille.
For whether[8] that he payde, or took by taille, 570
                                           credit

[1] Cp. Hl. nolde; Hn. noolde; E. ne wolde.
[2] E. toft; Ln. tofte; *rest* tuft.   [3] E. herys, erys.
[4] Hn. bristles; E. brustles; Pt. brysteles; Hl. Cp. berstles.
[5] *All but* Cp. *ins.* a.   [6] Hl. wyde; *rest* greet, gret.   [7] Hl. *om.* wel.
[8] E. Hn. wheither.

Algate he wayted so in his achat [1],   *purchase*
That he was ay biforn and in good stat [2].   *before others*
Now is nat that of God a ful fair grace,
That swich a lewed mannes wit shal pace   *surpass*
The wisdom of an heep of lerned men?   575
Of maistres hadde he mo than thryes ten,   *masters*
That were [3] of lawe expert and curious;   *careful*
Of which [4] ther were a doseyn [5] in that hous,
Worthy to been stiwardes of rente and lond
Of any lord that is in Engelond,   580
To make [6] him live by his propre good,
In honour dettelees, but [7] he were wood,   *mad*   *without debt*
Or live as scarsly as him list desire;
And able for to helpen al a shire
In any cas [8] that mighte falle or happe;   585
And yit this maunciple sette hir aller cappe.   *capped them all*

The REVE was a sclendre colerik man,
His berd was shave as ny as ever he can.
His heer was by his eres [9] round y-shorn.
His top was dokked [10] lyk a preest biforn.   590
Ful longe were his legges, and ful lene,
Y-lyk a staf, ther was no calf y-sene.
Wel coude he kepe a gerner and a binne;
Ther was noon auditour coude on [11] him winne.
Wel wiste he, by the droghte, and by the reyn,   595
The yeldyng of his seed, and of his greyn.
His lordes sheep, his neet, his dayerye,   *cattle*
His swyn, his hors, his stoor, and his pultrye,   *stock*
Was hoolly in this reves governing,

---

[1] E. Achaat.   [2] E. staat.   [3] E. weren.   [4] E. whiche.
[5] Cm. doseyn; E. duszeyne.   [6] E. maken.
[7] Cm. but; Cp. Pt. but if that; *rest* but if.   [8] E. Hn. caas.
[9] *All but* Hl. Ln. *ins.* ful.   [10] E. doked.   [11] E. of; *rest* on.

And by his covenaunt yaf the rekening,   600
Sin that his lord was twenty yeer of age ;
Ther coude no man bringe him in <u>arrerage</u>.   *arrears*
Ther nas baillif, ne <u>herde</u>, ne [1] other <u>hyne</u>,   *keeper servant*
That he [2] ne [3] knew his <u>sleighte</u> and his <u>covyne</u> ;   *sleight craft : dec-*
They were adrad of him, as of the deeth.   605
His <u>woning</u> was ful fair [4] up-on an heeth,
With grene treës shadwed [5] was his place.
He coude bettre than his lord purchace.
Ful riche he was <u>astored</u> prively,   *stored*
His lord wel coude he plesen subtilly,   610
To yeve and <u>lene</u> him of his owne [6] good,   *lend*
And have a thank, and [7] yet a <u>cote</u> [8], and hood.   *gown*
In youthe he lerned hadde [9] a good <u>mister</u> [10] ;   *trade?*
He was a wel good <u>wrighte</u>, a carpenter.   *workman*
This reve sat up-on a ful good <u>stot</u>,   *cob*   615
That was al <u>pomely</u> grey, and highte Scot.   *dappled*
A long surcote of <u>pers</u> up-on he hade,   *blue*
And by his syde he bar [11] a rusty blade.
Of Northfolk was this reve, of which I telle,
Bisyde a toun men clepen Baldeswelle.   620
Tukked he was, as is a frere, aboute,
And evere he rood the hindreste of our route.

A SOMNOUR [12] was ther with us in that place,
That hadde a fyr-reed cherubinnes face,
For <u>sawceflem</u> he was, with eyen narwe.   *pimpled* 625
[And quik] he was, and [chirped] as a sparwe,

---

[1] E. Hn. Cp. Pt. nor ; *rest* ne.   [2] Hl. they.   [3] E. Cm. *om.* ne.
[4] Hl. fair ; E. faire.
[5] E. Hn. shadwed ; Hl. i-schadewed ; Cm. I-schadewid ; Cp. Pt. shadewed ; Ln. schadowed.
[6] Hl. owne ; E. owene.   [7] E. *om.* and.   [8] E. gowne ; *rest* cote.
[9] *So* Hn. Hl. ; E. *and rest* hadde lerned.   [10] Cp. Hl. mester.
[11] E. baar.   [12] Cp. Pt. Somnour ; Hl. sompnour ; E. Hn. Somonour.

With scalled[1] browes blake, and piled berd; *plucked*
Of his visage children were aferd.
Ther nas quik-silver, litarge, ne brimstoon[2], *white lead*
Boras, ceruce, ne oille of tartre noon,   "   630
Ne oynement that wolde clense and byte,
That him mighte helpen of his[3] whelkes whyte, *pimples*
Ne of the knobbes sittinge on his chekes. *boils*
Wel loved he garleek, oynons, and eek lekes,
And for to drinken strong wyn, reed as blood. 635
Thanne wolde he speke, and crye as he were wood.
And whan that he wel dronken hadde the wyn,
Than wolde he speke no word but Latyn.
A fewe termes hadde he, two or thre,
That he had lerned out of som decree; 640
No wonder is, he herde it al the day;
And eek ye knowen wel, how that a Iay
Can clepen 'Watte,' as well as can the pope.
But who-so coude in other thing him grope, *test*
Thanne hadde he spent al his philosophye; 645
Ay '*Questio quid iuris*' wolde he crye.
He was a gentil harlot and a kynde;
A bettre felawe sholde men noght fynde.
He wolde suffre for a quart of wyn
A good felawe to have his [wikked sin] 650
A twelf-month, and excuse him atte fulle:
And prively a finch eek coude he pulle. *secretely pigeon*
And if he fond owher a good felawe, *anywhere*
He wolde techen him to have non awe,
In swich cas, of the erchedeknes[4] curs, 655
But-if a mannes soule were in his purs; *unless*
For in his purs he sholde y-punisshed be.

---

[1] E. Hn. Cm. scaled.   [2] Cp. Pt. bremston.
[3] E. the; *rest* his.   [4] Cp. erche-; E. erce-; Hl. arche-.

'Purs is the erchedeknes helle,' seyde he.
But wel I woot he lyed right in dede;
Of cursing oghte ech gulty man him[1] drede——　660
For curs wol slee right as assoilling saveth[2]——　*absolution*
And also war him of a *significavit*.　*writ of excommunication*
In daunger hadde he at his owne[3] gyse　*jurisdiction*
The yonge girles of the diocyse,　　　*assize*
And knew hir counseil, and was al hir reed.　*advis* 665 *or*
A gerland hadde he set up-on his heed,
As greet as it were for an ale-stake;
A bokeler[4] hadde he maad him of a cake.
　　With him ther rood[5] a gentil PARDONER
Of Rouncivale, his frend and his compeer,　*Ronces* 670 *alles*
That streight was comen fro the court of Rome.
Ful loude he song[6], 'Com hider, love, to me.'
This somnour bar to him a stif burdoun,　*bass sang a[deep]*
Was nevere trompe of half so greet a soun.　*trumpet*
This pardoner hadde heer as yelow as wex,　　675
But smothe it heng[7], as doth a strike of flex;　*hank*
By ounces henge his[8] lokkes that he hadde,　*small piece*
And ther-with he his[8] shuldres overspradde;
But thinne it lay, by colpons oon and oon;　*shreds*
But hood, for Iolitee, ne[9] wered he noon,　*amuse* 680 *men*
For it was trussed up in his walet.
Him thoughte, he rood al of the newe Iet;　*fashion*
Dischevele[10], save his cappe, he rood al bare.
Swiche glaringe eyen hadde he as an hare.
A vernicle hadde he sowed on[11] his cappe.　*veronica* 685
His walet lay[12] biforn him in his lappe,

---

[1] Cp. Ln. him ; Hl. Pt. to ; *rest om.*　　[2] Hl. saveth ; E. sauith.
[3] Hl. owne ; E. owene.　　　　[4] E. bokeleer.
[5] E. was ; *rest* rood, rode.　　[6] E. soong.　　[7] E. heeng.
[8] E. hise.　　[9] Hl. ne ; *rest omit.*　　[10] E. Discheuelee.
[11] Hl. Cp. on ; *rest* vp on.　　[12] Hl. lay ; *which the rest omit.*

Bret-ful of pardoun come[1] from Rome al hoot.
A voys he hadde as smal as hath a[2] goot.
No berd hadde he, ne nevere sholde have,
As smothe it was as it were late y-shave[3];   690
I trowe he were a gelding or a mare.

But of his craft, fro Berwik into Ware,
Ne was ther swich another pardoner.
For in his male he hadde a pilwe-beer,   *bag*
                                                 pillow case
Which that, he seyde, was our[4] lady veyl: 695
He seyde, he hadde a gobet of the seyl   *fragment*
That sëynt Peter hadde, whan that he wente
Up-on the see, til Iesu Crist him hente.   *took hold of*
He hadde a croys of latoun, ful of stones,   *brass*
And in a glas he hadde pigges bones.   700
But with thise relikes, whan that he fond
A povre person dwelling up-on lond,
Up-on a day he gat him more moneye
Than that the person gat in monthes tweye.
And thus with feyned flaterye and Iapes,   705
He made the person and the peple his apes.
But trewely to tellen, atte laste,
He was in chirche a noble ecclesiaste.
Wel coude he rede a lessoun or a storie,
But alderbest he song an offertorie; *best of all* 710 *Liturgy 238*
For wel he wiste, whan that song was songe,
He moste preche, and wel affyle his tonge,   *polish*
To winne silver, as he ful[5] wel coude;
Therefore he song so meriely[6] and loude.
      Now have I told you shortly[7], in a clause,   715 *discourse*

---

[1] Hl. Cm. come; *rest* comen.   [2] Hl. eny (*for* hath a).
[3] Hn. yshaue; E. shaue.   [4] *All* oure.   [5] Hl. right.
[6] Cp. Pt. Ln. so meriely; E. Hn. Cm. the murierly.
[7] E. Hl. shortly; *rest* soothly.

Thestat[1], tharray, the nombre, and eek the cause
Why that assembled was this compaignye
In Southwerk, at[2] this gentil hostelrye,
That highte the Tabard, faste by the Belle.
But now is tyme to yow for to telle   720
How that we baren us that ilke night,
Whan we were in that hostelrye alight.
And after wol I telle of our viage,
And al the remenaunt of our[3] pilgrimage.
But first I pray yow of your[4] curteisye,   725
That ye narette[5] it nat my vileinye,   *impute*
Thogh that I pleynly speke in this matere,
To telle yow hir wordes and hir chere;   *appearance*
Ne thogh I speke hir wordes proprely.
For this ye knowen al-so wel as I,   730
Who-so shal telle a tale after a man,
He moot reherce, as ny as evere he can,
Everich a word, if it be in his charge,
Al speke he never so rudeliche and[6] large; *free*
Or elles he moot telle his tale untrewe,   735
Or feyne thing, or fynde wordes newe.
He may nat spare, al-thogh he were his brother;
He moot as wel seye o word as another.
Crist spak him-self ful brode in holy writ, *plainly*
And wel ye woot, no vileinye is it.   740
Eek Plato seith, who-so that[7] can him rede,
The wordes mote be cosin to the dede.
Also I prey yow to foryeve it me,
Al have I nat set folk in hir degree   *although*
Here in this tale, as that they sholde stonde;   745

---

[1] Hl. Thestat; Hn. Thestaat; E. The staat; Cm. Cp. The estat.
[2] E. as; *rest* at.   [3] E. oure (*but* our *in* l. 723).
[4] E. youre; Hl. your.   [5] E. Hn. Cm. narette; Cp. Pt. Hl. ne rette.
[6] E. or; Hl. ne; *rest* and.   [7] *All but* Hl. *om.* that.

My wit is short, ye may wel understonde.   *wisdom*

    Greet chere[1] made our hoste us everichon,
And to the soper sette he us anon;
And served us with vitaille at the beste.
Strong was the wyn, and wel to drinke us leste. 750 *pleased*
A semely man our hoste[2] was with-alle   *comely*
For to han[3] been a marshal in an halle;
A large man he was with eyen stepe,   *glittering*
A fairer burgeys was ther noon in Chepe:
Bold of his speche, and wys, and wel y-taught,   755
And of manhod him lakkede[4] right naught.
Eek therto he was right a mery man,
And after soper pleyen he bigan,
And spak of mirthe amonges othere thinges,
Whan that we hadde maad our rekeninges;   760
And seyde thus: 'Now[5], lordinges, trewely
Ye ben to me right welcome hertely:
For by my trouthe, if that I shal nat lye,
I ne saugh[6] this yeer so mery[7] a compaignye
At ones in this herberwe as is now.   *lodging* 765
Fayn wolde I doon yow mirthe, wiste I how.
And of a mirthe I am right now bithoght,
To doon yow ese, and it shal coste noght.
    Ye goon to Caunterbury; God yow spede,
The blisful martir quyte yow your mede. *requite* 770 *reward*
And wel I woot, as ye goon by the weye,
Ye shapen yow to talen and to pleye;   *plan*
For trewely, confort ne mirthe is noon
To ryde by the weye doumb as a[8] stoon;
And therfore wol I maken yow disport, *diversion* 775

---

[1] E. chiere.   [2] Hl. ooste; E. hoost.   [3] Hl. han; *rest om.*
[4] Cm. Cp. lakkede; E. lakked.   [5] Hl. lo.
[6] Hl. ne saugh; *rest* saugh nat (seigh not, &c.).
[7] Hl. Cm. mery; E. myrie.   [8] E. the; Hn. *om*; *rest* a.

As I seyde erst, and doon yow som confort.
And if yow lyketh alle, by oon assent,
Now[1] for to stonden at my Iugement,
And for to werken as I shal yow seye,
To-morwe, whan ye ryden by the weye, 780
Now, by my fader soule, that is deed,
But[2] ye be merye[3], I wol yeve yow[4] myn heed.
Hold up your hond, withoute more speche.'
Our counseil was nat longe for to seche;
Us thoughte it was[5] noght worth to make it wys, 785 see p 165
And graunted him with-outen more avys,
And bad him seye his verdit[6], as him leste.
　'Lordinges,' quod he, 'now herkneth for the beste;
But tak[7] it not, I prey yow, in desdeyn;
This is the poynt, to speken short and pleyn, 790
That ech of yow, to shorte with our weye,
In this viage, shal telle tales tweye,
To Caunterbury-ward, I mene it so,
And hom-ward he shal tellen othere two,
Of aventures that whylom[8] han bifalle. 795
And which of yow that bereth him best of alle,
That is to seyn, that telleth in this cas[9] _condition_
Tales of best sentence and most solas[9], _mirth, enjoyment_
Shal han a soper at our aller cost
Here in this place, sitting by this post, 800
Whan that we come agayn fro Caunterbury.
And for to make yow the more mery[10],
I wol my-selven gladly[11] with yow ryde,

---

[1] _All but_ Hl. _om._ Now.　　[2] E. But if; _rest_ But.
[3] Hl. merye; E. myrie.　　[4] Hl. smyteth of.　　[5] Hl. nas.
[6] Cp. verdit; Pt. veredit; Hl. Ln. verdite; Cm. verdoit; E. Hn. voirdit.
[7] E. taak; Ln. tak; Cp. Pt. take; Hl. taketh.　　[8] Hl. ther.
[9] E. caas, solaas.　　[10] E. Hn. Cp. mury.
[11] Hl. myseluen gladly; E. my self goodly.

Right at myn owne cost, and be your gyde.
And who-so wol[1] my Iugement withseye *gainsay* 805
Shal paye al that we spenden by the weye.
And if ye vouche-sauf that it be so,
Tel me anon, with-outen wordes mo,
And I wol erly shape me therfore.'

This thing was graunted, and our othes swore 810
With ful glad herte, and preyden him also
That he wold[2] vouche-sauf for to do so,
And that he wolde been our governour,
And of our tales Iuge and reportour,
And sette a soper at a certeyn prys;   815
And we wold[3] reuled been at his devys,
In heigh and lowe[4]; and thus, by oon assent,
We been acorded to his Iugement.
And ther-up-on the wyn was fet anoon; *brought*
We dronken, and to reste wente echoon,   820
With-outen any lenger taryinge.
A-morwe, whan that[5] day bigan to springe[6],
Up roos our host, and was our aller[7] cok, *of us all*
And gadrede us togidre, alle in a flok,
And forth we riden, a litel more than pas[8],   825
Un-to the watering of seint Thomas.
And there our host bigan his hors areste,
And seyde; 'Lordinges, herkneth if yow leste.
Ye woot your forward[9], and I[10] it yow recorde. *agreement*
If even-song and morwe-song acorde,   830
Lat se now who shal telle the firste tale[11].
As evere mote I drinke wyn or ale,

---

[1] E. wole (*but* wol *in* l. 809).   [2] E. would.
[3] Hl. wolde; Pt. wold; *rest* wol, wolen, wiln. wil.
[4] Hl. lowe; E. lough.   [5] *So* E. Hn.; Hl. that the; *rest* the.
[6] E. gan for to sprynge.   [7] Hl. althur; Cp. alther; Pt. Ln. alder.
[8] E. paas.   [9] E. foreward (*badly*).   [10] E. Hn. *om.* I.
[11] Hl. ferst a tale.

Who-so be rebel to my Iugement
Shal paye for al that by the weye is spent.
Now draweth cut, er that we ferrer twinne; *farther* 835 *jou*
He which that hath the shortest[1] shal biginne.'
'Sire knight,' quod he, 'my maister and my lord,
Now draweth cut, for that is myn acord.
Cometh neer,' quod he, 'my lady prioresse;
And ye, sir clerk, lat be your shamfastnesse[2],   840
Ne studieth noght; ley hond to, every man.'

   Anon to drawen every wight bigan,
And shortly for to tellen, as it was,
Were it by aventure, or sort, or cas, *luck, destiny, cha*
The sothe is this, the cut fil to the knight,   845
Of which ful blythe and glad was every wight;
And telle he moste his tale, as was resoun, *right*
By forward[3] and by composicioun, *agreement*
As ye han herd; what nedeth wordes mo?
And whan this goode man saugh[4] it was so,   850
As he that wys was and obedient
To kepe his forward[3] by his free assent,
He seyde: 'Sin I shal biginne the game,
What, welcome be the[5] cut, a Goddes name!
Now lat us ryde, and herkneth what I seye.'   855

   And with that word we riden forth our weye;
And he bigan with right a mery[6] chere
His tale anon, and seyde in this manere.

**Heere endith the prolog of this book; and heere
bigynneth the first tale which is the Knyghte[s]
Tale.**

---

[1] E. Hn. shorteste.   [2] E. shamefastnesse.
[3] E. foreward (*badly*).   [4] *All insert* that *after* saugh (*needlessly*).
[5] Hl. thou.   [6] Cm. mery; E. myrie.
COLOPHON : *from* MS. Sloane 1685.

THE KNIGHTES TALE.

(GROUP A, ll. 859–3108 in the Six-text edition.)

Iamque domos patrias, Scithice post aspera gentis
Prelia laurigero, &c.

[Statius, *Theb.* xii. 519.]

WHYLOM, as olde stories tellen us,
Ther was a duk that highte Theseus;   (860)
Of Athenes he was lord and governour,
And in his tyme swich a conquerour,
That gretter was ther noon under the sonne.   5
Ful many a riche contree hadde he wonne;
That with his wisdom and his chivalrye
He conquered al the regne of Femenye,   *the Amazons*
That whylom was y-cleped Scithia;   *Hippolyte*
And weddede [1] the queen Ipolita,   *Scythia*   10
And broghte hir hoom with him in his contree
With muchel glorie and greet solempnitee,   (870) *festivity*
And eek hir yonge [2] suster Emelye.
And thus with victorie and with melodye
Lete I this noble duk to Athenes ryde,   15
And al his hoost, in armes him bisyde.
    And certes, if it nere to long to here,
I wolde han told yow [3] fully the manere,

[1] Cp. Hl. weddede; Cm. weddide; *the rest* wedded.
[2] E. faire; Pt. yenge; *the rest* yonge.
[3] Hl. han told yow; E. yow haue toold; *the rest* haue toold(told).

How wonnen was the regne of Femenye
By Theseus, and by his chivalrye ;   20
And of the grete bataille for the nones
Bitwixen Athenes and the [1] Amazones ;   (880)
And how asseged was Ipolita,
The faire hardy queen of Scithia ;
And of the feste that was at hir weddinge,   25
And of the tempest at hir hoom-cominge ;
But al that thing I moot as now forbere.
I have, God woot, a large feeld to ere,
And wayke been the oxen in my plough,   *weak*
The remenant of the tale is long ynough ;   *delay* 30
I wol nat letten eek noon of [2] this route, *company*
Lat every felawe telle his tale aboute,   (890)
And lat see now who shal the soper winne,
And ther I lefte, I wol ageyn biginne.

  This duk, of whom I make mencioun,   35
When he was come almost unto the toun,
In al his wele and in his moste pryde,   *prosperity*
He was war, as he caste his eye asyde,
Wher that ther kneled in the hye [3] weye
A compaignye of ladies, tweye and tweye,   40
Ech after other, clad in clothes blake ;
But swich a cry and swich a wo they make,   (900)
That in this world nis creature livinge,
That herde swich another weymentinge ;   *lamentation*
And of this cry they nolde nevere stenten, *cease* 45
Til they the reynes of his brydel henten.   *seized*

  ' What folk been ye, that at myn hoom-cominge
Perturben so my feste with cryinge ? '

---

[1] Tyrwhitt *has* the ; *which the* MSS. *omit.*
[2] Hl. létte eek non of al ; *the rest have* letten, *and omit* al.
[3] E. *om.* hye ; *the rest* hye, heighe, hihe, highe, high.

Quod Theseus, 'have ye so greet envye
Of myn honour, that thus compleyne and crye?   50
Or who hath yow misboden, or offended?   *injured*
And telleth me if it may been amended;   (910)
And why that ye been clothed thus in blak?'

   The eldest[1] lady of hem alle spak,
When she hadde swowned with a deedly chere,   55   *countenance*
That it was rewthe[2] for to seen and[3] here,   *pity*
And seyde: 'Lord, to whom Fortune hath yiven
Victorie, and as a conquerour to liven,
Noght greveth us your glorie and your[4] honour;
But we biseken mercy and socour.   60
Have mercy on our wo and our distresse.
Som droppe of pitee, thurgh thy gentillesse,   (920)   *through*
Upon us wrecched wommen lat thou falle.
For certes, lord, ther nis[5] noon of us alle,
That she nath[6] been a duchesse or a quene;   65
Now be we caitifs[7], as it is wel sene: *wretches*
Thanked be Fortune, and hir false wheel,
That noon estat assureth to be weel.
And certes, lord, to abyden youre presence,
Here in the temple of the goddesse Clemence   70   *clemency*
We han ben waytinge al this fourtenight;
Now help us, lord, sith it is in thy might.   (930)
I wrecche, which that wepe and waille[8] thus,   *wretch.*
Was whylom wyf to king Capaneus,
That starf at Thebes, cursed be that day!   *died*   75
And alle we, that been in this array,
And maken al this lamentacioun,
We losten alle our housbondes at that toun,

---

[1] Cm. eldest; E. eldeste.   [2] Ln. rewthe; Cm. reuthe; E. routhe.
[3] Hl. or; *rest* and.   [4] Hl. *om.* your.   [5] Hl. nys; *rest* is.
[6] E. Hn. Pt. Ln. ne hath.   [7] Cm. Hl. caytifs; E. caytyues.
[8] E. crie; Hn. Hl. waille; Cm. Cp. Pt. weile.

Whyl that the sege ther-aboute lay.
And yet¹ the olde Creon, weylaway !   80
That lord is now of Thebes the citee,
Fulfild of ire and of iniquitee,   (940)
He, for despyt, and for his tirannye,   *malicious anger*
To do the dede bodyes vileinye,
Of alle our lordes, whiche that ben slawe,   85
Hath² alle the bodyes on an heep y-drawe,
And wol nat suffren hem, by noon assent,
Neither to been y-buried nor y-brent,
But maketh houndes ete hem in despyt.'
And with that word, with-outen more respyt,   90
They fillen gruf, and cryden pitously,   *fell flat*
'Have on us wrecched wommen som mercy,   (950)
And lat our sorwe sinken in thyn herte.'
    This gentil duk doun from his courser sterte *leape*
With herte pitous, whan he herde hem speke.   95
Him thoughte that his herte wolde breke,
Whan he saugh hem so pitous and so mat³, *dejected*
That whylom weren of so greet estat³.
And in his armes he hem alle up hente,   *seized*
And hem conforteth in ful good entente ; *intention*100
And swoor his oth, as he was trewe knight,
He wolde doon so ferforthly his might   *as far* (960) *as*
Upon the tyraunt Creon hem to wreke,
That al the peple of Grece sholde speke
How Creon was of Theseus y-served,   105
As he that hadde his deth ful wel deserved.
And right anoon, with-outen more abood, *delay*
His baner he desplayeth, and forth rood
To Thebes-ward, and al his host bisyde ;

---

¹ *All but* Hl. *ins.* now.   ² E. He hath ; *rest* Hath.
³ E. maat, estaat.

No neer Athenes wolde he go ne ryde,   110
Ne take his ese fully half a day,
But onward on his wey that night he lay;   (970)
And sente anoon Ipolita the quene,
And Emelye hir yonge suster shene,
Un-to the toun of Athenës to dwelle;   115
And forth he rit; ther is namore to telle.

    The rede statue of Mars with spere and targe
So shyneth in his whyte baner large,
That alle the feeldes gliteren up and doun;
And by his baner born is his penoun   120
Of gold ful riche, in which ther was y-bete
The Minotaur which that he slough in Crete.   (980)
Thus rit this duk, thus rit this conquerour,
And in his host of chivalrye the flour,
Til that he cam to Thebes, and alighte   125
Faire in a feeld, ther as he thoughte fighte. *gracefully*
But shortly for to speken of this thing,
With Creon, which that was of Thebes king,
He faught, and slough him manly as a knight
In pleyn bataille, and putte the folk to flight;   130
And by assaut he wan the citee after,
And rente adoun bothe wal, and sparre, and rafter;
And to the ladyes he restored agayn   (991)
The bones of hir housbondes that were slayn,
To doon obsequies, as was tho the ~~gyse~~. *fashion* 135
But it were al to long for to devyse
The grete clamour and the waymentinge
That[1] the ladyes made at the brenninge
Of the bodyes, and the grete honour
That Theseus, the noble conquerour,   140
Doth to the ladyes, whan they from him wente;

[1] Hl. Which that.

D

But shortly for to telle is myn entente.   (1000)
Whan that this worthy duk, this Theseus,
Hath Creon slayn, and wonne Thebes thus,
Stille in that feeld he took al night his reste,   145 *quiet*
And dide with al the contree as him leste.

To ransake in the tas[1] of[2] bodyes dede,   *heap*
Hem for to strepe of harneys and of wede,   *clothing*
The pilours diden bisynesse and cure,
After the bataille and disconfiture. *defeat*   150
And so bifel, that in the tas[1] thei founde,
Thurgh-girt with many a grevous blody wounde, (1010) *pierced through*
Two yonge knightes ligging by and by,   *separately*
Bothe in oon armes, wroght ful richely ;   *one kind of arms*
Of whiche two, Arcita hight[3] that oon,   155
And that other knight hight[3] Palamon.
Nat fully quike, ne fully dede they were,   *alive*
But by hir cote-armures, and by hir gere,
The heraudes knewe hem best in special,   *specially*
As they that weren of the blood roial   160
Of Thebes, and of sustren two y-born.
Out of the tas[1] the pilours han hem torn,   (1020)
And han hem caried softe un-to the tente
Of Theseus, and he ful sone[4] hem sente
To Athenes[5], to dwellen in prisoun   165
Perpetuelly, he nolde no raunsoun.
And whan this worthy duk hath thus y-don,
He took his host, and hoom he rood anon
With laurer crowned as a conquerour ;
And there he liveth in Ioye and in honour   170
Terme of his[6] lyf ; what nedeth wordes mo ?

---

[1] E. Hn. Cm. taas ; Hl. cas ; Cp. Pt. Ln. caas ; *read* tas.
[2] E. of the ; Hn. Cm. of.   [3] Hl. hight ; E. highte.
[4] E. ful soone he.   [5] Hl. Tathenes for.   [6] E. Cm. *om.* his.

And in a tour, in angwish and in wo,   (1030)
This Palamon, and his felawe Arcite,
For everemore, ther may no gold hem quyte. *free*

   This passeth yeer by yeer, and day by day,   175
Til it fil ones, in a morwe of May,
That Emelye, that fairer was to sene
Than is the lilie vpon his [1] stalke grene,
And fressher than the May with floures newe—
For with the rose colour strof hir hewe,   180
I noot which was the fairer [2] of hem two—
Er it were day, as was hir wone to do,   (1040)
She was arisen, and al redy dight; *dressed*
For May wol have no slogardye [3] anight.   *sloth*
The sesoun priketh every gentil herte,   185
And maketh him out of his sleep to sterte,
And seith, 'Arys, and do thyn observaunce.'
This maked Emelye have remembraunce
To doon honour to May, and for to ryse.
Y-clothed was she fresh, for to devyse; *relate*   190
Hir yelow heer was broyded [4] in a tresse, *woven*
Bihynde hir bak, a yerde long, I gesse.   (1050)
And in the gardin, at the sonne up-riste,
She walketh up and doun, and as hir liste *as it pleased her*
She gadereth floures, party whyte and rede,   195
To make a sotil [5] gerland for hir hede,   *subtle = woven*
And as an aungel hevenly [6] she song.
The grete tour, that was so thikke and strong,
Which of the castel was the chief dongeoun,
(Ther as the knightes weren in prisoun,   200

[1] Hl. on hire.   [2] E. Hl. fyner; Cm. fynere; Hn. Cp. Pt. fairer.
[3] E. slogardrie; *rest* slogardye (sloggardye, sluggardie).
[4] E. Hn. Cm. Cp. broyded; Pt. breided; Ln. Hl. browded.
[5] Ln. sotil; Cp. sotyl; E. Hn. Cm. subtil; Pt. subtile; Hl. certeyn.
[6] Hl. Pt. heuenly; Cm. heueneliche; E. Hn. Cp. Ln. heuenysshly.

Of which I tolde yow, and tellen shal)
Was evene Ioynant to the gardin-wal,   *closely*   (1060) *joi*
Ther as this Emelye hadde hir pleyinge.
Bright was the sonne, and cleer that morweninge,
And Palamon, this woful prisoner,   205
As was his wone, by leve of his gayler,
Was risen, and romed in a chambre on[1] heigh,
In which he al the noble citee seigh,
And eek the gardin, ful of braunches grene,
Ther as this fresshe Emelye the shene   *beautiful*   210
Was in hir walk, and romed up and doun.
This sorweful prisoner, this Palamoun,   (1070)
Goth in the chambre, roming to and fro,
And to him-self compleyning of his wo;
That he was born, ful ofte he seyde, 'alas!'   215
And so bifel, by aventure or cas,   *hap*
That thurgh a window, thikke of many a barre
Of iren greet, and square as any sparre,
He caste his eye upon Emelya,
And ther-with-al he bleynte, and cryde 'a!' *blenched* 220
As though he stongen were un-to the herte.
And with that cry Arcite anon up-sterte, *in one* (1080) *ins*
And seyde, 'Cosin myn, what eyleth thee,
That art so pale and deedly on to see?
Why crydestow? who hath thee doon offence?   225
For Goddes love, tak al in pacience
Our prisoun, for it may non other be;
Fortune hath yeven us this adversitee.
Som wikke aspect or disposicioun
Of Saturne, by sum constellacioun,   230
Hath yeven us this, al-though we hadde it sworn; *see p!*
So stood the heven whan that we were born;   (1090)

---

[1] Hl. on; E. an.

We moste endure it[1]: this is the short and pleyn.'

  This Palamon answerde, and seyde ageyn,
'Cosyn, for sothe, of this opinioun *in truth* 235
Thou hast a veyn imaginacioun.
This prison caused me nat for to crye.
But I was hurt right now thurgh-out myn yë[2]
In-to myn herte, that wol my bane be.
The fairnesse of that lady that I see 240
Yond in the gardin romen to and fro,
Is cause of al my crying and my wo. (1100)
I noot wher[3] she be womman or goddesse;
But Venus is it, sothly, as I gesse.'
And ther-with-al on kneës doun[4] he fil, 245
And seyde: 'Venus, if it be thy wil
Yow in this gardin thus to transfigure,
Bifore me sorweful wrecche creature,
Out of this prisoun help that we may scapen.
And if so be my destinee be shapen 250
By eterne word to dyen in prisoun,
Of our linage have som compassioun, (1110)
That is so lowe y-broght by tirannye.'
And with that word Arcite gan espye
Wher-as this lady romed to and fro. 255
And with that sighte hir beautee hurte him so,
That if that Palamon was[5] wounded sore,
Arcite is hurt as moche as he, or more.
And with a sigh he seyde pitously:
'The fresshe beautee sleeth me sodeynly 260
Of hir that rometh in the yonder place;
And but I have hir mercy and hir grace, *pity* (1120) *favour*

---

[1] E. *om*. it; *the rest retain it*.
[2] Cm. Pt. ye; Hn. Iye; Cp. yhe; E. eye.
[3] Cm. wheþer; Hl. whethur. [4] Hl. Cp. a doun.
[5] E. *wrongly om*. was.

That I may seen hir atte leste weye,   *at the least*
I nam but deed ; ther nis[1] no more to seye.' *no better*
   This Palamon, whan he tho wordes herde,   265
Dispitously he loked, and answerde :   *angrily*
'Whether[2] seistow this in ernest or in pley?'
'Nay,' quod Arcite, 'in ernest, by my fey!
God help me so, me list ful evele pleye.' *it pleases me v...*
   This Palamon gan knitte his browes tweye :   *badly to*
   270
'It nere,' quod he, 'to thee no greet honour   *would not*
For to be fals, ne for to be traytour   (1130)
To me, that am thy cosin and thy brother
Y-sworn ful depe, and ech of us til[3] other,   *to*
That nevere, for to dyen in the peyne,   *torture*   275 *fo...*
   fear
Til that the[4] deeth departe shal us tweyne,
Neither of us in love to hindren[5] other,
Ne in non other cas, my leve brother ;   *hap*   *dear*
But that thou sholdest trewely forthren me
In every cas, and I shal forthren thee.   280
This was thyn ooth, and myn also, certeyn ;
I wot right wel, thou darst it nat withseyn.   (1140)
Thus artow[6] of my counseil, out of doute.
And now thou woldest falsly been aboute
To love my lady, whom I love and serve,   285
And evere shal, til that myn herte sterve.
Now[7] certes, fals Arcite, thou shalt nat so.
I loved hir first, and tolde thee my wo
As to my counseil, and[8] my brother sworn
To forthre me, as I have told biforn.   290
For which thou art y-bounden as a knight
To helpen me, if it lay in thy might,   (1150)

---

[1] E. is ; *rest* nys.   [2] E. Wheither.   [3] Cm. Pt. Ln. Hl. to.
[4] E. Ln. Hl. *om.* the.   [5] E. hyndre ; Cm. hynderyn.
[6] E. Hn. artow ; *rest* art thou.   [7] E. Nay ; *rest* Now.
[8] E. Cm. *ins.* to.

Or elles artow [1] fals, I dar wel seyn.'
This Arcitë ful proudly spak ageyn,
'Thou shalt,' quod he, 'be rather fals than I;   295
But [2] thou art fals, I telle thee utterly [3];
For *par amour* I loved hir first er thow.
What wiltow [4] seyn? thou wistest nat yet now
Whether she be a womman or goddesse.
Thyn is <u>affeccioun</u> *of holynesse*,   *sacred affection*   300
And myn is love, as to a creature;
For which I tolde thee myn aventure   *misfortune* (1160)
As to my cosin, and my brother sworn.
I <u>pose</u>, that thou lovedest hir biforn;   *suppose*
<u>Wostow</u> [5] nat wel the olde clerkes sawe,   *knewest*   305   *thou*
That 'who shal yeve a lover any lawe?
Love is a gretter lawe, by my <u>pan</u>,   *brain pan*
Than may be yeve to [6] any erthly man.'
And [7] therfore positif lawe and swich decree
Is broke [8] al-day for love, in <u>ech degree</u>.   *every*   310   *rank*
A man moot nedes love, maugree his <u>heed</u>.   *head*
He may nat flee it, thogh he sholde be deed,
Al be she mayde, or widwe, or elles wyf.   (1171)
And eek it is nat lykly, al thy lyf,
To stonden in hir <u>grace</u>; namore shal I;   *favour* 315
For wel thou wost thy-selven, verraily,
That thou and I be <u>dampned</u> to prisoun   *doomed*
Perpetuelly; us <u>gayneth</u> no raunsoun.   *avails*
We stryve [9], as dide the houndes for the boon,
They foughten al day, and yet hir part was noon;   320

---

[1] E. Hn. artow; *rest* art thou.   [2] E. Hn. And; *rest* But.
[3] Hl. Cm. uttirly; Cp. Pt. Ln. witterly; E. Hn. outrely.
[4] Cp. Pt. wilt thou; Hl. wolt thou.
[5] Cm. Wist thou; Hl. Ln. Wost thou; Pt. Woost thow.
[6] E. of; *rest* to.   [7] Hl. *om.* And.   [8] E. Cm. broken.
[9] Hn. Cm. Hl. stryue; *rest* stryuen.

Ther cam a kyte, whyl that [1] they were [2] wrothe,
And bar awey the boon bitwixe hem bothe.   (1180)
And therfore at the kinges court, my brother,
Ech man for him-self, ther is non other.
Love if thee list; for I love and ay shal;   325
And sothly, leve brother, this is al.
Here in this prisoun mote we endure,
And everich of us take his aventure.'

  Greet was the stryf and long bitwixe hem tweye,
If that I hadde leyser for to seye;   *leisure*   330
But to theffect. It happed on a day,   *the result*
(To telle it yow as shortly as I may)   (1190)
A worthy duk that highte Perotheus,
That felawe was un-to [3] duk Theseus
Sin thilke day that they were children lyte,   335
Was come to Athenes, his felawe to visyte,
And for to pleye, as he was wont [4] to do,
For in this world he loved no man so:
And he loved him as [5] tendrely ageyn.
So wel they loved, as olde bokes seyn,   340
That whan that oon was deed, sothly to telle,
His felawe wente and soughte him doun in helle;
But of that story list me nat to wryte.   (1201)
Duk Perotheus loved wel Arcite,
And hadde him knowe at Thebes yeer by yere;   345
And fynally, at requeste and preyere
Of Perotheus, with-oute [6] any raunsoun,
Duk Theseus him leet out of prisoun,
Frely to goon, wher that him liste over-al,   *every where*
In swich a gyse, as I you tellen shal.   *fashion*   350

[1] E. *om.* that.   [2] *All but* Cm. Hl. *ins.* so.
[3] E. to; Hl. to the; *rest* un-to.   [4] E. won; Cm. wone; *rest* wont.
[5] E. als; Hn. Cm. Hl. as.
[6] Hl. Cp. Pt. with-oute; *rest* with-outen.

This was the forward, pleynly for tendite,   *agreement*
Bitwixen Theseus and him Arcite :   (1210)
That if so were, that Arcite were y-founde
Evere in his lyf, by day or night, o.[1] stounde   *one moment*
In any contree of this Theseus,   355
And he were caught, it was acorded thus,
That with a swerd he sholde lese his heed ;
Ther nas noon other remedye ne reed,   *plan*
But taketh[2] his leve, and homward he him spedde ;
Let him be war, his nekke lyth to wedde !   *pledge*   360

How greet a sorwe suffreth now Arcite !
The deeth he feleth thurgh his herte smyte ;   (1220)
He wepeth, weyleth, cryeth pitously ;
To sleen him-self he wayteth prively.   *to kill himself unperceiva*
He seyde, 'Allas that[3] day that I[4] was born !   365
Now is my prisoun worse than biforn ;
Now is me shape eternally to dwelle
Noght[5] in[6] purgatorie, but in helle.
Allas ! that evere knew I Perotheus !
For elles hadde I dwelled[7] with Theseus   370
Y-fetered in his prisoun evere-moo.
Than hadde I been in blisse, and nat in wo.   (1230)
Only the sighte of hir, whom that I serve,
Though that I nevere hir grace may deserve,
Wolde han suffised right ynough for me.   375
O dere cosin Palamon,' quod he,
' Thyn is the victorie of this aventure,
Ful blisfully in prison maistow dure ;
In prison ? certes nay, but in[8] paradys !
Wel hath fortune y-turned thee the dys,   380

---

[1] Hl. o ; *rest* or.   [2] Hl. (*alone*) took.   [3] Hn. Hl. the.
[4] E. he ; *rest* I.   [5] Hn. Noght ; E. Nat ; Cm. Not ; *rest* Nought.
[6] E. (*alone*) ins. my.   [7] Hl. dweld.   [8] Cp. Pt. Ln. *om.* in.

That hast the sight of hir, and I thabsence.
For possible is, sin thou hast hir presence,   (1240)
And art a knight, a worthy and an able,
That by[1] som cas, sin fortune is chaungeable,
Thou maist to thy desyr som-tyme atteyne.   385
But I, that am exyled, and bareyne *devoid*
Of alle grace, and in so greet despeir,
That ther nis erthe, water, fyr, ne eir,
Ne creature, that of hem maked is,
That may me helpe[2] or doon confort in this.   390
Wel oughte I sterve in wanhope and distresse; *despai*
Farwel my lyf, my lust, and my gladnesse.   (1250)
Allas, why pleynen folk so in commune *commonly*
Of purveiaunce of God, or of fortune,   *providence*
That yeveth hem ful ofte in many a gyse *fashion* 395
Wel bettre than they can hem-self devyse?
Som man desyreth for to han richesse,
That cause is of his mordre[3] or greet siknesse.
And som man wolde out of his prison fayn, *gladly*
That in his hous is of his meynee slayn. *domestics* 400
Infinite harmes been in this matere;
We witen nat what thing[4] we prayen here. *knaw* (1260)
We faren as he that dronke is as a mous;
A dronke man wot wel[5] he hath an hous,
But he noot which the righte wey is thider;   405
And to a dronke man the wey is slider; *slippery*
And certes, in this world so faren we;
We seken faste after felicitee,
But we goon wrong ful often trewely.
Thus may we seyen[6] alle, and namely I,   410

[1] E. (*alone*) om. by.   [2] E. (*alone*) heele.
[3] Cp. Ln. mordre; E. Hn. moerdre; Cm. Pt. mordere; Hl. morthre.
[4] E. (*alone*) om. thing.   [5] E. Cm. *ins.* that.
[6] Hl. seyen; E. Hn. Cm. Cp. seyn.

That wende and hadde a greet opinioun,   *thought*
That if I mighte escapen from prisoun,   (1270)
Than hadde I been in Ioye and perfit hele,
Ther¹ now I am exyled fro my wele. *wealth*
Sin that I may nat seen yow, Emelye,   415
I nam but deed; ther nis no remedye.'
   Up-on that other syde Palamon,
Whan that he wiste Arcite was agon,
Swich sorwe he maketh, that the grete tour
Resouneth² of his youling and clamour.   420
The pure fettres on his shines grete   *very*   *legs*
Weren of his bittre salte teres wete.   (1280)
'Allas!' quod he, 'Arcita, cosin myn,
Of al our stryf, God woot, the fruyt is thyn.
Thow walkest now in Thebes at thy large,   425
And of my wo thou yevest litel charge.   *consideration*
Thou mayst, sin thou hast wisdom and manhede,
Assemblen alle the folk of our kinrede,
And make a werre so sharpe on this citee,
That by som aventure, or som tretee,   430
Thou mayst have hir to lady and to wyf,
For whom that I mot³ nedes lese my lyf.   (1290)
For, as by wey of possibilitee,
Sith thou art at thy large, of prison free,
And art a lord, greet is thyn avauntage,   435
More than is myn, that sterve here in a cage.
For I mot wepe and weyle, whyl I live,
With al the wo that prison may me yive⁴,
And eek with peyne that love me yiveth⁴ also,
That doubleth al my torment and my wo.'   440

---

¹ E. (*alone*) That.   ² E. Resouned; *rest* Resouneth.
³ *All* moste, most, muste; *but read* mot; *see* l. 437.
⁴ Hl. ȝyue; E. yeue.   ⁴ E. yeueth.

Ther-with the fyr of Ielousye[1] up-sterte
With-inne his brest, and hente him by the herte   *seize*
So woodly, that he lyk was to biholde   (1301)
The box-tree, or the asshen dede and colde.
Tho[2] seyde he; 'O cruel goddes, that governe   445
This world with bynding of your word eterne,
And wryten in the table of athamaunte[3] *adamant*
Your parlement, and your eterne graunte, *permission*
What is mankynde more un-to yow holde *esteemed*
Than is the sheep, that rouketh in the folde? *lies* 450
For slayn is man right as another beste[4],
And dwelleth eek in prison and areste[5], *custody* (1310)
And hath siknesse, and greet adversitee,
And ofte tymes giltelees[6], pardee.
What governaunce is in this prescience, *management* 455
That giltelees[6] tormenteth innocence?   *Fore knowledge*
And yet encreseth[7] this al my penaunce, *sorrow*
That man is bounden to his observaunce, *respect*
For Goddes sake, to letten of his wille,
Ther as a beest may al his lust fulfille.   460
And whan a beest is deed, he hath no peyne;
But man after his deeth[8] moot wepe and pleyne,
Though in this world he have care and wo: (1321)
With-outen doute it may stonden so.
The answere of this I lete[9] to divynis,   465
But wel I woot, that in this world gret pyne is.
Allas! I se a serpent or a theef,
That many a trewe man hath doon mescheef,

---

[1] Hl. Ielousye; E. Ialousie.   [2] Hl. Tho; E. Thanne.
[3] Hl. Cm. athamaunte; E. Atthamaunt.
[4] Cm. Hl. beste; E. beest.   [5] Cm. areste; Hl. arreste; E. arreest.
[6] Cm. Cp. Hl. giltelees; E. giltlees.
[7] Cm. Cp. Pt. Ln. encreseth; E. encresseth.
[8] *So* Hn. Cm. Hl.; *rest* after his deeth man.   [9] *So* Hl.; *rest* lete I.

Goon at his large, and wher him list may turne.
But I moot been in prison thurgh Saturne,   *goddess of*   470
And eek thurgh Iuno, Ialous and eek wood,   *women + marriage*
That hath destroyed wel ny al the blood   (1330)
Of Thebes, with his[1] waste walles wyde.
And Venus sleeth me on that other syde
For Ielousye[2], and fere of him Arcite.'   *fear*   475
                                                  stop
    Now wol I stinte of Palamon a lyte,
And lete him in his prison stille dwelle,
And of Arcita forth I wol yow telle.
The somer[3] passeth, and the nightes longe
Encresen[4] double wyse the peynes stronge   480
Bothe of the lovere and the prisoner.
I noot which hath the wofullere mester.   *necessity*(1340)
For shortly for to seyn, this Palamoun
Perpetuelly is dampned to prisoun,
In cheynes and in fettres to been deed;   485
And Arcite is exyled upon[5] his heed
For evere-mo as out of that contree,
Ne nevere-mo he shal his lady see.
Yow[6] loveres axe I now this questioun,
Who hath the worse, Arcite or Palamoun?   490
That oon may seen his lady day by day,
But in prisoun he moot[7] dwelle alway.   (1350)
That other wher him list may ryde or go,
But seen his lady shal he nevere-mo.
Now demeth as yow liste[8], ye that can,   *judge*   495
For I wol telle forth as I bigan.

Explicit prima Pars.   Sequitur pars secunda.

[1] E. hise.   [2] E. Ialousie.   [3] E. (*alone*) sonne.   [4] E. Encressen.
[5] Cm. Cp. Pt. vp (*perhaps rightly*).   [6] E. Now (*wrongly*).
[7] Hn. Cp. Pt. moot he.   [8] Ln. liste; Cm. lyste; Hl. luste; *rest* list.

Whan that Arcite to Thebes comen was,
Ful ofte a day he swelte and seyde 'allas,'   *fainted*
For seen his lady shal he nevere-mo.
And shortly to concluden al his wo,   500
So muche sorwe had[1] nevere creature
That is, or shal, whyl that the world may dure.
His sleep, his mete, his drink is him biraft,   *be* (1361) *20y*
That lene he wex[2], and drye as is a shaft.   *reed*
His eyen holwe, and grisly to biholde;   505
His hewe falwe[3], and pale as asshen colde,   *pale*
And solitarie he was, and evere allone,
And wailling al the night, making his mone.
And if he herde song or instrument,
Then wolde he wepe, he mighte nat be stent;   *stopped*   510
So feble eek were his spirits[4], and so lowe,
And chaunged so, that no man coude knowe   (1370)
His speche nor his vois, though men it herde.
And in his gere, for al the world he ferde   *manner, we*
Nat oonly lyk the loveres maladye   515
Of Hereos, but rather lyk manye   *Eros*
Engendred of humour malencolyk,
Biforen, in his[5] celle fantastyk.   *see p 176*
And shortly, turned was al up-so-doun
Bothe habit and eek disposicioun   520
Of him, this woful lovere daun Arcite.
What sholde I al-day of his wo endyte?   (1380)
Whan he endured hadde a yeer or two
This cruel torment, and this peyne and wo,
At Thebes, in his contree, as I seyde,   525

---

[1] Hl. Pt. Ln. had; *rest* hadde.   [2] E. Pt. wexeth.
[3] Hl. Cm. falwe; E. Hn. falow.   [4] E. spiritz.
[5] E. Biforn his owene; Cm. Be-forn hese owene; Hn. Cd. Pt. Ln
Biforn his; Hl. Byforne in his.

Up-on a night, in sleep as he him leyde,
Him thoughte how that the winged god Mercurie
Biforn him stood, and bad him to be murye.
His slepy yerde in hond he bar uprighte;
An hat he werede up-on[1] his heres brighte.   530
Arrayed was this god (as he[2] took keep)   *Reed*
As he was whan that Argus took his sleep;   (1390)
And seyde him thus: 'To Athenes shaltou wende;
Ther is thee shapen of thy wo an ende.'   *ordained*
And with that word Arcite wook and sterte.   535
'Now trewely, how sore that me smerte,'
Quod he, 'to Athenes right now wol I fare;
Ne for the drede of deeth shal I nat spare
To see my lady, that I love and serve;
In hir presence I recche nat to sterve.'   540
And with that word he caughte a greet mirour,
And saugh that chaunged was al his colour,   (1400)
And saugh his visage al in another kynde.
And right anoon it ran him in his mynde,
That, sith his face was so disfigured   545
Of maladye, the which he hadde endured,
He mighte wel, if that he bar him lowe,   *low estate*
Live in Athenes evere-more unknowe,
And seen his lady wel ny day by day.
And right anon he chaungede his array,   550
And cladde him as a povre laborer,
And al allone, save oonly a squyer,   (1410)
That knew his privetee and al his cas,   *secret*
Which was disgysed povrely, as he was,
To Athenes is he goon the nexte way.   *nearest* 555
And to the court he wente up-on a day,
And at the gate he profreth his servyse,

---

[1] E. vp *(perhaps rightly)*; *rest* vp-on.   [2] E. I; *rest* he.

To drugge and drawe, what so men wol devyse. *drudge*
direct

And shortly of this matere for to seyn,

He fil in office with a chamberleyn,   560

The which that dwelling was with Emelye.

For he was wys, and coude soon aspye   (1420)

Of every servaunt, which that serveth here.

Wel coude he hewen wode, and water bere,

For he was yong and mighty for the nones,   565 -

And ther-to he was strong[1] and big of bones

To doon that any wight can him devyse. *direct*

A yeer or two he was in this servyse,

Page of the chambre of Emelye the brighte ;

And 'Philostrate' he seide that he highte.   570

But half so wel biloved a man as he

Ne was ther nevere in court, of his degree ;   (1430)

He was so gentil of[2] condicioun,

That thurghout al the court was his renoun.

They seyden that it were a charitee   575

That Theseus wolde enhauncen his degree,

And putten him in worshipful servyse, *honourable*

Ther as he mighte his vertu excercyse.

And thus, with-inne a whyle, his name is spronge *wide sprede*

Bothe of his dedes, and his goode tonge,   580

That Theseus hath taken him so neer

That of his chambre he made him a squyer,   (1440)

And yaf him gold to mayntene his degree ;

And eek men broghte him out of his contree

From yeer to yeer ful prively his rente ; *revenue* 585

But honestly and slyly he it spente, *wisely*

That no man wondred how that he it hadde.

And thre yeer in this wyse his lyf he ladde,

And bar him so in pees and eek in werre,

---

[1] E. Cm. long; *rest* strong.   [2] E. Hl. *ins.* his.

Ther nas no man that Theseus hath derre. *dearer* 590
And in this blisse lete I now Arcite,
And speke I wol of Palamon a lyte.   (1450)
   In derknesse and horrible and strong prisoun
This seven yeer hath seten Palamoun,
Forpyned, what for wo and for distresse; *wasted* 595 *away*
Who feleth double soor[1] and[2] hevynesse
But Palamon? that love destreyneth so,
That wood out of his wit he goth for wo;
And eek therto he is a prisoner
Perpetuelly, noght oonly for a yeer.   600
Who coude ryme in English proprely
His martirdom? for sothe, it am nat I;   (1460)
Therefore I passe as lightly as I may.
It fel that in the seventhe yeer, in May,
The thridde night, (as olde bokes seyn,   605
That al this storie tellen more pleyn,)
Were it by aventure or destinee,
(As, whan a thing is shapen, it shal be,)
That, sone after the midnight, Palamoun,
By helping of a freend, brak his prisoun,   610
And fleeth the citee faste as he may go,
For he had yive[3] his gayler drinke so   (1470)
Of a clarree, maad of a certeyn wyn,
With[4] nercotikes and opie of Thebes fyn, *fine*
That al that night, thogh that men wolde him shake,
The gayler sleep, he mighte nat awake;   616
And thus he fleeth as faste as evere he may.
The night was short, and faste by the day,
That nedes-cost he moste[5] him-selven hyde, *necessarily*

---

[1] *So* E. Hn. Pt.; Cp. Ln. sore; Cm. Hl. sorwe.
[2] E. *om.* and.   [3] Hl. ȝiue; E. yeue.
[4] E. Of; *rest* With.
[5] E. moot; *rest* moste, most, muste.

And til a grove, faste ther besyde,   *to*   620
With dredful foot than[1] stalketh Palamoun. *crepe*
For shortly, this was his opinioun,   (1480)
That in that grove he wolde him hyde al day,
And in the night than wolde he take his way
To Thebes-ward, his frendes for to preye *pray* 625
On Theseus to helpe him to werreye; *war*
And shortly, outher he wolde lese his lyf,
Or winnen Emelye un-to his wyf;
This is theffect and his entente pleyn.
      Now wol I torne un-to[2] Arcite ageyn,   630
That litel wiste how ny that was his care, *sorow?*
Til that fortune had broght him in the snare. (1490)
      The bisy larke, messager of daye,
Saluëth in hir song the morwe graye;
And fyry Phebus ryseth up so brighte,   635
That al the orient laugheth of the lighte,
And with his[3] stremes dryeth in the greves *groves*
The silver dropes, hanging on the leves.
And Arcite[4], that is in the court roial
With Theseus, his squyer principal,   640
Is risen, and loketh on the myrie day.
And, for to doon his observaunce to May, (1500)
Remembring on the poynt of his desyr,
He on a[5] courser, sterting[6] as the fyr, *leaping*
Is riden in-to the feeldes, him to pleye,   645
Out of the court, were it a myle or tweye;
And to the grove, of which that I yow tolde,
By aventure his wey he gan to holde,

---

[1] E. Hn. Cm. thanne; *rest* than.   [2] E. Hn. Ln. to; *rest* vn-to.
[3] E. hise.   [4] Hl. Arcite; *rest* Arcita.
[5] E. Hn. Cm. a; *rest* his.
[6] Cp. Pt. Ln. Hl. stertyng; E. Hn. startlynge; Cm. stertelynge.

To maken him a gerland of the greves,
Were it of wodebynde or hawethorn-leves,   650
And loude he song ageyn the sonne shene: *towards*
'May, with alle thy floures and thy grene,   (1510)
Wel-come be thou, wel[1] faire fresshe May, *ful*
I[2] hope that I som grene gete may.'
And from his courser, with a lusty herte,   655
In-to the[3] grove ful hastily he sterte,
And in a path he rometh up and doun,
Ther as by aventure this Palamoun
Was in a bush, that no man mighte him see,
For sore afered[4] of his deeth[5] was he.   660
No-thing ne knew he that it was Arcite:
God wot he wolde have trowed it ful lyte.   (1520) *believed*
But soth is seyd, gon[6] sithen many yeres, *truly since*
That feeld hath eyen, and the wode hath eres.
It is ful fair a man to bere him evene, *well conduct* 665 *normally*
For al-day meteth men at unset stevene. *unexpected meeting*
Ful litel wot Arcite of his felawe,
That was so ny to herknen al his sawe, *discourse*
For in the bush he sitteth now ful stille.

  Whan that Arcite had romed al his fille,   670
And songen al the roundel lustily,
In-to a studie he fil al sodeynly,   (1530)
As doon thise loveres in hir queynte geres, *strange behaviour*
Now in the croppe[7], now doun in the breres, *top · briars*
Now up, now doun, as boket in a welle.   675
Right as the Friday, sothly for to telle,
Now it shyneth, now it reyneth faste,

---

[1] Hl. wel; *rest omit.*   [2] E. Hn. Cm. In; *rest* I.
[3] E. a; *rest* the.   [4] Hn. Hl. afered; Cm. ofered; *rest* aferd.
[5] E. (*alone*) *ins.* thanne.
[6] Hl. Pt. goon; Cm. Ln. gon; E. Hn. Cp. go.
[7] E. Hn. Cm. crop; Cp. Hl. Pt. croppe.

Right so can[1] gery Venus overcaste   *changeable*
The hertes of hir folk; right as hir day
Is gerful[2], right so chaungeth she array. *situation* 680
Selde is the Friday al the wyke[3] ylyke. *seldom*
Whan that Arcite had songe, he gan to syke, (1540) *sigh*
And sette him doun with-outen any more:
'Alas!' quod he, 'that day that I was bore!
How longe, Iuno, thurgh thy crueltee,   685
Woltow werreyen Thebes the citee?
Allas! y-broght is to confusioun
The blood roial of Cadme and Amphioun;
Of Cadmus, which that was the firste man
That Thebes bulte, or first the toun bigan,   690
And of the citee first was crouned king,
Of his linage am I, and his of-spring   (1550)
By verray ligne[4], as of the stok roial: *true lineage*
And now I am so caitif and so thral, *enslaved*
That he, that is my mortal enemy,   695
I serve him as his squyer povrely.
And yet doth Iuno me wel more shame,   *much*
For I dar noght biknowe myn owne[5] name, *acknowledge*
But ther as I was wont to highte[6] Arcite,
Now highte I Philostrate, noght worth a myte.   700
Allas! thou felle Mars, allas! Iuno,   *cruel*
Thus hath your ire our kinrede al fordo, *ruined* (1560)
Save only me, and wrecched Palamoun,
That Theseus martyreth in prisoun.
And over al this, to sleen me utterly[7],   705
Love hath his fyry dart so brenningly

---

[1] So E. Hn. Cm.; *rest* gan.
[2] E. gereful; Cp. geerful; Hl. grisful; *rest* gerful.
[3] Hl. wyke; Hn. Cp. wike; Pt. Ln. weke; Cm. wouke; E. wowke.
[4] Cm. Pt. Hl. lyne.   [5] Cp. Pt. Ln. owne; E. owene.   [6] Hl. hote.
[7] Hl. vtterly; E. outrely.

Y-stiked thurgh my trewe careful herte,   *sorrowful*
That shapen was my deeth erst than my sherte.   *before*
Ye sleen me with your eyen, Emelye ;
Ye been the cause wherfor that I dye.   710
Of al the remenant of myn other care
Ne sette I nat the mountaunce of a tare,   (1570)   *value*
So that I coude doon aught to your plesaunce.'
And with that word he fil doun in a traunce
A long[1] tyme ; and he afterward[2] upsterte.   715

    This Palamoun, that thoughte that thurgh his herte
He felte a cold swerd sodeynliche glyde,
For ire he quook, no lenger wolde he byde.
And whan that he had herd Arcites tale,
As he were wood, with face deed and pale,   720
He sterte him up out of the buskes[3] thikke,
And seyde : 'Arcite, false traitour wikke,   (1580)
Now artow[4] hent, that lovest my lady so,   *seized*
For whom that I have al this peyne and wo,
And art my blood, and to my counseil sworn,   725
As I ful ofte have told[5] thee heer-biforn,
And hast by-iaped heer duk Theseus,   *tricked*
And falsly chaunged hast thy name thus ;
I wol be deed, or elles thou shalt dye.
Thou shalt nat love my lady Emelye,   730
But I wol love hir only and namo[6] ;
For I am Palamoun, thy mortal fo.   (1590)
And though that I no wepne have in this place,
But out of prison am astert by grace,   *escaped*
I drede noght that outher thou shalt dye,   735

---

[1] E. Hn. longe ; Cm. long.
[2] Ln. he afterwarde ; E. after he ; Hl. *om.* he ; *rest* afterward he.
[3] Hl. bussches ; Cm. boschis ; Ln. boskes.
[4] E. Hn. artow ; *rest* art thou.   [5] E. Cm. seyd.
[6] E. Hn. namo ; Hl. Cm. no mo.

Or thou ne shalt nat loven Emelye.

Chees which thou wilt[1], for[2] thou shalt nat asterte.' *escape*

This Arcite, with ful despitous herte, *angry*

Whan he him knew, and hadde his tale herd,

As fiers as leoun pulled out a[3] swerd,   740

And seyde thus: 'by God that sit above,

Nere it that thou art sik and wood for love,   (1600)

And eek that thou no wepne hast in this place,

Thou sholdest nevere out of this grove pace, *pass*

That thou ne sholdest dyen of myn hond.   745

For I defye the seurtee and the bond   *security*

Which that thou seyst that I have maad to thee.

What, verray fool, think wel that love is fre,

And I wol love hir, maugre al thy might!

But, for as much thou art a worthy knight,   750

And wilnest to darreyne[4] hir by batayle,

Have heer my trouthe, to-morwe I wol nat fayle, *here*

With-outen witing of any other wight, *knowledge*(1611)

That heer I wol be founden as a knight,

And bringen harneys right ynough for thee;   755

And chees the beste, and leve the worste for me.

And mete and drinke this night wol I bringe

Ynough for thee, and clothes for thy beddinge.

And, if so be that thou my lady winne,

And sle me in this wode ther I am inne, *madness?*760

Thou mayst wel have thy lady, as for me.'

This Palamon answerde: 'I graunte it thee.'   (1620)

And thus they been departed til a-morwe,

When ech of hem had leyd his feith to borwe. *pledge*

    O Cupide, out of alle charitee !   765

O regne, that wolt no felawe have with thee !

---

[1] E. Hn. wolt.   [2] Hl. for; *rest* or.   [3] E. Hn. his.
[4] Cp. derreyne; Hl. dereyne.

Ful sooth is seyd, that love ne lordshipe
Wol noght, hir thankes, have no felaweshipe ;   *willingly*
Wel fynden that Arcite and Palamoun.
Arcite is riden anon un-to the toun,   770
And on the morwe, er it were dayes light,
Ful prively two harneys hath he dight,   *prepared* (1630)
Bothe suffisaunt and mete to darreyne   *contest*
The bataille in the feeld bitwix hem tweyne.
And on his hors, allone as he was born,   775
He carieth al this [1] harneys him biforn ;
And in the grove, at tyme and place y-set,
This Arcite and this Palamon ben met.
Tho [2] chaungen gan the colour in hir face ;
Right as the hunter [3] in the regne of Trace,   780
That stondeth at the gappe with a spere,
Whan hunted is the leoun or [4] the bere,   (1640)
And hereth him come russhing in the greves,
And breketh bothe bowes and the leves,
And thinketh, 'heer cometh my mortel enemy,   785
With-oute faile, he moot be deed, or I ;
For outher I moot sleen him at the gappe,
Or he moot sleen me, if that me mishappe :'
So ferden they, in chaunging of hir hewe,   *went*
As fer as everich of hem other knewe.   790
Ther nas no good day, ne no saluing ;
But streight with-outen word or rehersing,   (1650)
Everich of hem halp [5] for [6] to armen other,
As frendly as he were his owne [7] brother ;
And after that, with sharpe speres stronge   795
They foynen ech at other wonder longe.   *thrust*

---

[1] E. the ; Hn. Cm. Hl. this.   [2] Hl. Tho ; *rest* To.
[3] *So edd.* ; MSS. hunters, hunterys.   [4] E. and ; *rest* or.
[5] Cm. halp ; Cp. hilp ; E. Hn. heelp ; Hl. Pt. helpeth ; Ln. helpe.
[6] Hl. Ln. *om.* for.   [7] E. owene.

Thou mightest <u>wene</u> that this Palamoun   *think*
In his fighting were as [1] a wood leoun,
And as a cruel tygre was Arcite :
As wilde bores gonne they to smyte,   800
That frothen whyte as foom for ire wood.
Up to the ancle [2] foghte they in hir blood.   (1660)
And in this wyse I lete hem fighting dwelle ;
And forth I wol [3] of Theseus yow telle.

    The destinee, ministre general,   805
That executeth in the world over-al
The <u>purveiaunce</u>, that God hath <u>seyn</u> <u>biforn</u>,   *foresight.*
So strong it is, that though the world had sworn   *to a force*
The contrarie of a thing, by ye or nay,
Yet somtyme it shal fallen on a day   810
That falleth nat <u>eft</u> with-inne a thousand yere.   *again*
For certeinly oure <u>appetytes</u> here,   *desires*
Be it of werre, or pees, or hate, or love,   (1670)
Al is this [4] reuled by the <u>sighte</u> above.   *providence*
This <u>mene</u> I now by mighty Theseus,   *intend*   815
That for to honten is so desirous,
And namely at the grete hert in May,
That in his bed ther <u>daweth</u> him no day,   *dawneth*
That he nis clad, and redy for to ryde
With hunte and horn, and houndes him bisyde.   820
For in his hunting hath he swich delyt,
That it is al his Ioye and appetyt   (1680)
To been him-self the grete hertes bane,
For after Mars he serveth now Diane.

    Cleer was the day, as I have told er this,   825
And Theseus, with alle Ioye and blis,
With his Ipolita, the fayre quene,
And Emelye, clothed al in grene,

---

[1] Hl. as ; *rest omit.*   [2] E. anclee.   [3] E. wole.   [4] Hl. it.

On hunting be they riden roially.
And to the grove, that stood ful faste by,   830
In which ther was an hert, as men him tolde,
Duk Theseus the streighte wey hath holde.   (1690) *held*
And to the launde he rydeth him ful right,   *hunting grounds*
For thider was the hert wont have his flight,
And over a brook, and so forth in his weye.   835
This duk wol han a cours at him or tweye
With houndes, swiche as that[1] him list comaunde.   *please*
And whan this duk was come un-to the launde,
Under the sonne he loketh, and anon
He was war of Arcite and Palamon,   840
That foughten breme, as it were bores two;   *fiercely*
The brighte swerdes wenten to and fro   (1700)
So hidously, that with the leste strook
It semed as it wolde felle[2] an ook;
But what they were, no-thing he ne woot.   845
This duk his courser with his spores smoot,
And at a stert he was bitwix hem two,
And pullede out a swerd and cryed[3], 'ho!
Namore, up[4] peyne of lesing of your heed.
By mighty Mars, he shal anon be deed,   850
That smyteth any strook, that I may seen!
But telleth me what mister[5] men ye been,   *sort* (1710) *of*
That been so hardy for to fighten here   *bold*
With-outen Iuge or other officere,
As it were in a listes roially?'   855
This Palamon answerde hastily,
And seyde: 'sire, what nedeth wordes mo?
We have the deeth deserved[6] bothe two.

---

[1] Hn. Cp. Pt. that ; *rest om.*   [2] E. fille.
[3] E. cride ; Hn. Cp. Pt. cryed.   [4] E. Hn. Ln. vp-on ; *rest* vp.
[5] Hn. Cm. Cp. Pt. myster ; E. mystiers ; Ln. mester ; Hl. mestir.
[6] E. Hn. disserued.

Two woful wrecches been we, two caytyves,
That been encombred of our owne[1] lyves; *wearied* 860
And as thou art a rightful lord and Iuge,
Ne yeve us neither mercy ne refuge. *protection* (1720)
But[2] sle me first, for seynte charitee;
But sle my felawe eek as wel as me.
Or sle him first; for, though thou knowe[3] it lyte, 865
This is thy mortal fo, this is Arcite,
That fro thy lond is banished on his heed,
For which he hath deserved to be deed.
For this is he that cam un-to thy gate,
And seyde, that he highte Philostrate.   870
Thus hath he Iaped thee ful many a yeer,
And thou has maked him thy chief squyer;   (1730)
And this is he that loveth Emelye.
For sith the day is come that I shal dye,
I make pleynly my confessioun,   875
That I am thilke woful Palamoun,
That hath thy prisoun broken wikkedly.
I am thy mortal foo, and it am I
That loveth so hote Emelye the brighte,
That I wol dye present in hir sighte.   880
Therfore I axe deeth and my luwyse; *judgment*
But sle my felawe in the same wyse,   (1740)
For bothe han we deserved to be slayn.'
   This worthy duk answerde anon agayn,
And seide, 'This is a short conclusioun: 885
Youre owne[4] mouth, by your confessioun,
Hath dampned you, and I wol it recorde,
It nedeth noght to pyne yow with the corde.

---

[1] E. Hn. Cm. owene.   [2] *So in the* MSS.
[3] Hl. Hn. knowe; *rest* knowest.
[4] E. Hn. Cm. owene; Hl. Cp. Pt. owne.

Ye shul[1] be deed, by mighty Mars the rede!'
The quene anon, for verray wommanhede   890
Gan for to wepe, and so dide Emelye,
And alle the ladies in the compaignye.   (1750)
Gret pitee was it, as it thoughte hem alle,
That evere swich a chaunce sholde falle;
For gentil men they were, of greet estat[2],   895
And no-thing but for love was this debat[3];
And sawe hir bloody woundes wyde and sore;
And alle cryden, bothe lasse and more,   *less*
'Have mercy, lord, up-on us wommen alle!'
And on hir bare knees adoun they falle,   900
And wolde have kist his feet ther as he stood,
Til at the laste aslaked was his mood;   (1760) *appeased*
For pitee renneth sone in gentil herte.
And though he firste for ire quook and sterte, *quaked*
He hath considered shortly, in a clause,   905
The trespas of hem bothe, and eek the cause:
And al-though that his ire hir gilt accused, *censured*
Yet in his resoun he hem bothe excused;
And thus he thoghte wel, that every man
Wol helpe him-self in love, if that he can,   910
And eek delivere him-self out of prisoun;
And eek his herte hadde[4] compassioun   (1770)
Of wommen, for they wepen evere in oon;
And in his gentil herte he thoghte anoon,
And softe un-to himself he seyde : 'fy   915
Up-on a lord that wol have no mercy,
But been a leoun, bothe in word and dede,
To hem that been in repentaunce and drede,
As wel as to a proud despitous man,   *merciless*

---

[1] Hn. Pt. shul; Cm. Hl. schul; E. shal.   [2] E. estaat.
[3] E. debaat.   [4] Hl. Pt. Ln. had; *rest* hadde.

That wol maynteyne that he first bigan!   920
That lord hath litel of discrecioun,
That in swich cas can no divisioun,   (1780)
But weyeth pryde and humblesse after oon.'   *one manne*
And shortly, whan his ire is thus agoon,
He gan to loken up with eyen lighte,   925
And spak thise same wordes al on highte:— *aloud*
'The god of love, a! *benedicite,*
How mighty and how greet a lord is he!   . *prev*
Ayeins his might ther gayneth none obstacles, *against*
He may be cleped a god for his[1] miracles;   930
For he can maken at his owne[2] gyse
Of everich herte, as that him list devyse[3]. *direct* (1790)
Lo heer, this Arcite and this Palamoun,
That quitly weren out of my prisoun,   *free*
And mighte han lived in Thebes roially,   935
And witen I am hir mortal enemy,   *knew*
And that hir deth lyth in my might also,
And yet hath love, maugree hir eyen two,
Y-broght[4] hem hider bothe for to dye!
Now loketh, is nat that an heigh folye?   940
Who may nat[5] ben a fool, if that[6] he love?
Bihold, for Goddes sake that sit above,   (1800)
Se how they blede! be they noght wel arrayed?
Thus hath hir lord, the god of love, y-payed
Hir wages and hir fees for hir servyse!   945
And yet théy wenen for to been ful wyse *think*
That serven love, for aught that may bifalle!
But this is yet the beste game of alle,
That she, for whom they han this Iolitee,

[1] E. hise.   [2] E. Hn. Cm. owene; Cp. Pt. owne.
[3] E. diuyse.   [4] Hl. I-brought; *rest* Broght, Brought.
[5] *Not in the* MSS.   [6] Hl. if that; *rest* but if.

Can hem ther-for as moche thank as me ;   950
She woot namore of al this hote fare,
By God, than woot a cokkow or[1] an hare !   (1810)
But al moot ben assayed, hoot and cold ;   *must*
A man moot ben a fool, or yong or old ;
I woot it by my-self ful yore agoon :   955
For in my tyme a servant was I oon.
And therfore, sin I knowe of loves peyne,
And woot how sore it can a man distreyne,
As he that hath ben caught ofte in his las[2], *snare*
I yow foryeve al hoolly this trespas[3],   960
At requeste of the quene that kneleth here,
And eek of Emelye, my suster dere.   (1820)
And ye shul bothe anon un-to me swere,
That nevere-mo ye shul my contree[4] dere, *injure*
Ne make werre up-on me night ne day,   965
But been my frendes in al that ye may ;
I yow foryeve this trespas every del[5].'
And they him swore[6] his axing fayre and wel[5],
And him of lordshipe and of mercy preyde,
And he hem graunteth grace, and thus he seyde : 970
   'To speke of roial lynage and richesse,
Though that she were a quene or a princesse, (1830)
Ech of yow bothe is worthy, doutelees,
To wedden when tyme is, but nathelees[7]
I speke as for my suster Emelye,   975
For whom ye have this stryf and Ielousye[8],
Ye woot your-self she may not wedden two
At ones, though ye fighten evere-mo :

[1] E. Hn. Cp. of ; *rest* or.
[2] E. Hn. Cp. Pt. laas ; Cm. las ; Hl. Ln. lace.
[3] E. Pt. trespaas.   [4] Cp. Ln. Hl. coroune.
[5] E. deel, weel ; Hn. Cm. Cp. del, wel.
[6] Hl. Pt. swore ; *rest* sworen, sworne, sworyn.
[7] E. *wrongly repeats* doutelees.   [8] E. Ialousye.

That oon of yow, al be him <u>looth</u> or leef,   *displeasing or pleasin*
He moot go[1] pypen in an ivy-leef;   980
This is to seyn, she may nat now han bothe,
Al be ye nevere so Ielous[2], ne so wrothe.   (1840)
And <u>for-thy</u> I yow putte in this degree,   *therefore*
That ech of yow shal have his destinee
As him is shape; and herkneth in what wyse;   985
Lo, heer your ende of that I shal devyse.

   My wil is this, for <u>plat</u> conclusioun,   *plain*
With-outen any replicacioun,
If that yow lyketh, tak it for the beste,
That everich of yow shal goon wher him leste   990
Frely, with-outen raunsoun or daunger;
And this day fifty wykes, <u>fer ne ner</u>, *nor more* (1850) *is*
Everich of yow shal bringe an hundred knightes,
Armed for listes up <u>at alle rightes</u>, *rightly in all respect*
Al redy to darreyne hir by bataille.   995
And this <u>bihote</u> I yow with-outen faille   *promise*
Up-on my trouthe, and as I am a knight,
That whether[3] of yow bothe that hath might,
This is to seyn, that whether[3] he or thou
May with his hundred, as I spak of now,   1000
Sleen his contrarie, or out of listes dryve,
Him[4] shal I yeve Emelya[5] to wyve,   (1860)
To whom that fortune yeveth so fair a grace.
The listes shal I maken in this place,   *truely*
And God so <u>wisly</u> on my soule <u>rewe</u>, *pity* 1005
As I shal even Iuge been and trewe.
Ye shul non other ende with me maken,
That oon of yow ne shal be <u>deed</u> or taken.

---

[1] E. *om.* go.   [2] E. Hn. Cp. Ialouse.   [3] E. wheither.
[4] Hl. Him; Cp. Ln. That; E. Hn. Thanne; Cm. Pt. Than.
[5] *So* E. Cp. Ln.; Hl. Hn. Emelye.

And if yow thinketh this is wel y-sayd,
Seyeth your avys, and holdeth yow apayd.   1010   *satisfied*
This is your ende and your conclusioun.'

    Who loketh lightly now but Palamoun?   (1870)
Who springeth up for Ioye but Arcite?
Who couthe telle, or who couthe it[1] endyte,
The Ioye that is maked in the place   1015
Whan Theseus hath doon so fair a grace?
But doun on knees wente every maner wight,
And thanked[2] him with al hir herte and might,
And namely the Thebans ofte[3] sythe.   *times*
And thus with good hope and with herte blythe   1020
They take hir leve, and hom-ward gonne they ryde
To Thebes, with his olde walles wyde.   (1880)

Explicit secunda pars.   Sequitur pars tercia.

    I trowe men wolde deme it necligence,   *believe*
If I foryete to tellen the dispence   *expense*
Of Theseus, that goth so busily   1025
To maken up the listes roially;
That swich a noble theatre as it was,
I dar wel seyn that[4] in this world ther nas.
The circuit a myle was aboute,
Walled of stoon, and diched al with-oute.   1030
Round was the shap, in manere of compas[5],   *circle*
Ful of degrees, the heighte of sixty pas,   *steps* (1890)
That, whan a man was set on o degree,
He lette nat his felawe for to see.   *hindered*

    Est-ward ther stood a gate of marbel[6] whyt,   1035

[1] E. Cm. Hl. *om.* it.
[2] Hl. thanked; Cm. thankede; Cp. Pt. Ln. thonked; E. Hn. thonken.
[3] E. often; Ln. oft; Pt. mony; *rest* ofte.   [4] Hl. that; *rest om.*
[5] E. compaas.   [6] E. Hn. marbul.

West-ward, right swich another in the opposit.
And shortly to concluden, swich a place
Was noon in erthe, as in so litel space;
For in the lond ther nas no crafty man,
That geometrie or ars-metrik can,   *arithmetic*   1040
Ne portreyour[1], ne kervere of images,
That Theseus ne yaf him[2] mete and wages   (1900)
The theatre for to maken and devyse.   *plan*
And for to doon his ryte and sacrifyse,
He est-ward hath up-on the gate above,   1045
In worship of Venus, goddesse of love,
Doon make an auter and an oratorie;   *chapel*
And west-ward, in the mynde and in memorie[3]   *memory*
Of Mars, he maked hath right swich another,
That coste largely of gold a fother.   *load*   1050
And north-ward, in a touret on the wal,
Of alabastre whyt and reed coral   (1910)
An oratorie riche for to see,
In worship of Dyane of chastitee,
Hath Theseus doon wroght in noble wyse.   1055
But yet hadde I foryeten to devyse
The noble kerving, and the portreitures,
The shap, the contenaunce, and the figures,
That weren in thise oratories thre.

First in the temple of Venus maystow se   1060
Wroght on the wal, ful pitous to biholde,
The broken slepes, and the sykes colde;   *sighs* (1920)
The sacred teres, and the waymenting;
The fyry strokes of[4] the desiring,
That loves servaunts in this lyf enduren;   1065

---

[1] Hl. purtreyour; Hn. purtreyour; E. portreitour.
[2] Cp. Pt. Cm. him; Hl. hem; *rest om.*
[3] *So* Hl.; E. (*wrongly*) And on the westward, in memorie.
[4] E. and; *rest* of.

The othes, that hir covenants assuren; *confirm*
Plesaunce and hope, desyr, fool-hardinesse,
Beautee and youthe, bauderie, richesse, *bawdry*
Charmes and force, lesinges, flaterye, *lies*
Dispense, bisynesse, and Ielousye [1], *expense*   1070 *care*
That wered of yelwe goldes [2] a gerland, *turnsols (marigolds)*
And a cokkow sitting on hir [3] hand;   (1930)
Festes, instruments, caroles, dounces,
Lust and array, and alle the circumstaunces *state, dress*
Of love, whiche that I rekne and rekne shal [4], 1075 *reckon*
By ordre weren peynted on the wal,
And mo than I can make of mencioun.
For soothly, al the mount of Citheroun, *Cithaeron*
Ther Venus hath hir principal dwelling,
Was shewed on the wal in portreying,   1080
With al the gardin, and the lustinesse.
Nat was foryete the porter Ydelnesse,   (1940)
Ne Narcisus the faire of yore agon, *years ago*
Ne [5] yet the folye of king Salamon,
Ne yet [6] the grete strengthe of Hercules [7],   1085
Thenchauntements of Medea and Circes,
Ne of Turnus, with the hardy fiers corage,
The riche Cresus, caytif in servage.
Thus may ye seen that wisdom ne richesse,
Beautee ne sleighte, strengthe, ne [8] hardinesse, 1090 *craft boldness*
Ne may with Venus holde champartye; *partnership*
For as hir list the world than may she gye.   (1950) *please guide*
Lo, alle thise folk so caught were in hir las,
Til they for wo ful ofte seyde 'allas!'

---

[1] E. Hn. Cp. Ialousye.   [2] Hl. guldes.   [3] Cp. Ln. Cm. his.
[4] Cm. I reken and rekne shal; Hn. I rekned and rekne shal; E.
I rekned haue and rekne shal (*too long*).
[5] E. Cm. And; *rest* Ne.   [6] E. And eek; Hn. Ne yet; Hl. Ne eek.
[7] E. Hn. Cm. Ercules.   [8] E. Hn. Pt. *om.*

Suffyceth heer ensamples oon or two,   1095
And though I coude rekne a thousand mo.

The statue of Venus, glorious for to see,
Was naked fleting in the large see,
And fro the navele doun al covered was
With wawes grene, and brighte as any glas.   1100
A citole in hir right hand hadde she,   *small harp*
And on hir heed, ful semely for to see,   (1960)
A rose gerland, fresh and wel smellinge;
Above hir heed hir dowves flikeringe.
Biforn hir stood hir sone Cupido,   1105
Up-on his shuldres winges hadde he two;
And blynd he was, as it is[1] ofte sene;
A bowe he bar and arwes brighte and kene.

Why sholde I noght as wel eek telle yow al
The portreiture, that was up-on the wal   1110
With-inne the temple of mighty Mars the rede?
Al peynted was the wal, in lengthe and brede,   (1970)
Lyk to the estres of the grisly place,   *inner parts*
That highte the grete temple of Mars in Trace,
In thilke colde frosty regioun,   1115
Ther as Mars hath his sovereyn mansioun.

First on the wal was peynted a foreste[2],
In which ther dwelleth neither man ne beste[3],
With knotty knarry bareyn treës olde   *knotty*
Of stubbes sharpe and hidous to biholde;   1120
In which ther ran a rumbel[4] in[5] a swough,   *gust of wind*
As though a storm sholde bresten[6] every bough:
And downward from[7] an hille, under a bente,   (1981)
Ther stood the temple of Mars armipotente,   *plain*
                                              mighty in arms

---

[1] E. was; *rest* is.   [2] Hl. foreste; E. forest.   [3] Hl. beste; E. best.
[4] *So* E; Cm. ru*m*bil; Hn. rombul; Cp. Ln. rombel; Hl. swymbul.
[5] E. Pt. and; *rest* in.   [6] Ln. berste; Hl. berst.   [7] Hn. Hl. on.

Wroght al of burned steel, of which thentree[1] 1125 *entrance burnished*
Was long and streit, and gastly for to see. *narrow horrible*
And ther-out cam a rage and such a vese[2], *draught*
That it made al the gates[3] for to rese. *quake*
The northren light in at the dores shoon,
For windowe on the wal ne was ther noon, 1130
Thurgh which men mighten any light discerne.
The dores were[4] alle of adamant eterne, (1990)
Y-clenched overthwart and endelong *fastened, athwart, length ways*
With iren tough; and, for to make it strong,
Every piler, the temple to sustene, 1135
Was tonne-greet, of iren bright and shene. *round like a tun*
   Ther saugh I first the derke[5] imagining *plotting*
Of felonye, and al[6] the compassing; *craft*
The cruel ire, as[7] reed as any glede; *hot coal*
The pykepurs, and eek[8] the pale drede; 1140
The smyler with the knyf under the cloke;
The shepne brenning with the blake smoke; (2000) *stables*
The tresoun of the mordring in the bedde;
The open werre, with woundes al bi-bledde;
Contek, with blody knyf and sharp manace; 1145 *contest menace*
Al ful of chirking was that sory place. *chirping of birds*
The sleere of him-self yet saugh I ther,
His herte-blood hath bathed al his heer; *hair*
The nayl y-driven in the shode a-night; *temple*
The colde deeth, with mouth gaping up-right. 1150
Amiddes of the temple sat meschaunce,
With disconfort and sory contenaunce. (2010)
Yet saugh I woodnesse laughing in his rage; *madness*

[1] E. Hn. the entree.
[2] Cp. vese; Cm. wese; E. Hn. Ln. veze; Hl. prise.
[3] E. Hn. Cm. gate.   [4] E. Hn. Pt. dore was.
[5] E. Hn. dirke.   [6] E. Cm. *om.*
[7] Hl. Ln. as; *rest om.*   [8] E. Cm. *om.*

Armed compleint, outhees [1], and fiers outrage.   *outery*
The careyne in the bush [2], with throte y-corve :   1155
A thousand slayn, and nat [3] of qualm y-storve ;   *sickness do*
The tiraunt, with the prey by force y-raft ;   *bereft*
The toun destroyed, ther was no-thing laft.
Yet sawgh I brent the shippes hoppesteres ;   *dancing*
The hunte strangled with the wilde beres :   1160
The sowe freten the child right in the cradel ;   *eating*
The cook y-scalded, for al his longe ladel.   (2020)
Noght was foryeten by the infortune of Marte ;
The carter over-riden with his carte,
Under the wheel ful lowe he lay adoun.   1165
Ther were also, of Martes divisioun,
The barbour [4], and the bocher, and the smith
That forgeth sharpe swerdes on his stith.   *anvil*
And al above, depeynted in a tour,
Saw I conquest sittinge in greet honour,   1170
With the sharpe swerde [5] over his heed
Hanginge by a sotil twynes threed.   (2030)
Depeynted was the slaughtre of Iulius,
Of grete Nero, and of Antonius ;
Al be that thilke tyme they were unborn,   1175
Yet was hir deeth depeynted ther-biforn,
By manasinge of Mars, right by figure ;   *menace*
So was it shewed in that portreiture
As is depeynted in the sterres [6] above,
Who shal be slayn or elles deed for love.   1180
Suffyceth oon ensample in stories olde,
I may not rekne hem alle, thogh I wolde.   (2040)
    The statue of Mars up-on a carte stood,   *chariot*

---

[1] Cm. outes.   [2] E. Cp. Ln. busk ; Cm. bosch ; Hn. Pt. bussh.
[3] E. *alone ins.* oon.   [4] E. Cm. laborer ; *rest* barbour.
[5] Pt. Ln. swerde ; *rest* swerd.
[6] Hl. sterres ; E. Pt. certres ; *rest* sertres.

Armed, and loked grim as he were wood;
And over his heed ther shynen two figures   1185
Of sterres, that been cleped in scriptures,   *called*
That oon Puella, that other Rubeus.
This god of armes was arrayed thus :—
A wolf ther stood biforn him at his feet
With eyen rede, and of a man he eet;   1190
With sotil[1] pencel was depeynt[2] this storie,
In redoutinge of Mars and of his glorie.   *reverend* (2050)

   Now to the temple of Diane the chaste
As shortly as I can I wol me haste,
To telle yow al the descripcioun.   1195
Depeynted been the walles up and doun
Of hunting and of shamfast chastitee.   *modest*
Ther saugh I how woful Calistopee,   *Callisto*
Whan that Diane agreved was with here,
Was turned from a womman to a bere,   1200
And after was she maad the lode-sterre;
Thus was it peynt[3], I can say yow no ferre;   (2060)
Hir sone is eek a sterre, as men may see.
Ther saugh I Dane, y-turned til a tree,
I mene nat the goddesse Diane,   1205 *Peneus*
But Penneus doughter, which that highte Dane.   *Daphne*
Ther saugh I Attheon an hert y-maked,
For vengeaunce that he saugh Diane al naked;
I saugh how that his[4] houndes have him caught,
And freten him, for that they knewe him naught. 1210 *eat*
Yet peynted was[5] a litel forther-moor,
How Atthalante hunted the wilde boor,   (2070)
And Meleagre[6], and many another mo,

---

[1] Cm. sotyl; E. soutil.
[2] *All* depeynted (*badly*).
[3] *All* peynted; *see* l. 1191.
[4] E. Hn. hise.
[5] E. *om.* was.
[6] E. Hn. Meleagree.

For which Diane wroughte him[1] care and woo.   *woe*

Ther saugh I many another wonder storie,   1215

The whiche me list nat drawen to memorie.   *call to*
                                             memory

This goddesse on an hert ful[2] hye seet,

With smale houndes al aboute hir feet;

And undernethe hir feet she hadde a mone,   *moon*

Wexing it was, and sholde wanie sone.   1220

In gaude grene hir statue clothed was,   *bright*

With bowe in honde, and arwes in a cas.   (2080)

Hir eyen caste she ful lowe adoun,

Ther Pluto hath his derke regioun.

A womman travailinge was hir biforn,   1225

But, for hir child so longe was unborn,

Ful pitously Lucyna gan she calle,

And seyde, 'help, for thou mayst best of alle.'

Wel couthe he peynten lyfly that it wroghte,

With many a florin he the hewes boghte.   *clours* 1230

    Now been thise[3] listes maad, and Theseus,

That at his grete cost arrayed thus   (2090)

The temples and the theatre every del,   *part*

Whan it was doon, him lyked wonder wel.

But stinte I wol of Theseus a lyte,   1235

And speke of Palamon and of Arcite.

    The day approcheth of hir retourninge,

That everich sholde an hundred knightes bringe,

The bataille to darreyne, as I yow tolde ;   *contest*

And til Athenes, hir covenant[4] for[5] to holde,   1240

Hath everich of hem broght an hundred knightes

Wel armed for the werre at alle rightes.   *in all* (2100)

And sikerly, ther trowed many a man   *believed* *resp*

That nevere, sithen that the world bigan,

So in the MSS.   [2] E. Cp. Pt. *ins.* wel.   [3] E. the.
[4] E. couenantz.   [5] Hl. (*alone*) om. for.

As for to speke of knighthod of hir hond,   1245
As fer as God hath maked see or lond,
Nas, of so fewe, so noble a compaignye.
For every wight that loved chivalrye,   *being willing*
And wolde, his thankes, han a passant name,   *surpassing*
Hath preyed[1] that he mighte ben of that game; 1250 *sport*
And wel was him, that ther-to chosen was.

For if ther fille to-morwe swich a cas[2],   (2110)
Ye knowen wel, that every lusty knight,
That loveth paramours, and hath his might,
Were it in Engelond, or elles-where,   1255
They wolde, hir thankes, wilnen to be there.
To fighte for a lady, *benedicite!*
It were a lusty sighte for to see.
And right so ferden they with Palamon.
With him ther wenten knightes many oon;   1260
Som wol ben armed in an habergeoun,   *hauberk*
In a[3] brest-plat and in a light gipoun; *cassok* (2120)
And somme woln have a peyre plates large; *pair*
And somme woln have a Pruce sheld, or a targe;
Somme woln been armed on hir legges weel, 1265 *well*
And have an ax, and somme a mace of steel.
Ther nis no newe gyse, that it nas old.
Armed were they, as I have you told,
Everich after his opinioun.

   Ther maistow seen coming with Palamoun   1270
Ligurge him-self, the grete king of Trace;
Blak was his berd, and manly was his face.   (2130)
The cercles of his eyen in his heed,   *pupils ?*
They gloweden bitwixe yelow and reed;
And lyk a griffoun loked he aboute,   1275

---

[1] E. preyd; Hn. prayd; Hl. Cm. preyed.   [2] E. Cp. Pt. caas.
[3] Hl. In a; E. And in; Hn. Cm. Cp. Ln. And in a.

With kempe heres on his[1] browes stoute;   *shaggy h*

His[1] limes grete, his[1] braunes harde and stronge,   *mus*

His[1] shuldres brode, his[1] armes rounde and longe.

And as the gyse was in his contree,   *fashion*

Ful hye up-on a char of gold stood he,   1280

With foure white boles in the trays.   *bulls*

In-stede of cote-armure over his harnays,   (2140)

With nayles yelwe[2], and brighte as any gold,

He hadde a beres skin, col-blak, for-old.   *very old*

His longe heer was kembd bihynde his bak,   1285

As any ravenes fether it shoon for-blak.   *very black*

A wrethe of gold arm-greet, of huge wighte,   *arm's wi*

Upon his heed, set ful of stones brighte,   *weig*

Of fyne rubies and of dyamaunts.

Aboute his char[3] ther wenten whyte alaunts,   *hunt* 1290

Twenty and mo, as grete as any steer,

To hunten at the leoun or the deer,   (2150)

And folwed him, with mosel faste y-bounde,   *muzzel*

Colers[4] of golde, and torets[5] fyled rounde.   *ring swi*

An hundred lordes hadde he in his route   *company* 1295

Armed ful wel, with hertes sterne[6] and stoute.

  With Arcita, in stories as men fynde,

The grete Emetreus, the king of Inde,

Up-on a stede bay, trapped in steel,

Covered in cloth of gold diapred wel,   *variegated* 1300

Cam ryding lyk the god of armes, Mars.

His cote-armure was of cloth of Tars,   *silk*   (2160)

Couched with perles whyte and rounde and grete.   *inla*

His sadel was of brend gold newe y-bete;   *burnished*

---

[1] E. hise.   [2] Hn. yelwe; E. yelewe.   [3] E. chaar.
[4] Pt. Ln. Colers; Cp. Coleres; E. Hl. Colerd; Hn. Colered; Cm. Colerid.
[5] E. *tourettes*; Cp. Hl. torettes (*better* torets).   [6] E. Hn. stierne.

A mantelet [1] upon his shuldre hanginge   1305
Bret-ful [2] of rubies reede, as fyr sparklinge. *brimfull*
His crispe heer lyk ringes was y-ronne, *curled* *clustered*
And that was yelow, and glitered as the sonne.
His nose was heigh, his eyen bright citryn, *yellow*
His lippes rounde, his colour was sangwyn,   1310
A fewe fraknes in his face y-spreynd, *freckles* *scattered*
Betwixen yelow and somdel blak y-meynd,   (2170) *mingled*
And as a leoun he his loking caste.
Of fyve and twenty yeer his age I caste. *suppose*
His berd was wel bigonne for to springe;   1315
His voys was as a trompe thunderinge.
Up-on his heed he wered of laurer grene
A gerlond fresh and lusty for to sene.
Up-on his hand he bar, for his deduyt, *pleasure*
An egle tame, as eny lilye whyt.   1320
An hundred lordes hadde he with him there,
Al armed, sauf hir heddes, in al [3] hir gere,   (2180) *except*
Ful richely in alle maner thinges.
For trusteth wel, that dukes, erles, kinges,
Were gadered in this noble compaignye,   1325
For love, and for encrees of chivalrye.
Aboute this king ther ran on every part
Ful many a tame leoun and lepart [4].
And in this wyse thise lordes, alle and some, *one and all*
Been on the Sonday to the citee come   1330
Aboute pryme, and in the toun alight. *1st ¼ p - 241*
    This Theseus, this duk, this worthy knight,   (2190)
Whan he had broght hem in-to his citee,
And inned hem, everich in [5] his degree, *lodged*
He festeth hem, and doth so greet labour   1335

[1] E. Cm. Pt. mantel.   [2] E. Brat-ful.   [3] Hl. *om.* al.
[4] Hl. Cp. lepart; E. leopard.   [5] E. in; Pt. after; *rest* at.

To esen hem, and doon hem al honour,
That yet men weneth that no mannes [1] wit   *think*
Of noon estat ne coude amenden it.
The minstralcye, the service at the feste,   *minstrelsy*
The grete yiftes to the moste [2] and leste,   1340
The riche array of Theseus paleys,
Ne who sat first ne last up-on the deys,   (2200)
What ladies fairest been or best daunsinge,
Or which of hem can dauncen best and singe,
Ne who most felingly speketh of love: 1345
What haukes sitten on the perche above,
What houndes liggen on [3] the floor adoun:
Of al this make I now no mencioun;
But al [4] theffect, that thinketh me the beste;
Now comth [5] the poynt, and herkneth if yow leste.   *please*

The Sonday night, er day bigan to springe,   1351
When Palamon the larke herde singe,   (2210)
Although it nere nat day by houres two,
Yet song the larke, and Palamon also.
With holy herte, and with an heigh corage   *great* 1355
                                                spirit
He roos, to wenden on his pilgrimage
Un-to the blisful Citherea benygne,
I mene Venus, honurable and dygne.
And in hir houre he walketh forth a pas [6]   *at foot pace*
Un-to the listes, ther hir temple was,   1360
And doun he kneleth, and with [7] humble chere   *countenance*
And herte soor, he seide as ye shul here [8].   *sore* (2220)
   'Faireste of faire, o lady myn Venus,
Doughter to [9] Iove, and spouse of [10] Vulcanus,
Thou gladere of the mount of Citheroun,   *made* 1365

---

[1] E. maner.   [2] E. Hn. meeste; Cm. Cp. meste; *rest* most. *glad*
[3] E. Cm. Hl. in; *rest* on.   [4] Hl. of.   [5] Hn. comth; E. cometh.
[6] E. paas.   [7] E. with ful; *rest* and with.
[8] E. and seyde in this manere.   [9] Hn. Hl. of.   [10] E. Cm. of; *rest* to.

For thilke love thou haddest to Adoun,
Have pitee of my bittre teres smerte,   *smarting*
And tak myn humble preyere at[1] thin herte.
Allas! I ne have no langage to telle
Theffectes ne the torments of myn helle;   1370
Myn herte may myne harmes nat biwreye;   *reveal*
I am so confus, that I can noght seye.   (2230)
But mercy, lady bright, that knowest wele[2]
My thought, and seest what harmes that I fele[3],
Considere al this, and rewe up-on my sore,   *pity* 1375
As wisly as I shal for evermore,   *truly*
Emforth my might, thy trewe servant be,   *even with*
And holden werre alway with chastitee;
That make I myn avow, so ye me helpe.
I kepe noght of armes for to yelpe,—*boast*   1380 *care*
Ne I ne axe[4] nat to-morwe[5] to have victorie,
Ne renoun in this caas, ne veyne glorie *hap* (2240)
Of pris of armes blowen up and doun,
But I wolde have fully possessioun
Of Emelye, and dye in thy servyse;   1385
Fynd thou the manere how, and in what wyse.
I recche nat, but it may bettre be,
To have victorie of hem, or they of me,
So that I have my lady in myne armes.
For though so be that Mars is god of armes,   1390
Your vertu is so greet in hevene above,   *power*
That, if yow list, I shal wel have my love.   (2250) *please*
Thy temple wol I worshipe everemo,
And on thyn auter, wher I ryde or go,
I wol doon sacrifice, and fyres bete.   *light*   1395
And if ye wol nat so, my lady swete,

---

[1] Hl. to.   [2] Cm. Hl. wel.   [3] Cm. Hl. fel.
[4] Hl. aske.   [5] Hl. Ln. to morn.

Than preye I thee, to-morwe with a spere
That Arcita me thurgh the herte bere.   *pierce*
Thanne rekke I noght, whan I have lost my lyf,
Though that Arcita winne hir to his wyf.   1400
This is theffect and ende of my preyere,
Yif me my love, thou blisful lady dere.'   (2260)
Whan thorisoun[1] was doon of Palamon,
His sacrifice he dide, and that anon
Ful pitously, with alle circumstaunces[2],   1405
Al telle I noght as now his observaunces[3].
But atte laste the statue of Venus shook,
And made a signe, wher-by that he took
That his preyere accepted was that day.
For thogh the signe shewed a delay,   1410
Yet wiste he wel that graunted was his bone;   (2269)
And with glad herte he wente him hoom ful sone. *praye*
    The thridde houre inequal that Palamon
Bigan to Venus temple for to gon,
Up roos the sonne, and up roos Emelye,   1415
And to the temple of Diane gan[4] hye.
Hir maydens, that she thider with hir ladde,
Ful redily with hem the fyr they hadde[5],
Thencens, the clothes, and the remenant al
That to the sacrifyce longen shal;   *belong*   1420
The hornes fulle of meth[6], as was the gyse; *mead*
Ther lakked noght to doon hir sacrifyse.   (2280)
Smoking the temple, ful of clothes faire, *perfuming*
This Emelye with herte debonaire *gracious*
Hir body wessh with water of a welle;   1425
But how she dide hir ryte I dar nat telle.

---

[1] Hl. thorisoun; *rest* the orison (orisoun).
[2] E. Cm. circumstaunce.   [3] E. Cm. observaunce.
[4] Pt. Hl. *ins.* she.   [5] E. ladde; *rest* hadde.
[6] Cp. Pt. Ln. methe; Hl. meth; E. meeth; Hn. mede.

But it be any thing in general;
And yet it were a game to heren al;   *pleasure*
To him that meneth wel, it were no charge: *harm*
But it is good a man ben at his large.   *free*   1430
Hir brighte heer was kempt[1], untressed al;   *combed*
A coroune of a grene ook cerial   *cerrus oak*   (2290)
Up-on hir heed was set ful fair and mete.
Two fyres on the auter gan she bete,   *kindle*
And dide hir thinges, as men may biholde   1435
In Stace of Thebes, and thise bokes olde.
Whan kindled was the fyr, with pitous chere   *countenance*
Un-to Diane she spak, as ye may here.
  'O chaste goddesse of the wodes grene,
To whom bothe hevene and erthe and see is sene,
Quene of the regne of Pluto derk and lowe,   1441
Goddesse of maydens, that myn herte hast knowe
Ful many a yeer, and woost what I desyre,   (2301)
As keep me fro thy vengeaunce and thyn ire,
That Attheon[2] aboghte cruelly[3].   *atoned for*   1445
Chaste goddesse, wel wostow that I
Desyre to been a mayden al my lyf,
Ne nevere wol I be no love ne wyf.
I am, thou woost, yet of thy compaignye,
A mayde, and love hunting and venerye,   *chasing* 1450
And for to walken in the wodes wylde,
And noght to been a wyf, and be with chylde.
Nought wol I knowe the compaignye of man. (2311)
Now help me, lady, sith ye may and can,
For tho thre formes that thou hast in thee.   1455 *see p. 189*
And Palamon, that hath swich love to me,
And eek Arcite, that loveth me so sore,
This grace I preye thee with-oute more,

---

[1] E. kempd.   [2] Hl. Atheon.   [3] Hl. trewely.

As[1] sende love and pees bitwixe hem two;

And fro me torne awey hir hertes so,   1460

That al hir hote love, and hir desyr,

And al hir bisy torment, and hir fyr   *anxious* (2320)

Be queynt, or turned in another place;

And if so be thou wolt do me no grace,

Or[2] if my destinee be shapen so,   1465

That I shal nedes have oon of hem two,

As sende me him that most desyreth me.

Bihold, goddesse of clene chastitee,

The bittre teres that on my chekes falle.

Sin thou art mayde, and kepere of us alle,   1470

My maydenhode thou kepe and wel conserve,

And whyl I live a mayde, I wol thee serve.'   (2330)

    The fyres brenne up-on the auter clere,

Whyl Emelye was thus in hir preyere;

But sodeinly she saugh a sighte queynte, *stranger*1475

For right anon oon of the fyres queynte, *quenched*

And quiked agayn, and after that anon   *revive*

That other fyr was queynt, and al agon;

And as it queynte, it made a whistelinge,

As doon thise wete brondes in hir[3] brenninge,   1480

And at the brondes ende out-ran anoon

As it were blody dropes many oon;   (2340)

For which so sore agast was Emelye,

That she was wel ny mad, and gan to crye,

For she ne wiste what it signifyed;   1485

But only for the fere thus hath[4] she cryed, *terror*

And weep, that it was pitee for to here.

And ther-with-al Diane gan appere,

With bowe in hond, right as an hunteresse,

---

[1] Hn. As ; *rest* And.   [2] E. And ; *rest* Or.

[3] Hl. (*only*) As doth a wete brond in his.   [4] Pt. Hl. *om.* hath.

And seyde: 'Doghter, stint thyn hevinesse. *stop* 1490
Among the goddes hye it is affermed,
And by eterne[1] word write[2] and confermed, (2350)
Thou·shalt ben wedded un-to oon of tho
That han for thee so muchel care and wo;
But un-to which of hem I may nat telle. 1495
Farwel, for I ne may no lenger dwelle.
The fyres which that on myn auter brenne
Shul thee declaren[3], er that thou go henne, *hence*
Thyn aventure of love, as in this cas.' *chance*
And with that word, the arwes in the cas[4] 1500
Of the goddesse clateren faste and ringe, *rattled*
And forth she wente, and made a vanisshinge; (2360)
For which this Emelye astoned was,
And seyde, 'What amounteth this, allas!
I putte me in thy proteccioun, 1505
Diane, and in thy disposicioun.'
And hoom she goth anon the nexte weye. *nearest way*
This is theffect, ther is namore to seye.

The nexte houre of Mars folwinge this,
Arcite un-to the temple walked is *has* ·510
Of fierse[5] Mars, to doon his sacrifyse,
With alle the rytes of his payen wyse. *pagan* (2370)
With pitous herte and heigh devocioun,
Right thus to Mars he seyde his orisoun:
'O stronge god, that in the regnes colde 1515
Of Trace honoured art and lord y-holde,
And hast in every regne and every lond
Of armes al the brydel in thyn hond,
And hem fortunest as thee list devyse, *make fortunate: direct*
Accept of me my pitous sacrifyse. 1520

---

[1] *So all.* [2] Hl. write; Pt. writt; *rest* writen. [3] E. Cp. Hl. declare.
[4] E. cas. [5] E. Hn. fierse; Cm. ferse; Hl. fyry.

If so be that my youthe may deserve,
And that my might be worthy for to serve   (2380)
Thy godhede, that I may been oon of thyne,
Than preye I thee to rewe up-on my pyne.   *pity, gris*
For thilke peyne, and thilke hote fyr,   1525
In which thou whylom brendest for desyr,

.   .   .   .

For thilke sorwe that was in thyn herte,   (2391)
Have routhe as wel up-on my peynes smerte.   *pity*
I am yong and unkonning, as thou wost,   *ignorant* 1535
And, as I trowe, with love offended most,
That evere was any lyves creature;   *living*
For she, that doth me al this wo endure,
Ne reccheth nevere wher I sinke or flete.
And wel I woot, er she me mercy hete,   *promise* 1540
I moot with strengthe winne hir in the place;
And wel I woot, withouten help or grace   (2400)
Of thee, ne may my strengthe noght availle.
Than help me, lord, to-morwe in my bataille,
For thilke fyr that whylom brente thee,   1545
As wel as thilke fyr now brenneth me;
And do that I to-morwe have victorie.
Myn be the travaille, and thyn be the glorie!
Thy soverein temple wol I most honouren
Of any place, and alwey most labouren   1550
In thy plesaunce and in thy craftes stronge,
And in thy temple I wol my baner honge,   (2410)
And alle the armes of my compaignye;
And evere-mo, un-to that day I dye,
Eterne fyr I wol biforn thee fynde.   *provide*   1555
And eek to this avow I wol me bynde:
My berd, myn heer that hongeth long adoun,
That nevere yet ne felte offensioun

Of rasour nor of shere, I wol the yive,
And ben thy trewe servant whyl I live.   1560
Now lord, have routhe up-on my sorwes sore,   *pity*
Yif me [1] victorie, I aske thee namore.'   (2420)

    The preyere stinte of Arcita the stronge,   *finished*
The ringes on the temple-dore that honge,
And eek the dores, clatereden ful faste,   1565
Of which Arcita som-what him agaste.
The fyres brende up-on the auter brighte,
That it gan al the temple for to lighte ;
And swete smel the ground anon up-yaf,   *gave up*
And Arcita anon his hand up-haf,   *up-heaved*   1570   *lifted*
And more encens in-to the fyr he caste,
With othere rytes mo ; and atte laste   (2430)
The statue of Mars bigan his hauberk ringe.
And with that soun he herde a murmuringe
Ful lowe and dim, that sayde thus, 'Victorie.'   1575
For which he yaf to Mars honour and glorie.
And thus with Ioye, and hope wel to fare,
Arcite anon un-to his inne is fare,
As fayn as fowel is of the brighte sonne.   *joyful*

    And right anon swich stryf ther is bigonne   1580
For thilke graunting, in the hevene above,
Bitwixe Venus, the goddesse of love,   (2440)
And Mars, the sterne god armipotente,
That Iupiter was bisy it to stente ;   *stop*
Til that the pale Saturnus the colde,   1585
That knew so manye of aventures olde,   *adventures*
Fond in his olde experience an [2] art,
That he ful sone hath plesed every part.
As sooth is sayd, elde hath greet avantage,
In elde is bothe wisdom and usage ;   *knowing*   1590

---

[1] *All insert* the ; (*read* victórie).   [2] E. Pt. and.

out.

Men may the olde at-renne, and [1] noght at-rede.   out.

Saturne anon, to stinten stryf and drede,   (2450)

Al be it that it is agayn his kynde,

Of al this stryf he gan remedie fynde.

'My dere doughter Venus,' quod Saturne,   1595

'My cours, that hath so wyde for to turne,

Hath more power than woot any man.   knows

Myn is the drenching in the see so wan;   drowing

Myn is the prison in the derke cote;

Myn is the strangling and hanging by the throte;   1600

The murmure, and the cherles rebelling,

The groyning, and the pryve empoysoning: (2460) p

I do vengeance and pleyn correccioun,

Whyl I dwelle in the [2] signe of the leoun.

Myn is the ruine of the hye halles,   1605

The falling of the toures and of the walles

Up-on the mynour or the carpenter.

I slow Sampsoun in [3] shaking the piler;

And myne be the maladyes colde,

The derke tresons [4], and the castes olde;   plot 1610

My loking is the fader of pestilence.

Now weep namore, I shal doon diligence   (2470)

That Palamon, that is thyn owene knight,

Shal have his lady, as thou hast him hight.   promised

Though Mars shal helpe his knight, yet nathelees

Bitwixe yow ther moot be som tyme pees,   peace 1616

Al be ye noght of o complexioun,

That causeth al day swich divisioun.

I am thin ayel, redy at thy wille;   grandfather

Weep thou namore, I wol thy lust fulfille.'   1620

Now wol I stinten of the goddes above,

---

[1] Hl. Pt. but; *rest* and.   [2] E. *om.* the.

[3] Hl. in; *rest om.*   [4] Hl. tresoun.

Of Mars, and of Venus, goddesse of love,   (2480)
And telle yow, as pleynly as I can,
The grete effect, for which that I bigan.

Explicit tercia pars. Sequitur pars quarta.

Greet was the feste in Athenes that day,   1625
And eek the lusty seson of that May
Made every wight to been in swich plesaunce,
That al that Monday Iusten they and daunce,   *joust*
And spenden it in Venus heigh servyse.
But by the cause that they sholde aryse   1630
Erly, for to seen the grete fight,
Unto hir reste wente they at night.   (2490)
And on the morwe, whan that day gan springe,
Of hors and harneys, noyse and clateringe
Ther was in[1] hostelryes al aboute;   1635
And to the paleys rood ther many a route *company*
Of lordes, up-on stedes and palfreys.
Ther maystow seen devysing of herneys [*directing*] *preparation*
So uncouth and so riche, and wroght so weel *unknown, rare*
Of goldsmithrie, of browding, and of steel;   1640 *embroidery*
The sheeldes brighte, testers, and trappures; *helmets*
Gold-hewen[2] helmes, hauberks, cote-armures;   (2500)
Lordes in paraments on hir courseres, *ornamental clothes*
Knightes of retenue, and eek squyeres
Nailinge[3] the speres, and helmes bokelinge, 1645 *buckling*
Gigginge[4] of sheeldes, with layneres lacinge; *fitting whiplashes lacing*
Ther as need is, they weren no-thing ydel;
The fomy stedes on the golden brydel
Gnawinge, and faste the armurers also

---

[1] E. *ins.* the.   [2] Hl. Gold-beten.
[3] Hl. Rayhyng.   [4] Hl. Girdyng.

With fyle and hamer prikinge to and fro; *piercing* 1650
Yemen on fote, and communes many oon
With shorte staves, thikke as they may goon; (2510)
Pypes, trompes, nakers[1], clariounes, *cornets , clarions*
That in the bataille blowen blody sounes;
The paleys ful of peples up and doun,   1655
Heer thre, ther ten, holding hir questioun,
Divyninge of thise Thebane knightes two. *guessing*
Somme seyden thus, somme seyde it shal be so;
Somme helden with him with the blake berd,
Somme with the balled, somme with the thikke herd; 1660 *with* *ha*
Somme sayde, he loked grim and he wolde fighte;
He hath a sparth of twenty pound of wighte. (2520) *ba* *a*
Thus was the halle ful of divyninge,
Longe after that the sonne gan to springe.

   The grete Theseus, that of his sleep awaked 1665
With minstralcye and noyse that was maked,
Held yet the chambre of his paleys riche,   *stayed in*
Til that the Thebane knightes, bothe y-liche
Honoured, were into the paleys fet.
Duk Theseus was at a window set,   1670
Arrayed right as he were a god in trone.
The peple presseth thider-ward ful sone   (2530)
Him for to seen, and doon heigh reverence,
And eek to herkne his hest and his sentence. *command meaning*
An heraud on a scaffold made an ho[2],   1675
Til al the noyse of the[3] peple was y-do;
And whan he saugh the peple of noyse[4] al stille,
Tho shewed he the mighty dukes wille.   *then*
   ' The lord hath of his heigh discrecioun
Considered, that it were destruccioun   1680

---

[1] E. nakerers (*wrongly*).   [2] E. Hn. Pt. oo.
[3] E. *om.* the.   [4] E. Cm. the noyse of peple.

To gentil blood, to fighten in the gyse
Of mortal bataille now in this empryse;   *(2540)* enterprise
Wherfore, to shapen that they shul not dye,   ordain
He wol his firste purpos modifye.
No man therfor, up peyne of los of lyf,   1685
No maner shot, ne[1] pollax, ne short knyf, sling?   pole axe
Into the listes sende, or[2] thider bringe;
Ne short swerd for to stoke, with poynt bytinge,   stab sharp
No man ne drawe, ne bere by his syde.
Ne no man shal un-to his felawe ryde   1690
But o cours, with a sharp y-grounde spere;   sharpened
Foyne, if him list, on fote, him-self to were.   *(2550)* thrust
And he that is at meschief, shal be take,   misfortune: defend
And noght slayn, but be broght un-to the stake
That shal ben ordeyned on either syde;   1695
But thider he shal by force, and ther abyde.
And if so falle[3], the chieftayn[4] be take   befell
On either syde, or elles sleen his make,   slain his companion
No lenger shal the turneyinge laste.
God spede yow; goth forth, and ley on faste.   1700
With long swerd and with maces fight[5] your fille.
Goth now your wey; this is the lordes wille.'   *(2560)*

    The voys of peple touchede the hevene,
So loude cryden[6] they with mery[7] stevene: voice
'God save swich a lord, that is so good,   1705
He wilneth no destruccioun of blood!'
Up gon the trompes and the melodye.
And to the listes rit the compaignye   rides
By ordinaunce, thurgh-out the citee large,   plan
Hanged with cloth of gold, and nat with sarge.   1710

---

[1] E. Cm. *om.* ne.   [2] E. Cm. Ln. ne.   [3] E. be.
[4] Cm. cheuynteyn; Cp. cheuentein; Hl. cheuenten.
[5] Hl. fight; Ln. fihten; *rest* fighteth.
[6] Cm. cryedyn; E. cride.   [7] E. murie.

Ful lyk a lord this noble duk gan ryde,
Thise two Thebanes[1] up-on either syde ;   (2570)
And after rood the quene, and Emelye,
And after that another compaignye,
Of oon and other, after hir degree.   171
And thus they passen thurgh-out the citee,
And to the listes come they by tyme.
It nas not of the day yet fully pryme,
Whan set was Theseus ful riche and hye,
Ipolita the quene and Emelye,   1720
And other ladies in degrees aboute.
Un-to the seetes presseth al the <u>route</u> ; *assembly* (2580)
And west-ward, thurgh the gates under Marte,
Arcite, and eek the hundred of his parte,
With baner reed is entred right anon ;   1725
And in that selve moment Palamon
Is under Venus, est-ward in the place,   *bold*
With baner whyt, and <u>hardy</u> <u>chere</u> and face. *countena-*
In al the world, to seken up and doun,
So even with-outen variacioun,   1730
Ther nere swiche compaignyes tweye.
For ther nas noon so wys that coude seye,   (2590)
That any hadde of other avauntage
Of <u>worthinesse</u>, ne of estaat, ne age, *bravery*
So even were they[2] chosen, for to <del>gesse</del>. *deem* 1735
And in two <u>renges</u> faire they hem <u>dresse</u>. *ranks*
in
Whan that hir names rad were everichoon, *order*
That in hir nombre <del>gyle</del> were ther noon, *deceit*
Tho were the gates shet, and cried was loude :
'Do[3] now your devoir, yonge knightes proude !'   1740
   The heraudes lefte hir priking up and doun ;
Now ringen trompes loude and clarioun ;   (2600)

[1] E. Hn. Hl. Thebans; *see* l. 1765.   [2] E. *om.* they.   [3] Hl. Dooth

Ther is namore to seyn, but west and est
In goon the speres ful <u>sadly</u> in <u>arest</u>; *firmly   the rest*
In goth the sharpe spore in-to the syde.   1745
Ther seen men who can Iuste, and who can ryde;
Ther shiveren shaftes up-on sheeldes thikke;
He feleth thurgh the <u>herte-spoon</u> the prikke. *navel*
Up springen speres twenty foot on highte;
Out goth the swerdes as the silver brighte.   1750
The helmes they to-hewen and <u>to-shrede</u>; *to cut in shreds*
Out <u>brest</u> the blood, with sterne stremes rede. (2610) *burst*
With mighty maces the bones they to-breste.
He thurgh the thikkeste of the throng gan threste.
Ther stomblen[1] steedes stronge, and doun goth alle.
<u>He</u> rolleth under foot as doth a balle.   1756
He <u>foyneth</u> on his feet with his <u>tronchoun</u>, *one... another*
And he him hurtleth with his hors adoun. *thrust   spear shaft*
He thurgh the body is hurt, and <u>sithen</u> take, *afterwards*
Maugree his <u>heed</u>, and broght un-to the stake, 1760 *head*
As <u>forward</u> was, right ther he moste abyde; *agreement*
Another lad is on that other syde.   (2620)
And som tyme doth hem Theseus to reste,
Hem to refresshe[2], and drinken if hem leste.
Ful ofte a-day han thise Thebanes two   1765
Togidre y-met, and wroght his felawe wo;
Unhorsed hath ech other of hem tweye.
Ther nas no tygre in the vale of <u>Galgopheye</u>, *Gargaphia*
Whan that hir whelp is stole, whan it is lyte,
So cruel on the hunte, as is Arcite   1770
For Ielous herte upon this Palamoun:
Ne in <u>Belmarie</u> ther nis so fel leoun, *Benamarin* (2630)
That hunted is, or for his hunger wood,
Ne of his praye desyreth so the blood,

---

[1] E. Cm. semblen.   [2] E. fresshen.

As Palamon to sleen his foo Arcite.   1775
The Ielous strokes on hir helmes byte;
Out renneth blood on bothe hir sydes rede.
    Som tyme an ende ther is of every dede;
For er the sonne un-to the reste wente,
The stronge king Emetreus gan hente *seize*   1780
This Palamon, as he faught with Arcite,
And made his swerd depe in his flesh to byte; (2640)
And by the force of twenty is he take
Unyolden, and y-drawe unto the stake.   *unyielded*
And in the rescous[1] of this Palamoun *rescue*   1785
The stronge king Ligurge is born adoun;
And king Emetreus, for al his strengthe,
Is born out of his sadel a swerdes lengthe,
So hitte him Palamon er he were take;
But al for noght, he was broght to the stake.   1790
His hardy herte mighte him helpe naught;
He moste abyde, whan that he was caught,   (2650)
By force, and eek by composicioun. *moreover agreeme*
    Who sorweth now but woful Palamoun,
That moot namore goon agayn to fighte?   1795
And whan that Theseus hadde seyn this sighte,
Un-to the folk that foghten thus echon
He cryde, 'Ho! namore, for it is don!
I wol be trewe Iuge, and no partye. *not partied*
Arcite of Thebes shal have Emelye,   1800
That by his fortune hath hir faire y-wonne.' *well*
Anon ther is a noyse of peple bigonne   (2660)
For Ioye of this, so loude and heigh with-alle,
It semed that the listes sholde falle.
    What can now faire Venus doon above?   1805
What seith she now? what doth this quene of love?

---

[1] E. rescous; Pt. rescowe; *rest* rescous.

But wepeth so, for wanting of hir wille,
Til that hir teeres in the listes fille;
She seyde: 'I am ashamed, doutelees.'
Saturnus seyde: 'Doghter, hold thy pees.   1810
Mars hath his wille, his knight hath al his bone,   *prayer*
And, by myn heed, thou shalt ben esed sone.' (2670)   *accomodated*
    The trompes with the loude minstralcye,   *minstrelsy*
The heraudes, that ful loude yolle and crye,
Been in hir wele for Ioye of daun Arcite.   *weal* 1815   *lord*
But herkneth me, and stinteth now a lyte,
Which a miracle ther bifel anon.   *what*
This fierse[1] Arcite hath of his helm y-don,
And on a courser, for to shewe his face,
He priketh endelong the large place,   1820
Loking upward up-on this[2] Emelye;
And she agayn him caste a frendlich yë,   ✓ (2680) *towards*
(For wommen, as to speken in comune,
They folwen al the favour of fortune),[3]
And she[4] was al his chere, as in his herte.   1825
Out of the ground a furie[5] infernal sterte,
From Pluto sent, at requeste of Saturne,
For which his hors for fere gan to turne,
And leep asyde, and foundred as he leep;   *fell down*
And, er that Arcite may taken keep,   *heed* 1830
He pighte him on the pomel of his heed,   *pitched*   *top*
That in the place he lay as he were deed,   (2690)
His brest to-brosten with his sadel-bowe.   *broken*
As blak he lay as any cole or crowe,
So was the blood y-ronnen in his face.   1835
Anon he was y-born out of the place

---

[1] Cm. ferse; E. fierse.   [2] E. Pt. *om.* this.
[3] E. Hn. Cm. *omit* ll. 1823, 1824.   [4] Hn. she; *rest om.*
[5] E. furie; Hn. Cm. furye; *rest* fyr, fir, fire, fyre; *see note.*

With herte soor, to Theseus paleys.
Tho was he corven out of his harneys,   *cut armour*
And in a bed y-brought ful faire and blyve,   *neatly,*
For he was yet in memorie and alyve[1],   1840   *qui*
And alway crying after Emelye.

Duk Theseus, with al his compaignye,   (2700)
Is comen hoom to Athenes his citee,
With alle blisse and greet solempnitee.
Al be it that this aventure was falle,   1845
He nolde noght disconforten hem alle.
Men seyde eek, that Arcite shal nat dye,
He shal ben heled of his maladye.
And of another thing they were as fayn,   *glad*
That of hem alle was ther noon y-slayn,   1850
Al were they sore y-hurt, and namely oon,
That with a spere was thirled his brest-boon.   (2710) *pie*
To othere woundes, and to broken armes,
Some hadden salves, and some hadden charmes,
Fermacies of herbes, and eek save   *medicines*   1855 *so*
They dronken, for they wolde hir limes have.   *limbs*
For which this noble duk, as he wel can,
Conforteth and honoureth every man,
And made revel al the longe night,
Un-to the straunge lordes, as was right.   1860
Ne ther was holden no disconfitinge,   *defeat*
But as a Iustes or a tourneyinge;   (2720)
For soothly ther was no disconfiture,   *misery*
For falling nis nat but an aventure;
Ne to be lad with fors un-to the stake   1865
Unyolden, and with twenty knightes take,
O persone allone, with-outen mo,   *more*
And haried forth by arme[2], foot, and to,

---

[1] Hl. Pt. on lyue.   [2] E. Hn. Cm. arm.

And eek his stede driven forth with staves,
With footmen, bothe yemen and eek knaves,   1870 *servants*
It nas aretted him no vileinye,   *deemed*
Ther may no man clepen it[1] cowardye.   (2730)

    For which anon duk Theseus leet crye,
To stinten alle rancour and envye,
The gree as wel of o syde as of other,   1875 *superiority*
And either syde y-lyk as otheres brother;
And yaf hem yiftes after hir degree,
And fully heeld a feste dayes three;
And conveyed[2] the kinges worthily
Out of his toun a Iournee largely.   *freely*   1880
And hoom wente every man the righte way.
Ther was namore, but 'far[3] wel, have good day!'
Of this bataille I wol namore endyte,   (2741)
But speke of Palamon and of Arcite.

    Swelleth the brest of Arcite, and the sore   1885
Encresseth at his herte more and more.
The clothered blood, for any lechecraft,   *physician's skill*
Corrupteth[4], and is in his bouk y-laft,   *body left*
That nother veyne-blood, ne ventusinge,   *cupping*
Ne drinke of herbes may ben his helpinge.   1890
The vertu expulsif, or animal,
Fro thilke vertu cleped natural,   (2750)
Ne may the venim voyden, ne expelle.   *poison expel*
The pypes of his longes gonne to swelle,
And every lacerte in his brest adoun   *muscle* 1895 *below*
Is shent with venim and corrupcioun.   *destroyed*
Him gayneth neither, for to gete his lyf,   *obtain*
Vomyt upward, ne dounward laxatif;
Al is to-brosten thilke regioun,
Nature hath now no dominacioun.   1900

---

[1] Hl. *ins.* no.   [2] E. conuoyed.   [3] E. fare.   [4] Hl. Pt. Corrumpith.

And certeynly, ther nature wol nat wirche,
Fare-wel, phisyk! go ber the man to chirche. (2760)
This al and som, that Arcita moot dye, *long + short*
For which he sendeth after Emelye,
And Palamon, that was his cosin dere;   1905
Than seyde he thus, as ye shul after here.

 'Naught may the woful spirit in myn herte
Declare o poynt of alle my sorwes smerte *partick*
To yow, my lady, that I love most;
But I biquethe the service of my gost   1910
To yow aboven every creature,
Sin that my lyf ne[1] may no lenger dure. *last* (2770)
Allas, the wo! allas, the peynes stronge,
That I for yow have suffred, and so longe!
Allas, the deeth! allas, myn Emelye!   1915
Allas, departing of our compaignye!
Allas, myn hertes quene! allas, my wyf!
Myn hertes lady, endere of my lyf! *see p 222*
What is this world? what asketh men to have?
Now with his love, now in his colde grave   1920
Allone, with-outen any compaignye.
Fare-wel, my swete fo! myn Emelye!   (2780)
And softe tak me in your armes tweye,
For love of God, and herkneth what I seye.

 I have heer with my cosin Palamon   1925
Had stryf and rancour, many a day a-gon,
For love of yow, and for my Ielousye[2].
And Iupiter so ~~gye~~ wis my soule, *certain   guide*
To speken of a servant proprely, *lover*
With alle circumstaunces trewely,   1930
That is to seyn, trouthe, honour, and[3] knighthede,

---

[1] Tyrwhitt *supplied* ne; *it is not in the* MSS.
[2] E. Cm. Cp. Ialousye.   [3] Cp. Pt. Hl. and; *rest om.*

Wisdom, humblesse, ~~estaat~~, and heigh kinrede, (2790) *condition*
Fredom, and al that longeth to that art,
So Iupiter have of my soule part,
As in this world right now ne knowe I non   1935
So worthy to be loved as Palamon,
That serveth yow, and wol doon al his lyf.
And if that evere ye shul been a wyf,
Foryet nat Palamon, the gentil man.'
And with that word his speche faille gan,   1940
For[1] fro his feet[2] up to his brest was come
The cold of deeth, that hadde him overcome. (2800)
And yet more-over[3], in his armes two
The vital strengthe is lost, and al ~~ago.~~ *gone*
Only the intellect, with-outen more,   1945
That dwelled in his herte syk and sore,
Gan faillen, when the herte felte deeth,
Dusked his eyen two, and failled breeth.
But on his lady yet caste he his yë;
His laste word was, 'mercy, Emelye!'   1950
His spirit chaunged hous, and wente ther,
As I cam nevere, I can nat tellen wher. (2810)
Therfor I stinte, I nam no divynistre;
Of soules fynde I nat in this registre,
Ne me ne list thilke opiniouns to telle   1955
Of hem, though that they wryten wher they dwelle.
Arcite is cold, ther Mars his soule ~~gye~~; *where & hope Mars*
Now wol I speken forth of Emelye.   *will his soul guide*

    Shrighte Emelye, and howleth Palamon,
And Theseus his suster took anon   1960
Swowninge, and bar[4] hir fro the corps away.
What helpeth it to tarien forth the day, (2820)
To tellen how she weep, bothe eve and morwe?

[1] E. And. [2] E. Hl. Cm. herte. [3] *All but* Hl. *ins.* for. [4] E. baar.

For in swich cas wommen can[1] have swich sorwe,
Whan that hir housbonds been[2] from hem ago, 1965
That for the more part they sorwen so,
Or elles fallen in swich maladye,
That at the laste certeynly they dye.

Infinite been the sorwes and the teres
Of olde folk, and folk[3] of tendre yeres,   1970
In al the toun, for deeth of this Theban,
For him ther wepeth bothe child and man ;   (2830)
So greet a weping was ther noon certayn,
Whan Ector was y-broght, al fresh y-slayn,
To Troye ; allas ! the pitee that was ther,   1975
Cracching of chekes, rending[4] eek of heer. *scratching*
' Why woldestow be deed,' thise wommen crye,
' And haddest gold ynough, and Emelye ?'
No man mighte gladen Theseus,
Savinge his olde fader Egeus,   1980
That knew this worldes transmutacioun,
As he had seen it chaungen[5] up and doun,   (2840)
Ioye after wo, and wo after gladnesse :
And shewed hem ensamples and lyknesse.

' Right as ther deyed nevere man,' quod he,   1985
' That he ne livede in erthe in som degree, *station*
Right so ther livede nevere man,' he seyde,
' In al this world, that som tyme he ne deyde.
This world nis but a thurghfare ful of wo,
And we ben pilgrimes, passinge to and fro ;   1990
Deeth is an ende of every worldly[6] sore.'
And over al this yet seyde he muchel more   (2850)
To this effect, ful wysly to enhorte *encourage*
The peple, that they sholde hem reconforte.

---

[1] Hl. can; *rest om.*   [2] E. housbond is.
[3] E. eek; *rest* folk.   [4] E. Hn. Cm. Pt. rentynge.
[5] Hn. chaungen; Hl. torne; *rest om.*   [6] E. worldes.

Duk Theseus, with al his ~~bisy~~ cure, *industrious* 1995 *care*
Caste [1] now wher that the sepulture
Of good Arcite may best y-maked be,
And eek most honurable in his degree.
And at the laste he took conclusioun,
That ther as first Arcite and Palamoun   2000
Hadden for love the bataille hem bitwene,
That in that <u>selve</u> grove, <u>swote</u> and grene, *same* (2860) *sweet*
Ther as he hadde his amorous desyres,
His compleynt, and for love his hote fyres,
He wolde make a fyr, in which thoffice [2]   2005
Funeral [3] he mighte al accomplice;
And leet comaunde anon to hakke and hewe
The okes olde, and leye hem on a rewe
In <u>colpons</u> wel arrayed for to brenne ; *Bundles*
His officers with swifte feet they renne,   2010
And ryde anon at his comaundement.
And after this, Theseus hath y-sent   (2870)
After a bere, and it al over-spradde
With cloth of gold, the richest that he hadde.
And of the same suyte he cladde Arcite ;   2015
Upon his hondes hadde he gloves whyte ;
Eek on his heed a coroune of laurer grene,
And in his hond a swerd ful bright and kene.
He leyde him bare the visage on the bere,
Therwith he weep that pitee was to here.   2020
And for the peple sholde seen him alle,
Whan it was day, he broghte him to the halle, (2880)
That roreth of the crying and the soun.
Tho cam this woful Theban Palamoun,
With <u>flotery</u> berd, and ruggy [4] asshy heres, *wavy* 2025 *rough*

---

[1] Hn. Caste ; E. Cast.   [2] E. the office ; Hl. thoffice.
[3] *So in the* MSS.   [4] E. rugged.

In clothes blake, y-dropped al with teres;
And, passing othere of weping, Emelye,
The rewfulleste of al the compaignye.   *most sorrowful*
In as muche as the service sholde be
The more noble and riche in his degree,   2030
Duk Theseus leet forth three stedes bringe,
That trapped were in steel al gliteringe,   (2890)
And covered with the armes of daun Arcite.
Up-on thise stedes, that weren [1] grete and white,
Ther seten [2] folk, of which oon bar his sheeld,   2035
Another his spere up [3] in his hondes heeld;
The thridde bar with him his bowe Turkeys,   *equipmen*
Of brend gold was the cas, and eek the harneys;   *case*
And riden forth a pas with sorweful chere   *quiver*
Toward the grove, as ye shul after here.   2040
The nobleste of the Grekes that ther were
Upon hir shuldres carieden the bere,   (2900)
With slake [4] pas, and eyen rede and wete,
Thurgh-out the citee, by the maister-strete,
That sprad was al with blak, and wonder hye   2045
Right of the same is al [5] the strete y-wrye.   *covered*
Up-on the right hond wente old Egeus,
And on that other syde duk Theseus,
With vessels in hir hand of gold wel fyn,
Al ful of hony, milk, and blood, and wyn;   2050
Eek Palamon, with ful greet compaignye;
And after that cam woful Emelye,   (2910)
With fyr in honde, as was that tyme the gyse,
To do thoffice [6] of funeral servyse.
    Heigh labour, and ful greet apparaillinge   *great*   2055
                                                  preparation

---

[1] Hl. that weren; *rest om.*   [2] E. Ln. sitten.
[3] E. *om.* up.   [4] Ln. slake; *rest* slak.
[5] Hl. al; *rest om.*   [6] *So* Hl. Cp.; *rest* the office.

Was at the service and the fyr-makinge,
That with his grene top the heven raughte, *reached*
And twenty fadme of brede the armes¹ straughte; *breadth stretched*
This is to seyn, the bowes were so brode.
Of stree first ther was leyd ful many a lode. 2060 *straw*
But how the fyr was maked up on highte,
And eek the names how² the treës highte, (2920) *aspen*
As ook, firre, birch, asp, alder, holm, popler, *holly*] *chestnut*
Wilow, elm, plane, ash, box, chasteyn, lind, laurer, *lime*
Mapul, thorn, beech, hasel, ew, whippeltre, 2065 *cornel tree*
How they weren feld³, shal nat be told for me;
Ne how the goddes ronnen up and doun,
Disherited⁴ of hir habitacioun,
In which they woneden in reste and pees,
Nymphes⁵, Faunes, and Amadrides; *Hamadryads* 2070
Ne how the bestes and the briddes alle
Fledden for fere, whan the wode was falle; (2930)
Ne how the ground agast was of the light, *terrified*
That was nat wont to seen the sonne bright;
Ne how the fyr was couched first with stree, 2075 *laid*
And than⁶ with drye stokkes⁷ cloven a three,
And than⁶ with grene wode and spycerye, *spices*
And than⁶ with cloth of gold and with perrye, *jewelry*
And gerlandes hanging with ful many a flour,
The mirre, thencens, with al so greet odour; 2080 *myrrh incense*
Ne how Arcite lay among al this,
Ne what richesse aboute his body is; (2940)
Ne how that Emelye, as was the gyse,
Putte in the fyr of funeral servyse;
Ne how she swowned whan men made the⁸ fyr, 2085

¹ Hl. tharme.   ² E. that.   ³ E. fild.   ⁴ Hl. Disheryt.
⁵ E. Cm. Nymphus.   ⁶ Pt. Ln. than; *rest* thanne.
⁷ E. Cp. stokkes; *rest* stikkes.   ⁸ E. *om.* the.

Ne what she spak, ne what was hir desyr;
Ne what Ieweles men in the fyr tho[1] caste,   *those*
Whan that the fyr was greet and brente faste;
Ne how som caste hir sheeld, and som hir spere,
And of hir vestiments, whiche that they were,   2090
And cuppes ful of wyn, and milk, and blood,
Into the fyr, that brente as it were wood;   (2950)
Ne how the Grekes with an huge route   *company*
Thryës[2] riden al the fyr[3] aboute
Up-on the left hand, with a loud shoutinge,   2095
And thryës with hir speres clateringe;
And thryës how the ladies gonne crye;
Ne[4] how that lad was hom-ward Emelye;
Ne how Arcite is brent to asshen colde;
Ne how that liche-wake was y-holde   *watch over[100] dea*
Al thilke night, ne how the Grekes pleye
The wake-pleyes, ne kepe I nat to seye;   (2960)
Who wrastleth best naked, with oille enoynt,
Ne who that bar him best, in no disioynt.   *difficult situat*
I wol nat tellen eek how that they goon   2105
Hoom til Athenes whan the pley is doon.
But shortly to the poynt than wol I wende,
And maken of my longe tale an ende.

By processe and by lengthe of certeyn yeres
Al stinted is the moorning and the teres   2110
Of Grekes, by oon general assent.
Than semed me ther was a parlement   (2970)
At Athenes, up-on certeyn poynts and cas;   *particulars*
Among the whiche poynts y-spoken was   *conditions*
To have with certeyn contrees alliaunce,   2115

---

[1] Hl. tho; *rest om.*
[2] *So all but* Hl., *which has* Thre tymes; *see l.* 2096.
[3] E. place.   [4] E. Hn. And.

And have fully of Thebans obeisaunce.
For which this noble Theseus anon
Leet senden after gentil Palamon,   *caused to*
Unwist of him what was the cause and why;
But in his blake clothes sorwefully   2120
He cam at his comaundement in hye.   *haste*
Tho sente Theseus for Emelye.   (2980)
Whan they were set, and hust was al the place,   *sat*
And Theseus abiden hadde a space
Er any word cam from his wyse brest,   2125
His eyen sette he ther as was his lest,   *pleasure*
And with a sad visage he syked stille,   *sighed quietly*
And after that right thus he seyde his wille.   *quietly*
   'The firste moevere of the cause above,
Whan he first made the faire cheyne of love,   2130
Greet was theffect, and heigh was his entente;
Wel wiste he why, and what ther-of he mente; (2990)
For with that faire cheyne of love he bond
The fyr, the eyr, the water, and the lond
In certeyn boundes, that they may nat flee;   2135
That same prince and that[1] moevere,' quod he,
'Hath stablissed[2], in this wrecched world adoun,
Certeyne dayes and duracioun
To al that is[3] engendred in this place,   *produced*
Over the whiche day they may nat pace,   *pass*   2140
Al mowe they yet tho dayes wel abregge;   *are able   shorten*
Ther needeth[4] non auctoritee allegge[5],   (3000)
For it is preved by experience,
But that me list declaren my sentence.
Than may men by this ordre wel discerne,   2145

[1] Hn. Ln. that; *rest (except* Hl.) that same; Hl. and moeuere eek.
[2] Hl. Ln. stabled.   [3] Hl. alle that er; Cp. alle that beth.
[4] E. Cp. *ins.* noght.   [5] Hl. tallegge; Hn. to allegge; Cm. to legge.

That thilke moevere stable is and eterne.
Wel may men knowe, but it be a fool,
That every part deryveth [1] from his hool.   *whole*
For nature hath nat take [2] his biginning
Of no partye ne [3] cantel of a thing,   *corner   part* 2150
But of a thing that parfit is and stable,
Descending so, til it be corrumpable.   (3010)
And therfore of his wyse purveiaunce,   *providence*
He hath so wel biset his ordinaunce,   *plan*
That speces of thinges and progressiouns   2155
Shullen endure by successiouns,
And nat eterne be, with-oute lye [4]:
This maistow understonde and seen at [5] eye.   *at a glance*
    'Lo the ook, that hath so long a norisshinge
Fro tyme that it first biginneth springe,   2160
And hath so long a lyf, as we may see,
Yet at the laste wasted is the tree.   (3020)
    'Considereth eek, how that the harde stoon
Under our feet, on which we trede and goon,   *go*
Yit wasteth it, as it lyth by the weye.   2165
The brode river somtyme wexeth dreye.
The grete tounes [6] see we wane and wende.
Than may ye see that al this thing hath ende.
    'Of man and womman seen we wel also,
That nedeth in oon of thise termes two,   *must of* 2170
This is to seyn, in youthe or elles age,   *necessity*
He moot ben deed, the king as shal a page;   (3030)
Som in his bed, som in the depe see,
Som in the large feeld, as men may se.
Ther helpeth noght, al goth that ilke weye.   2175

---

[1] E. dirryueth.   [2] Hl. Ln. take; *rest* taken; E. Cm. *om.* nat.
[3] Hl. ne; E. Hn. Cm. Pt. or of.
[4] *So* Hl.; *rest* eterne, with-outen any lye.   [5] E. it.
[6] E. toures.

Thanne may I seyn that[1] al this thing moot deye.
What maketh this but Iupiter the king?
The which[2] is prince and cause of alle thing,
Converting al un-to his propre welle, *source*
From which it is deryved, sooth to telle.   2180
And here-agayns no creature on lyve
Of no degree availleth for to stryve.   (3040)
   'Thanne is it wisdom, as it thinketh me,
To maken vertu of necessitee,
And take it wel, that we may nat eschue, *avoid* 2185
And namely that to us alle is due.
And who-so gruccheth ought, he doth folye, *grumble*
And rebel is to him that al may gye.
And certeinly a man hath most honour
To dyen in his excellence and flour,   2190
Whan he is siker of his gode name; *certain* (3049)
Than hath he doon his freend, ne him, no shame.
And gladder oghte his freend ben of his deeth,
Whan with honour up-yolden is his breeth,
Than whan his name apalled is for age; *weak* 2195
For al forgeten is his vasselage. *valour*
Than is it best, as for a worthy fame,
To dyen whan that he[3] is best of name.
The contrarie of al this is wilfulnesse.
Why grucchen we? why have we hevinesse,   2200
That good Arcite, of chivalrye[4] flour
Departed is, with duetee and honour   (3060)
Out of this foule prison of this lyf?
Why grucchen heer his cosin and his wyf
Of his wel-fare that loved hem so wel?   2205
Can he hem thank? nay, God woot, never a del,

---

[1] E. Cm. *om.* that.   [2] *So* Hl.; *rest* That.
[3] Hl. whan a man.   [4] Hl. Cp. Pt. Ln. *ins.* the.

That bothe his soule and eek hem-self offende,   *hemse*
And yet they mowe hir lustes nat amende.   *are able*
  'What may I conclude of this longe serye,   *train of argument*
But after wo I rede us to be merye,   *advise*   2210
And thanken Iupiter of al his grace?
And er that we departen from this place,   (3070)
I rede that[1] we make, of sorwes two,   *advice*
O parfyt Ioye, lasting evere-mo:
And loketh now wher most sorwe is her-inne,   2215
Ther wol we first amenden and biginne.
  'Suster,' quod he, 'this is my fulle assent,
With al thavys heer of my parlement,
That gentil Palamon, your[2] owene knight,
That serveth yow with wille, herte, and might,   2220
And evere hath doon, sin that ye first him knewe,
That ye shul, of youre grace, up-on him rewe,   (3080)
And taken him for housbonde and for lord: *have pity*
Leen[3] me youre hond, for this is our acord.
Lat see now of your wommanly pitee.   2225
He is a kinges brother sone, pardee;   *soon*
And, though he were a povre bacheler,   *apprentice knig...*
Sin he hath served yow so many a yeer,
And had for yow so greet adversitee,
It moste been considered, leveth me;   *believe*   2230
For gentil mercy oghte to passen right.'   *should surpass* *just*
   Than seyde he thus to Palamon ful right;   (3090)
'I trowe ther nedeth litel sermoning
To make yow assente to this thing.
Com neer, and tak your lady by the hond.'   2235
Bitwixen hem was maad anon the bond,
That highte matrimoine or mariage,
By al the counseil and the baronage.

---

[1] Hl. that; *rest om.*   [2] E. thyn.   [3] Hn. Leen; *rest* Lene.

And thus with alle blisse and melodye
Hath Palamon y-wedded Emelye.   2240
And God, that al this wyde world hath wroght,
Sende him his love, that hath[1] it dere a-boght. (3100)
For now is Palamon in alle wele,   *prosperity*
Living in blisse, in richesse, and in hele;   *health*
And Emelye him loveth so tendrely,   2245
And he hir serveth al-so[2] gentilly,
That nevere was ther no word hem bitwene
Of Ielousye[3], or any other tene.   *vexation*
Thus endeth Palamon and Emelye;
And God save al this faire compaignye!   *graceful* 2250

Here is ended the knightes tale.

[1] E. *om.* hath.   [2] Hl. al so; *rest* so.   [3] E. Hn. Cp. Ialousye.

THE NONNE PREESTES TALE.

(GROUP B, ll. 4011–4636 in the Six-text edition.)

Here biginneth the Nonne Preestes Tale of the Cok and Hen, Chauntecleer and Pertelote.

A POVRE widwe somdel stope[1] in age,   (4011)
Was whylom dwelling in a narwe cotage,
Bisyde a grove[2], stondyng in a dale.
This widwe, of which I telle yow my tale,
Sin thilke day that she was last a wyf,   5
In pacience ladde a ful simple lyf,
For litel was hir catel and hir rente;
By housbondrye, of such as God hir sente,
She fond hir-self, and eek hir doghtren two.   (4019)
Three large sowes hadde she, and namo,   10
Three kyn[3], and eek a sheep that highte Malle.
Ful sooty was hir bour, and eek hir halle,
In which she eet ful many a sclendre meel.
Of poynaunt sauce hir neded never a deel.
No deyntee morsel passed thurgh hir throte;   15
Hir dyete was accordant to hir cote.
Repleccioun ne made hir nevere syk;
Attempree dyete was al hir phisyk,
And exercyse, and hertes suffisaunce.
The goute lette hir no-thing for to daunce,   20

---

[1] E. Cm. stape; Ln. stoupe; *rest* stope.   [2] E. greue.
[3] E. keen; Hn. Hl. Cp. kyn.

Ne poplexye[1] shente nat hir heed ;   (4031)
No wyn ne drank she, neither whyt ne reed ;
Hir bord was served most with whyt and blak,
Milk and broun breed, in which she fond no lak,
Seynd bacoun, and somtyme an ey or tweye,   25
For she was as it were a maner deye.

   A yerd she hadde, enclosed al aboute
With stikkes, and a drye dich with-oute,
In which she hadde a cok, hight[2] Chauntecleer,
In al the land of crowing nas his peer.   30
His vois was merier[3] than the merye[4] orgon   (4041)
On messe-dayes that in the chirche gon ;
Wel sikerer was his crowing in his logge,
Than is a clokke, or an abbey orlogge.
By nature knew he[5] ech ascencioun   35
Of[6] equinoxial in thilke toun ;
For whan degrees fiftene were ascended,
Thanne crew he, that it mighte nat ben amended.
His comb was redder than the fyn coral,
And batailed, as it were a castel-wal.   40
His bile was blak, and as the Ieet[7] it shoon ; (4051)
Lyk asur were his legges, and his toon ;
His nayles whytter than the lilie flour,
And lyk the burned[8] gold was his colour.
This gentil cok hadde in his governaunce   45
Sevene hennes, for to doon al his plesaunce,
Whiche were his sustres and his paramours,
And wonder lyk to him, as of colours.
Of whiche the faireste hewed on hir throte

---

[1] E. Hn. Napoplexie ; *rest* Ne poplexie.
[2] E. Hn. heet ; *rest* that hight.   [3] E. Hn. Cm. murier.
[4] E. Cm. murie.   [5] Hl. knew he ; E. Pt. he crew ; *rest* he knew.
[6] E. Ln. *ins.* the.   [7] Hl. geet ; Pt. Ln. gete.
[8] Hl. Cp. Pt. Ln. burnischt.

Was cleped faire damoysele Pertelote.   50
Curteys she was, discreet, and debonaire,   (4061)
And compaignable, and bar hir-self so[1] faire,
Sin thilke day that she was seven night old,
That trewely she hath the herte in hold
Of Chauntecleer loken in every lith;   55
He loved hir so, that wel him was therwith.
But such a Ioye was it to here hem singe,
Whan that the brighte sonne gan[2] to springe,
In swete accord, 'my lief is faren in londe.'
For thilke tyme, as I have understonde,   60
Bestes and briddes coude speke and singe.   (4071)

    And so bifel, that in a[3] dawenynge,
As Chauntecleer among his wyves alle
Sat on his perche, that was in the halle,
And next him sat this faire Pertelote,   65
This Chauntecleer gan gronen in his throte,
As man that in his dreem is drecched sore.
And whan that Pertelote thus herde him rore,
She was agast, and seyde, 'o herte deere,
What eyleth yow, to grone in this manere?   70
Ye ben a verray sleper, fy for shame!'   (4081)
And he answerde and seyde thus, 'madame,
I pray yow, that ye take it nat agrief:
By God, me mette[4] I was in swich meschief
Right now, that yet myn herte is sore afright.   75
Now God,' quod he, 'my swevene rede[5] aright,
And keep my body out of foul prisoun!
Me mette, how that I romed up and doun
Withinne our yerde, wher as I saugh a beste,
Was lyk an hound, and wolde han maad areste   80

---

[1] Hl. ful.   [2] E. Cm. Ln. bigan.   [3] E. Pt. the.
[4] E. thoughte.   [5] E. Hn. recche; Cm. reche; *rest* rede, reed.

Upon my body, and wolde[1] han had me deed. (4091)
His colour was bitwixe yelwe and reed;
And tipped was his tail, and bothe his eres
With blak, unlyk the remenant of his heres;
His snowte smal, with glowinge eyen tweye.   85
Yet of his look for fere almost I deye;
This caused me my groning, douteles.'

'Avoy!' quod she, 'fy on yow, herteles!
Allas!' quod she, 'for, by that God above,
Now han ye lost myn herte and al my love;   90
I can nat love a coward, by my feith.   (4101)
For certes, what so any womman seith,
We alle desyren, if it mighte be,
To han housbondes hardy, wyse, and free,
And secree, and no nigard, ne no fool,   95
Ne him that is agast of every tool,
Ne noon avauntour, by that God above!
How dorste ye sayn for shame unto youre love,
That any thing mighte make yow aferd?
Have ye no mannes herte, and han a berd?   100
Allas! and conne ye been agast of swevenis?   (4111)
No-thing, God wot, but vanitee, in sweven is.
Swevenes engendren of replecciouns,
And ofte of fume, and of complecciouns,
Whan humours been to habundant in a wight.   105
Certes this dreem, which ye han met to-night,
Cometh of the[2] grete superfluitee
Of youre rede *colera*, pardee,
Which causeth folk to dremen[3] in here dremes
Of arwes, and of fyr with rede lemes,   110
Of grete bestes, that they wol hem byte,   (4121)

---

[1] E. Hn. Cm. *om.* wolde.   [2] E. *om.* the, *and has* greet.
[3] E. Hn. Cm. dreden.

Of contek, and of whelpes grete and lyte;
Right as the humour of malencolye
Causeth ful many a man, in sleep, to crye,
For fere of blake beres, or boles blake [1],   115
Or elles, blake develes wole him take.
Of othere humours coude I telle also,
That werken many a man in sleep ful wo;
But I wol passe as lightly as I can.

   Lo Catoun, which that was so wys a man,   120
Seyde he nat thus, ne do no fors of dremes? (4131)
Now, sire,' quod she, 'whan we [2] flee fro the bemes,
For Goddes love, as tak som laxatyf;
Up peril of my soule, and of my lyf,
I counseille yow the beste, I wol nat lye,   125
That both of colere, and of malencolye
Ye purge yow; and for ye shul nat tarie,
Though in this toun is noon apotecarie,
I shal my-self to herbes techen yow,
That shul ben for your hele, and for your prow; 130
And in our yerd tho herbes shal I fynde,   (4141)
The whiche han of here propretee, by kynde,
To purgen yow binethe, and eek above.
Forget not this, for Goddes owene love!
Ye been ful colerik of compleccioun.   135
Ware the sonne in his ascencioun
Ne fynde yow nat repleet of humours hote;
And if it do, I dar wel leye a grote,
That ye shul have a fevere terciane,
Or an agu, that may be youre bane.   140
A day or two ye shul have digestyves   (4151)

---

[1] *So* E. Hn. Cm.; Hl. Cp. of beres and of boles; Ln. Pt. of beres
and boles.
[2] E. ye; *rest* we.

Of wormes, er ye take your laxatyves,
Of lauriol, centaure, and fumetere,
Or elles of ellebor, that groweth there,
Of catapuce, or of gaytres [1] beryis,   145
Of erbe yve, growing in our yerd, that [2] mery is;
Pekke hem up right as they growe, and ete hem in.
Be mery, housbond, for your fader kyn!
Dredeth no dreem; I can say yow namore.'

   ' Madame,' quod he, '*graunt mercy* of your lore.
But natheles, as touching daun Catoun,   (4161)
That hath of wisdom such a gret renoun,
Though that he bad no dremes for to drede,
By God, men may in olde bokes rede
Of many a man, more of auctoritee   155
Than evere Catoun was, so moot I thee,
That al the revers seyn of this sentence,
And han wel founden by experience,
That dremes ben significaciouns,
As wel of Ioye as [3] tribulaciouns   160
That folk enduren in this lyf present.   (4171)
Ther nedeth make of this noon argument;
The verray preve sheweth it in dede.
Oon of the gretteste auctours [4] that men rede
Seith thus, that whylom two felawes wente   165
On pilgrimage, in a ful good entente;
And happed so, thay come into [5] a toun,
Wher as ther was swich congregacioun
Of peple, and eek so streit of herbergage,
That they ne founde as muche as o cotage,   170

[1] Cp. Ln. gaytres; E. gaitrys; Hn. gaytrys; Hl. gaytre; Cm. gattris;
Pt. gatys.
[2] Ln. that; Hn. they; *rest* ther.   [3] E. Cm. Cp. Ln. Hl. *ins.* of.
[4] Cm. autourys; Hl. auctorite; *rest* auctour (*sic*).
[5] E. Hn. coomen in; Cm. comyn in.

In which they bothe mighte y-logged[1] be.   (4181)
Wherfor thay mosten, of necessitee,
As for that night, departen compaignye;
And ech of hem goth to his hostelrye,
And took his logging as it wolde falle.   175
That oon of hem was logged in a stalle,
Fer in a yerd, with oxen of the plough;
That other man was logged wel y-nough,
As was his aventure, or his fortune,
That us governeth alle as in commune.   180
And so bifel, that, long er it were day,   (4191)
This man mette in his bed, ther as he lay,
How that his felawe gan up-on him calle,
And seyde, 'allas! for in an oxes[2] stalle
This night I shal be mordred ther I lye.   185
Now help me, dere brother, or I dye;
In alle haste com to me,' he sayde.
This man out of his sleep for fere abrayde;
But whan that he was wakned of his sleep,
He turned him, and took of this[3] no keep;   190
Him thoughte his dreem nas but a vanitee.   (4201)
Thus twyes in his sleping dremed he.
And atte thridde tyme yet his felawe
Com, as him thoughte, and seide, 'I am now slawe;
Bihold my bloody woundes, depe and wyde!   195
Arys up erly in the morwe-tyde,
And at the west gate of the toun,' quod he,
'A carte ful of donge ther shaltow see,
In which my body is hid ful prively;
Do thilke carte arresten boldely.   200
My gold caused my mordre, sooth to sayn;'   (4211)
And tolde him every poynt how he was slayn,

---

[1] E. logged.   [2] Hl. Cp. Ln. oxe.   [3] E. it.

With a ful pitous face, pale of hewe.
And truste wel, his dreem he fond ful trewe;
For on the morwe, as sone as it was day,   205
To his felawes in he took the way;
And whan that he cam to this oxes[1] stalle,
After his felawe he bigan to calle.
The hostiler answerde him anon,
And seyde, 'sire, your felawe is agon,   210
As sone as day he wente out of the toun.'   (4221)
This man gan fallen in[2] suspecioun,
Remembring on his dremes that he mette,
And forth he goth, no lenger wolde he lette,
Unto the west gate of the toun, and fond   215
A dong-carte, as it were[3] to donge lond,
That was arrayed in that same wyse
As ye han herd the dede man devyse;
And with an hardy herte he gan to crye
Vengeaunce and Iustice of this felonye:—   220
'My felawe mordred is this same night,   (4231)
And in this carte[4] he lyth gapinge upright.
I crye out on the ministres,' quod he,
'That sholden kepe and reulen this citee;
Harrow! allas! her lyth my felawe slayn!'   225
What sholde I more un-to this tale sayn?
The peple out-sterte, and caste the cart to grounde,
And in the middel of the dong they founde
The dede man, that mordred was al newe.

    O blisful God, that art so Iust and trewe!   230
Lo, how that thou biwreyest mordre alway!   (4241)
Mordre wol out, that se we day by day.

---

[1] Hl. Cp. Ln. oxe.   [2] Hl. *ins.* a; Cp. Pt. Ln. *ins.* gret (grete).
[3] *So* E; Hn. Cm. Hl. wente as it were; Cp. Pt. Ln. as he went.
[4] E. Hn. Cm. *ins.* heere.

Mordre is so wlatsom and abhominable
To God, that is so Iust and resonable,
That he ne wol nat suffre it heled be;   235
Though it abyde a yeer, or two, or three,
Mordre wol out, this[1] my conclusioun.
And right anoon[2], ministres of that toun
Han hent the carter, and so sore him pyned,
And eek the hostiler so sore engyned,   240
That thay biknewe hir wikkednesse anoon,   (4251)
And were an-hanged by the nekke-boon.

'Here may men seen that dremes been to drede.
And certes, in the same book I rede,
Right in the nexte chapitre after this,   245
(I gabbe nat, so have I Ioye or[3] blis,)
Two men that wolde han passed over see,
For certeyn cause, in-to a fer contree,
If that the wind ne hadde been contrarie,
That made hem in a citee for to tarie,   250
That stood ful mery upon an haven-syde.   (4261)
But on a day, agayn the even-tyde,
The wind gan chaunge, and blew right as hem leste.
Iolif and glad they wente un-to hir reste,
And casten hem ful erly for to saille;   255
But[4] to that oo man fel a greet mervaille.
That oon of hem, in sleping as he lay,
Him mette a wonder dreem, agayn the day;
Him thoughte a man stood by his beddes syde,
And him comaunded, that he sholde abyde,   260
And seyde him thus, 'if thou to-morwe wende, (4271)
Thou shalt be dreynt; my tale is at an ende.'
He wook, and tolde his felawe what he mette,

---

[1] Cp. Pt. Ln. Hl. *ins.* is (*perhaps rightly*).
[2] Hl. *ins.* the.   [3] Cp. Ln. and.
[4] *All here ins.* herkneth (herken).

And preyde him his viage for[1] to lette;
As for that day, he preyde him to abyde[2].　265
His felawe, that lay by his beddes syde,
Gan for to laughe, and scorned him ful faste.
'No dreem,' quod he, 'may so myn herte agaste,
That I wol lette for to do my thinges.
I sette not a straw by thy dreminges,　270
For swevenes been but vanitees and Iapes.　(4281)
Men dreme al-day of owles or of apes,
And eek[3] of many a mase therwithal;
Men dreme of thing that nevere was ne shal.
But sith I see that thou wolt heer abyde,　275
And thus for-sleuthen wilfully thy tyde,
God wot it reweth me; and have good day.'
And thus he took his leve, and wente his way.
But er that he hadde halfe his cours y-seyled,
Noot I nat why, ne what mischaunce it eyled,　280
But casuelly the shippes botme rente,　(4291)
And ship and man under the water wente
In sighte of othere shippes it[4] byside,
That with hem seyled at the same tyde.
And therfor, faire Pertelote so dere,　285
By swiche ensamples olde[5] maistow lere,
That no man sholde been to reccheless
Of dremes, for I sey thee, doutelees,
That many a dreem ful sore is for to drede.

'Lo, in the lyf of seint Kenelm, I rede,　290
That was Kenulphus sone, the noble king　(4301)
Of Mercenrike, how Kenelm mette a thing;
A lyte er he was mordred, on a day,
His mordre in his avisioun he say.

[1] E. Hn. Hl. *om.* for; *cf.* l. 255.　[2] E. Hn. byde.
[3] Hl. eke; *rest om.*　[4] Cp. Pt. him; Ln. hem; Hl. ther.
[5] E. *ins.* yet.

I

His norice him expouned every del   295
His swevene, and bad him for to kepe him wel
For traisoun; but he nas but seven yeer old,
And therfore litel tale hath he told
Of any dreem, so holy was[1] his herte.
By God, I hadde levere than my sherte   300
That ye had rad his legende, as have I.   (4311)
Dame Pertelote, I sey yow trewely,
Macrobeus, that writ the avisioun
In Affrike of the worthy Cipioun,
Affermeth dremes, and seith that they been   305
Warning of thinges that men after seen.
And forther-more, I pray yow loketh wel
In the olde testament, of Daniel,
If he held dremes any vanitee.
Reed eek of Ioseph, and ther shul ye see   310
Wher dremes ben somtyme (I sey nat alle)   (4321)
Warning of thinges that shul after falle.
Loke of Egipt the king, daun Pharao,
His bakere and his boteler[2] also,
Wher they ne felte noon effect in dremes.   315
Who so wol seken actes of sondry remes,
May rede of dremes many a wonder thing.
   'Lo Cresus, which that was of Lyde king,
Mette he nat that he sat upon a tree,
Which signified he sholde anhanged be?   320
Lo heer Andromacha[3], Ectores wyf,   (4331)
That day that Ector sholde lese his lyf,
She dremed on the same night biforn,
How that the lyf of Ector sholde be lorn,

---

[1] E. is; *rest* was.
[2] Cm. Ln. boteler; Pt. botelere; E. Hn. butiller.
[3] E. Adromacha.

If thilke day he wente in-to bataille;   325
She warned him, but it mighte nat availle;
He wente for to fighte natheles,
But [1] he was slayn anoon of Achilles.
But thilke tale is al to long to telle,
And eek it is ny day, I may nat dwelle. 330
Shortly I seye, as for conclusioun, (4341)
That I shal han of this avisioun
Adversitee; and I seye forther-more,
That I ne telle of laxatyves no store,
For they ben venimous [2], I woot it [3] wel; 335
I hem defye [4], I love hem nevere a del.
 'Now let us speke of mirthe, and stinte al this;
Madame Pertelote, so have I blis,
Of o thing God hath sent me large grace;
For whan I see the beautee of your face, 340
Ye ben so scarlet-reed about youre yën, (4351)
It maketh al my drede for to dyen;
For, also siker as *In principio*,
Mulier est hominis confusio;
Madame, the sentence of this Latin is— 345
Womman is mannes Ioye and al his blis.

  . . . . . .

I am so ful of Ioye and of solas 350
That I defye [4] bothe sweven and dreem.' (4361)
And with that word he fley [5] doun fro the beem,
For it was day, and eek his hennes alle;
And with a chuk he gan hem for to calle,
For he had [6] founde a corn, lay in the yerd. 355
Roial [7] he was, he was namore aferd;

---

[1] Hn. And. [2] E. Hn. Cm. venymes. [3] Cp. Pt. Ln. right.
[4] E. Cp. diffye. [5] Hn. Cm. fley; E. fly; Hl. Cp. fleigh.
[6] E. Hn. Cm. hadde. [7] Cm. Ln. Royal; *rest* Real; *but see* l. 364.

He loketh as it were a grim leoun;
And on his toos[1] he rometh up and doun,　　360
Him deyned[2] not to sette his foot to grounde. (4371)
He chukketh, whan he hath a corn y-founde,
And to him rennen thanne his wyves alle.
Thus roial, as a prince is in his[3] halle,
Leve I this Chauntecleer in his pasture;　　365
And after wol I telle his aventure.

　　Whan that the month in which the world bigan,
That highte March, whan God first maked man,
Was complet, and y-passed[4] were also,
Sin March bigan, thritty dayes and two[5],　　370
Bifel that Chauntecleer, in al his pryde, 　　(4381)
His seven wyves walking by his syde,
Caste up his eyen to the brighte sonne,
That in the signe of Taurus hadde y-ronne
Twenty degrees and oon, and somwhat more;　　375
And[6] knew by kynde, and by noon other lore,
That it was pryme, and crew with blisful stevene.
'The sonne,' he sayde, ' is clomben up on hevene
Fourty degrees and oon, and more, y-wis.
Madame Pertelote, my worldes blis,　　380
Herkneth thise blisful briddes how they singe, (4391)
And see the fresshe floures how they springe;
Ful is myn hert of revel and solas.'
But sodeinly him fil a sorweful cas;
For evere the latter ende of Ioye is wo.　　385
Got woot that worldly Ioye is sone ago;
And if a rethor coude faire endyte,
He in a chronique[7] saufly mighte it write,

---

[1] Hl. toon.　　　[2] Cm. deyneth.　　　[3] E. Cm. an.
[4] *All the* MSS. *read* passed.　　[5] Hl. tway monthes and dayes tuo.
[6] Cp. Pt. Ln. He.　　　[7] Hl. Cp. cronique ; *rest* cronicle.

As for a sovereyn notabilitee.
Now every wys man, lat him herkne me;   390
This storie is al-so trewe, I undertake,   (4401)
As is the book of Launcelot de Lake,
That wommen holde in ful gret reverence.
Now wol I torne[1] agayn to my sentence.

  A col-fox, ful of sly iniquitee,   395
That in the grove hadde woned yeres three,
By heigh imaginacioun forn-cast,
The same night thurgh-out the hegges brast
Into the yerd, ther Chauntecleer the faire
Was wont, and eek his wyves, to repaire;   400
And in a bed of wortes stille he lay,   (4411)
Til it was passed undern[2] of the day,
Wayting his tyme on Chauntecleer to falle
As gladly doon thise homicydes alle,
That in awayt liggen to mordre men.   405
O false mordrer, lurking in thy den!
O newe Scariot, newe Genilon!
False dissimilour, O Greek Sinon,
That broghtest Troye al outrely to sorwe!
O Chauntecleer, acursed be that morwe,   410
That thou into that yerd flough[3] fro the bemes! (4421)
Thou were ful wel y-warned by thy dremes,
That thilke day was perilous to thee.
But what that God forwot mot nedes be,
After the opinioun of certeyn clerkis.   415
Witnesse on him, that any perfit clerk is,
That in scole is gret altercacioun
In this matere, and greet disputisoun,
And hath ben of an hundred thousand men.

---

[1] E. come.   [2] E. Hn. Pt. vndren.
[3] E. Hn. flauh; Cm. flaw; Cp. fley3e; Hl. flough.

But I ne can not bulte it to the bren, 420
As can the holy doctour Augustyn, (4431)
Or Boece, or the bishop Bradwardyn,
Whether[1] that Goddes worthy forwiting
Streyneth me nedely for to doon[2] a thing,
(Nedely clepe I simple necessitee); 425
Or elles, if free choys be graunted me
To do that same thing, or do it noght,
Though God forwot it, er that it was wroght;
Or if his witing streyneth nevere a del
But by necessitee condicionel. 430
I wol not han to do of swich matere; (4441)
My tale is of a cok, as ye may[3] here,
That took his counseil of his wyf, with sorwe,
To walken in the yerd upon that morwe
That he had met the dreem, that I of tolde. 435
Wommennes counseils been ful ofte colde;
Wommannes counseil broghte us first to wo,
And made Adam fro[4] paradys to go,
Ther as he was ful mery, and wel at ese.
But for I noot, to whom it mighte displese, 440
If I counseil of wommen wolde blame, (4451)
Passe over, for I seyde[5] it in my game.
Rede auctours, wher they trete of swich matere,
And what thay seyn of wommen ye may here.
Thise been the cokkes wordes, and nat myne; 445
I can noon harme of no womman divyne.

Faire in the sond, to bathe hire merily,
Lyth Pertelote, and alle hir sustres by,
Agayn the sonne; and Chauntecleer so free
Song merier[6] than the mermayde in the see; 450

---

[1] E. Wheither.   [2] E. nedefully to doon.
[3] Hl. Cp. Pt. schal (schuln).   [4] E. out of.   [5] E. seye.   [6] E. murier.

For Phisiologus seith sikerly,   (4461)
How that they singen wel and merily.
And so bifel, that as he caste his yë,
Among the wortes, on a boterflye,
He was war of this fox that lay ful lowe.   455
No-thing ne liste him thanne for to crowe,
But cryde anon, 'cok, cok,' and up he sterte,
As man that was affrayed in his herte.
For naturelly a beest desyreth flee
Fro his contrarie, if he may it see,   460
Though he never erst had seyn it with his yë. (4471)
    This Chauntecleer, whan he gan him espye,
He wolde han fled, but that the fox anon
Seyde, 'Gentil sire, allas! wher wol ye gon?
Be ye affrayed of me that am your freend?   465
Now certes, I were worse than a feend,
If I to yow wolde harm or vileinye.
I am nat come your counseil for tespye;
But trewely, the cause of my cominge
Was only for to herkne how that ye singe.   470
For trewely ye have as mery a stevene,   (4481)
As eny aungel hath, that is in hevene;
Therwith ye han in musik more felinge
Than hadde Boece, or any that can singe.
My lord your fader (God his soule blesse!)   475
And eek your moder, of hir gentilesse,
Han in myn hous y-been, to my gret ese;
And certes, sire, ful fayn wolde I yow plese.
But for men speke of singing, I wol[1] saye,
So mote I brouke wel myn eyen tweye,   480
Save yow, I herde[2] nevere man so[3] singe,   (4491)
As dide your fader in the morweninge;

---

[1] E. *ins.* yow.   [2] E. herde I.   [3] E. yet.

Certes, it was of herte, al that he song.
And for to make his voys the more strong,
He wolde so peyne him, that with both his yĕn   485
He moste winke, so loude he wolde cryen,
And stonden on his tiptoon therwithal,
And strecche forth his nekke long and smal.
And eek he was of swich discrecioun,
That ther nas no man in no regioun   490
That him in song or wisdom mighte passe.   (4501)
I have weel rad in daun Burnel the Asse,
Among his vers, how that ther was a cok,
For that a prestes sone yaf him a knok
Upon his leg, whyl he was yong and nyce,   495
He made him for to lese his benefyce.
But certeyn, ther nis no comparisoun
Bitwix[1] the wisdom and discrecioun
Of your fader, and of his subtiltee.
Now singeth, sire, for seinte charitee,   500
Let se, conne ye your fader countrefete?'   (4511)
This Chauntecleer his winges gan to bete,
As man that coude his tresoun nat espye,
So was he ravisshed with his flaterye.

  Allas! ye lordes, many a fals flatour   505
Is in your courtes, and many a losengeour,
That plesen yow wel more, by my feith,
Than he that soothfastnesse unto yow seith.
Redeth Ecclesiaste of flaterye;
Beth war, ye lordes, of hir trecherye.   510

  This Chauntecleer stood hye up-on his toos,   (4521)
Strecching his nekke, and held his eyen cloos,
And gan to crowe loude for the nones;
And daun Russel the fox sterte[2] up at ones,

---

[1] E. Cm. Cp. Bitwixe.   [2] E. Hn. Cm. stirte.

And by the gargat[1] hente Chauntecleer,   515
And on his bak toward the wode him beer,
For yet ne was ther no man that him sewed.
O destinee, that mayst nat ben eschewed!
Allas, that Chauntecleer fleigh fro the bemes!
Allas, his wyf ne roghte nat of dremes!   520
And on a Friday fil[2] al this meschaunce.   (4531)
O Venus, that art goddesse of plesaunce,
Sin that thy servant was this Chauntecleer,
And in thy service dide al his poweer,
More for delyt, than world to multiplye,   525
Why woldestow suffre him on thy day to dye?
O Gaufred, dere mayster soverayn,
That, whan thy worthy king Richard was slayn
With shot, compleynedest his deth so sore,
Why ne hadde I now thy sentence and thy lore, 530
The Friday for to chide, as diden ye?   (4541)
(For on a Friday soothly slayn was he.)
Than wolde I shewe yow how that I coude pleyne
For Chauntecleres drede, and for his peyne.

　　Certes, swich cry ne lamentacioun   535
Was nevere of ladies maad, whan Ilioun
Was wonne, and Pirrus with his streite swerd,
Whan he hadde hent king Priam by the berd,
And slayn him (as saith us *Eneydos*),
As maden alle the hennes in the clos,   540
Whan they had seyn of Chauntecleer the sighte. (4551)
But sovereynly[3] dame Pertelote shrighte,
Ful louder than dide Hasdrubales wyf,
Whan that hir housbond hadde lost his lyf,
And that the Romayns hadde brend Cartage,   545

---

[1] E. Hn. gargat; Cm. Hl. garget; Ln. gorge.
[2] *So* E. Hn. Cm.　　　　　　　[3] E. sodeynly.

She was so ful of torment and of rage,
That wilfully into the fyr she sterte,
And brende hir-selven with a stedfast herte.
O woful hennes, right so cryden ye,
As, whan that Nero brende the citee   550
Of Rome, cryden senatoures wyves,   (4561)
For that hir housbondes losten alle hir lyves;
Withouten gilt this Nero hath hem slayn.
Now wol I torne[1] to my tale agayn:
    This sely widwe, and eek hir doghtres two,   555
Herden thise hennes crye and maken wo,
And out at dores sterten thay anoon,
And syen the fox toward the grove goon,
And bar upon his bak the cok away;
And[2] cryden, 'Out! harrow! and weylaway!   560
Ha, ha, the fox!' and after him they ran,   (4571)
And eek with staves many another man;
Ran Colle our dogge, and Talbot, and Gerland,
And Malkin, with a distaf in hir hand;
Ran cow and calf, and eek[3] the verray hogges   565
So were they[4] fered for berking of the dogges
And shouting of the men and wimmen eke,
They ronne so, hem thoughte hir herte breke.
They yelleden[5] as feendes doon in helle;
The dokes cryden as men wolde hem quelle;   570
The gees for fere flowen over the trees;   (4581)
Out of the hyve cam the swarm of bees;
So hidous was the noyse, a! *benedicite!*
Certes, he Iakke Straw, and his meynee,
Ne maden nevere shoutes half so shrille[6],   575

---

[1] E. Now turne I wole.   [2] Pt. They.
[3] E. *om.* eek.   [4] Hl. were they; *rest om.*
[5] E. yolleden.   [6] E. Ln. shille.

Whan that they wolden any Fleming kille,
As thilke day was maad upon the fox.
Of bras thay broghten bemes, and of box,
Of horn, of boon, in whiche they blewe and pouped,
And therwithal thay shryked [1] and they houped; 580
It semed as that hevene sholde falle.   (4591)
Now, gode men, I pray yow herkneth alle!
   Lo, how fortune turneth sodeinly
The hope and pryde eek [2] of hir enemy!
This cok, that lay upon the foxes bak,   585
In al his drede, un-to the fox he spak,
And seyde, 'sire, if that I were as ye,
Yet sholde [3] I seyn (as wis God helpe me),
Turneth agayn, ye proude cherles alle!
A verray pestilence up-on yow falle!   590
Now am I come un-to this [4] wodes syde,   (4601)
Maugree your heed, the cok shal heer abyde;
I wol him ete in feith, and that anon.'—
The fox answerde, 'In feith, it shal be don,'—
And as he spak that word, al sodeinly   595
This cok brak from his mouth deliverly,
And heighe up-on a tree he fleigh anon.
And whan the fox saugh that he was y-gon [5],
'Allas!' quod he, 'O Chauntecleer, allas!
I have to yow,' quod he, 'y-doon trespas,   600
In-as-muche as I maked yow aferd,   (4611)
Whan I yow hente, and broghte out of the [6] yerd;
But, sire, I dide it in [7] no wikke entente;
Com doun, and I shal telle yow what I mente.
I shal seye sooth to yow, God help me so.'   605

---

[1] E. Hn. skriked.   [2] E. *om.* eek.   [3] E. wolde.
[4] E. the.   [5] Hl. i-goon; *rest* gon, goon.
[6] E. Hn. into this.   [7] E. of.

'Nay than,' quod he, 'I shrewe us bothe two,
And first I shrewe my-self, bothe blood and bones,
If thou bigyle me [1] ofter than ones.
Thou shalt namore, thurgh thy flaterye
Do me to singe and winke with myn yë.   610
For he that winketh, whan he sholde see,   (4621)
Al wilfully, God lat him never thee!'
'Nay,' quod the fox, 'but God yive him meschaunce,
That is so undiscreet of governaunce,
That iangleth whan he sholde holde his pees.'   615
   Lo, swich it is for to be recchelees,
And necligent, and truste on flaterye.
But ye that holden this tale a folye,
As of a fox, or of a cok and hen,
Taketh the moralitee [2], good men.   620
For seint Paul seith, that al that writen is,   (4631)
To our doctryne it is y-write, y-wis.
Taketh the fruyt, and lat the chaf be stille.
   Now, gode God, if that it be thy wille,
As seith my lord, so make us alle good men;   625
And bringe us to his heighe blisse.   Amen.

Here is ended the Nonne [3] preestes tale.

---

[1] E. Hn. Hl. *ins.* any.   [2] Tyrwhitt *inserts* therof.
          [3] Cp. Nonne; E. Hn. Nonnes.

NOTES.

In the Notes, 'CH. 2' refers to the Clarendon Press edition of Chaucer's Prioresses Tale, &c.; and 'CH. 3' to the same of Chaucer's Man of Law's Tale, &c.

THE PROLOGUE.

1. *Aprille.* It appears that Chaucer's Prologue refers to the 16th and 17th of April. See Man of Law's Prol. ll. 1–6; and CH. 2, p. 129 and p. xi.

soote, sweet; from A.S. *swōt*, orig. an adv.; cf. A.S. *swēte*, adj.

4. *vertu*, power, corresponding to the A.S. *miht*, might.

4–6. Hawes seems to have had Chaucer's opening lines in view in the first and second stanzas, chap. i, of his Pastime of Pleasure :—

> 'When that Aurora did well appeare
> In the depured ayre and cruddy firmament,
> Forth then I walked without impediment
>
> Into a medowe both gaye and glorious,
> Whiche Flora depainted with many a colour,
> Lyke a place of pleasure moste solacious,
> Encensyng out the aromatike odoure
> Of Zepherus breath, whiche that every floure
> Through his fume doth alwaye engender.'

Lydgate (Minor Poems, ed. Halliwell, pp. 243, 244) copies Chaucer still more closely in his description of *Ver* (spring).

On the other hand, Chaucer seems to have had in his mind some passage like the following account in Vincent of Beauvais, *Speculum Naturale*, lib. xv. c. 66, entitled *De Vere* :—'Sol vero ad radices herbarum et arborum penetrans, humorem quem ibi coadunatum hyeme reperit, attrahit; herba vero, vel arbor suam inanitionem sentiens a terra attrahit humorem, quem ibi sui similitudine adiuuante calore Solis transmutat, sicque reuiuiscit; inde est quod quidam mensis huius temporis *Aprilis* dicitur, quia tunc terra praedicto modo aperitur.'

5. Chaucer twice refers again to *Zephirus*, in his translation of Boethius, bk. i. met. 5; bk. ii. met. 3.

7. *yonge sonne.* The sun is here said to be young because it had not long entered upon its annual course through the signs of the zodiac.

8. *the Ram.* 'The difficulty here really resides in the expression "his halfe cours," which means what it says, viz. "his half-course," and not, as Tyrwhitt unfortunately supposed, "half his course." The results of the two explanations are quite different. Taking Chaucer's own expression as it stands, he tells us that, a little past the middle of April, "the young sun has run his half-course in the Ram." Turning to Fig. 1 (in The Astrolabe, ed. Skeat) we see that, against the month "Aprilis" there appears in the circle of zodiacal signs, the *latter* half (roughly speaking) of Aries, and the *former* half of Taurus. Thus the sun in April runs a half-course in the Ram and a half-course in the Bull. "The former of these was completed," says the poet; which is as much as to say, that *it was past the eleventh of April.*

	March.	April.	May.
	Aries.	Taurus.	Gemini.

The sun had, in fact, only just completed his course through the first of the twelve signs, as the said course was supposed to begin at the vernal equinox. This is why it may well be called "the yonge sonne," an expression which Chaucer repeats under similar circumstances in the Squyeres Tale, Part ii. l. 39.'—Chaucer's Astrolabe, ed. Skeat, p. xlvii. Mr. Brae, in his edition of Chaucer's Astrolabe, shews that Chaucer *never* refers to the *constellations*, but always to the *signs*. 'Also twelue monþes ben in the ȝere, and eueriche monþe þe sonne entreþ into a *signe* as it falleþ for þe monþe. And so in March þey entreþ into þe Weþer; in Auerel in-to þe Boole.'—Trevisa's transl. of Higden's Polychronicon, ii. 207.

10. *open ye.*

'Hit bifelle bytwyxte March and Maye,
Whan kynd corage begynneth to pryke,
Whan frith and felde[s] wexen gaye, ...
Whan lovers slepen *with oþyn yȝe,*
As nightyngalis on grene tre.'
The Sowdone of Babyloyne, ll. 41–46.

12, 13. Professor Ten Brink thinks that a colon should be placed after *pilgrimages*, and *wenden* understood after *palmers*. According to ordinary English construction the verb *longen* must be supplied after palmers, and *seken* before *To ferne halwes.*

13. *palmer*, originally one who had made a pilgrimage to the Holy Land and brought home a *palm*-branch as a token. Chaucer, says Tyrwhitt, seems to consider all pilgrims to foreign parts as palmers. The essential difference between the two classes of persons here mentioned, the palmer

and the pilgrim, was, that the latter had 'some dwelling-place, a palmer had none; the pilgrim travelled to some certain place, the palmer to all, and not to any one in particular; the pilgrim might go at his own charge, the palmer must profess wilful poverty; the pilgrim might give over his profession, the palmer must be constant;' Blount's Glossographia. See note to P. Plowman, v. 523 (Clar. Press, smaller edition).

> 'But a prest that a *palmer* was
> A *palme* in his hand he had,
> And in a slaveyn he was clad.'—Tundal's Poems, p. 14.

14. *ferne halwes*, distant saints, i. e. shrines. Here *ferne = ferrene =* distant, foreign; cf. 'þrie kinges . . . comen fram *verrene* londes;' O.E. Miscel. p. 27. Also 'this man of *ferne* londe,' i. e. from a distant land; Havelok, 2031. 'To *ferne* peoples;' Chaucer's Boethius, bk. ii. met. 7. See Mätzner. *Ferne* also means 'ancient,' but not here.

halwes, saints; cp. Scotch *Hallow-e'en*, the eve of All Hallows, or All Saints; here applied to their shrines.

Chaucer has: 'to go seken *halwes*,' to go (on a pilgrimage) to seek saints' shrines; C. T. 6239.

16. *wende*, go; pret. *wente*, Eng. *went*. The old preterite of *go* (A.S. *gangan*) was *giéng*, which gave place to *eode*, *ȝede*, or *yode*, from the root *i* (cf. Lat. *i-re*) of the weak conjugation. Spenser uses *yode* as a past tense, but also *yeed* (wrongly) as a gerund (F. Q. ii. 4. 2).

17. *The holy blisful martir*, Thomas à Becket. On pilgrimages, see Saunders, Chaucer, p. 15; and Erasmus, *Peregrinatio religionis ergo*.

18. *holpen*, pp. of *helpen*. The older preterites of this verb are *heolp*, *help*, *halp*. *Seke*, sick, rimes to *seke*, seek; this apparent repetition is only allowed when the repeated word is used in two different senses.

20. *Tabard*. Of this word Speght gives the following account in his Glossary to Chaucer:—' Tabard—a jaquet or slevelesse coate, worne in times past by noblemen in the warres, but now only by heraults (heralds), and is called theyre "coate of armes in servise." It is the signe of an inne in Southwarke by London, within the which was the lodging of the Abbot of Hyde by Winchester. This is the hostelry where *Chaucer* and the other Pilgrims mett together, and, with Henry Baily their hoste, accorded about the manner of their journey to Canterbury. And whereas through time it hath bin much decayed, it is now by Master *J. Preston,* with the Abbot's house thereto adgoyned, newly repaired, and with convenient rooms much encreased, for the receipt of many guests.' The inne is well described in Saunders (on Chaucer), p. 19. The *Taberdars* of Queen's College, Oxford, were scholars supposed originally to have worn the *tabard*, since called, by mistake, the Talbot.

23. *hostelrye*, a lodging, inn, house, residence. *Hostler* properly signifies the keeper of an inn, and not, as now, the servant of an inn who

looks after the horses. (The A.S. *hors-hús* signifies an inn—another term was *gæst-hús;* and *hors-herde* = an inn-keeper.)

24. *wel* is here used like our word *full.*

25. *by aventure y-falle,* by adventure (chance) fallen (into company).

26. *felawshipe,* fellowship, from M.E. *felawe,* companion, fellow.

29. *esed atte beste,* accommodated or entertained in the best manner. *Easement* is still used as a law term, signifying accommodation.

atte = M.E. *atþan* = *attan* or *atten,* A.S. *æt þám.* In the older stages of the language we find *atte* used only before masc. and neuter nouns beginning with a consonant; the corresponding feminine form is *atter* (A.S. *æt þære*), which is not used by Chaucer.

30. *to reste* = at rest. Spenser has *to friend* = for friend; F. Q. i. 1. 28.

33. *forward,* agreement. 'Fals was here *foreward* so forst is in May,' i.e. their agreement was as false as a frost in May; Ritson's Ancient Songs, i. 30.

34. *ther as I yow devyse,* to that place that I tell you of (sc. Canterbury); *ther* in M. E. frequently signifies *where; devyse* = to speak of, describe.

35. *whyl,* whilst; Eng. *while,* time. Cp. M.E. *hwilum, hwile, whilen,* awhile. The form in *-es* (*whiles,* the reading of some MSS.) is comparatively a modern adverbial form, and may be compared with M.E. *hennes, thennes,* hence, thence; *ones, twies, thries,* once, twice, thrice; of which older forms are found in *-enne* and *-e* respectively.

37. 'It seemeth to me it is reasonable.'

Me thinketh = me thinks, where *me* is the dative before the impersonal vb. *thinken,* to appear, seem; cp. *me liketh, me list,* it pleases me. So the phrase *if you please* = if it *please you,* you being the *dative* and not the nominative case. *semed me,* = it seemed to me, occurs in l. 39.

41. *inne.* In M.E. *in* is the preposition, and *inne* the adverb.

43. *Knight.* It was a common thing in this age for knights to seek employment in foreign countries which were at war. Tyrwhitt cites from Leland the epitaph of a knight of this period, Matthew de Gourney, who had been at the battle of Benamaryn, at the siege of Algezir, and at the battles of Crecy, Poitiers, &c. See note to l. 51.

worthy, worthy, is here used in its literal signification of distinguished, honourable. See ll. 47, 50.

For notes on the dresses, &c., of the pilgrims, see Todd's Illustrations of Chaucer, p. 227; and Fairholt's Costume in England, 1885, i. 129. Also Warton, Hist. Eng. Poetry, sect. 17.

45. *chivalrye,* knighthood; also the manners, exercises, and exploits of a knight.

48. *ferre,* the comp. of *fer,* far. Cf. M.E. *derre,* dearer, *sarre,* sorer, &c.

49. *hethenesse,* heathen lands, as distinguished from *Cristendom,* Christian countries.

51. *Alisaundre*, in Egypt, 'was won, and immediately after abandoned in 1365, by Pierre de Lusignan, King of Cyprus;' Tyrwhitt. Froissart (Chron. bk. iii. c. 22) gives the epitaph of Pierre de Lusignan, king of Cyprus, who 'conquered in battle .. the cities of Alexandria in Egypt, Tripoli in Syria, Layas in Armenia, Satalia in Turkey, with several other cities and towns, from the enemies of the faith of Jesus Christ;' tr. by Johnes, vol. ii. p. 138.

52. *he hadde the bord bigonne.* Here *bord* = board, table, so that the phrase signifies 'he had been placed at the head of the dais, or *table* of state.' Warton, in his Hist. of Eng. Poetry, ed. 1840, ii. 209 (ed. 1871, ii. 373), aptly cites a passage from Gower which is quite explicit as to the sense of the phrase. See Gower, Conf. Amantis, bk. viii. ed. Pauli, iii. 299. We there read that a knight was honoured by a king by being set at the head of the middle table in the hall.

'And he, *which had his prise deserved*,
    After the kinges owne word,
    Was maad *beginne a middel bord*.'

The context shews that this was at supper-time, and that the knight was placed in this honourable position by the marshal of the hall.

It thus appears that the proposal made by Mr. Marsh to explain *bord* as meaning 'a tournament' is quite uncalled for. Once more, in Sir Beves of Hamptoun, ed. Kölbing (E. E. T. S.), p. 104, we find in one text (l. 2122)—

'Thow schelt this dai be priour,
    And beginne oure deis' [*daïs*];

where another text has (l. 1957) the reading—

'Palmer, thou semest best to me,
    Therfore men shal worshyp the;
    Begyn the borde, I the pray.'

See also Murray's Dict., s.v. *Board*.

53, 54. *Pruce.* When our English knights wanted employment, 'it was usual for them to go and serve in Pruce, or Prussia, with the knights of the Teutonic order, who were in a state of constant warfare with their heathen neighbours in *Lettow* (Lithuania), *Ruce* (Russia), and elsewhere.' —Tyrwhitt. Similarly, Gower (Conf. Amant. bk. iv, ed. Pauli, ii. 56) says that knights were expected to make 'rodes,' i.e. raids

'Somtime in *Pruce*, somtime in Rodes;' &c.

54. Walsingham, in his History, ed. Riley, ii. 197, tells us that, in 1390, no less a person than Henry, earl of Derby (afterwards Henry IV) set out for Prussia (*profectus est in le Pruys*), where 'devicit exercitum Regis de *Lettowe*, captis quatuor Ducibus,' &c. Warton, Hist. Eng. Poetry, ed. 1840, ii. 210, remarks—'Thomas duke of Gloucester, youngest son of Edw. III, and Henry earl of Derby, afterwards Henry IV, travelled into Prussia; and, in conjunction with the grand Masters

and Knights of Prussia and Livonia, fought the infidels of Lithuania. Lord Derby was greatly instrumental in taking Vilna, the capital of that country, in the year 1390. Here is a seeming compliment to some of these expeditions.' Hackluyt, in his Voyages, ed. 1598, i. 122, cites and translates the passage from Walsingham referred to above.

56–58. *Gernade*, Granada. 'The city of Algezir was taken from the Moorish King of *Granada* in 1344.'—T. It is the modern *Algeciras* on the S. coast of Spain, near Cape Trafalgar.

Belmarye and *Tramissene* (Tramessen), l. 62, were Moorish kingdoms in Africa, as appears from a passage in Froissart (bk. iv. c. 24) cited by Tyrwhitt. Johnes's translation has—' Tunis, Bugia, Morocco, Benmarin, Tremeçen.' Cf. Kn. Tale, l. 1772. Benmarin is called *Balmeryne* in Barbour's Bruce, xx. 393; cf. *Belmore*, Sowdone of Babylon, 3122.

Lyeys, in Armenia, was taken from the Turks by Pierre de Lusignan about 1367. It is the *Layas* mentioned by Froissart (see note to l. 51), and the modern *Ayas*; see Marco Polo, ed. Yule, i. 15.

Satalye (Attalia, now Adalia, on the S. coast of Asia Minor) was taken by the same prince soon after 1352.—T. See Acts xiv. 25.

Palatye (Palathia, see l. 65), in Anatolia, was one of the lordships held by Christian knights after the Turkish conquests.—T. Cf. Froissart, bk. iii. c. 23.

59. *the Grete See.* The name Great Sea is applied by Sir J. Maundeville (cap. 7) to that part of the Mediterranean which washes the coast of Palestine, to distinguish it from the two so-called inland seas, the sea of Tiberias and the Dead Sea. Cf. its proper name in Scripture, Numb. xxxiv. 6, 7; Josh. i. 4.

60. *aryve*, arrival or disembarkation of troops. Tyrwhitt, following the Ellesmere and other MSS., reads *armee*.

be = *ben*, been. Cf. *ydo* = *ydon*, done, &c.

62. *foughten*, pp. fought. This verb belongs to the strong, and not, like the past participles *soght*, *broght*, to the weak conjugation.

63. *slayn : hadde* must be supplied from l. 61.

67. *sovereyn prys*, exceeding great renown.

70. *vileinye*, any conduct unbecoming a gentleman. 'The *villain* is, *first*, the serf or peasant, *villanus*, because attached to the *villa* or farm. He is, *secondly*, the peasant, who, it is further taken for granted, will be churlish, selfish, dishonest, and generally of evil moral conditions, these having come to be assumed as always belonging to him, and to be permanently associated with his name, by those . . . who in the main commanded the springs of language. At the *third* step nothing of the meaning which the etymology suggests—nothing of *villa*—survives any longer; the peasant is wholly dismissed, and the evil moral conditions of him who is called by this name, alone remain.'—Trench; English Past and Present, ch. 7.

71. *no maner wight*, no kind of person whatever.

74. 'His horses were good, but he himself was not gaudily dressed.'

75. *gipoun*, a diminutive of *gipe*, a short cassock, a tight-fitting vest.

76. *habergeoun*, though etymologically an augmentative, is practically a diminutive of *hauberk*, but often used as synonymous with it. 'It was a defence of an inferior description to the hauberk; but when the introduction of plate-armour, in the reign of Edward III, had supplied more convenient and effectual defences for the legs and thighs, the long skirt of the hauberk became superfluous; from that period the *habergeon* alone seems to have been worn.'—Way, note to Promptorium Parvulorum, p. 220.

> 'And Tideus, aboue his *Habergeoun*,
>   A *gipoun* hadde, hidous, sharpe, and hoor,
> Wrought of the bristles of a wilde Boor.'
>
> Lydgate, Siege of Thebes, pt. ii.

77, 78. 'For he had just returned from his journey, and went to perform his pilgrimage (which he had vowed for a safe return) in his knightly array.'

79. *squyer*=esquire, one who attended on a knight, and bore his lance and shield. See Strutt, Sports and Pastimes, Introd. § 8.

80. *lovyer*, lover. The *y* in this word is not euphonic as in some modern words; *lovyer* is formed from the verb *lovie*, A.S. *lufian*, to love.

bacheler, a young aspirant to knighthood. Cf.

> 'Wightly Olyuer upsterte
>   As *bacheler*, doughti of dede.'
>
> The Sowdone of Babylone, l. 1211.

82. *yeer*. In the older stages of the language, *year*, *goat*, *swine*, &c., being neuter nouns, underwent no change in the nom. case of the plural number; but after numerals the *genitive* case was usually required.

I gesse, I should think. In M.E. *gesse* signifies to judge, believe, suppose. See Kn. Tale, l. 192.

85. *chivachye*. Fr. *chevauchée*. It most properly means an expedition with a small party of *cavalry*; but is often used generally for any military expedition. Holinshed calls it a *rode* (i.e. *raid*); cf. note to l. 53 above.

87. *born him wel*, conducted himself well, behaved bravely.

88. *lady grace*, lady's grace. In the earlier stages of our language the genitive of feminine nouns terminated in -*e*, so that *lady* is for *ladye*. Cf. the modern phrase 'Lady-day,' as compared with 'Lord's day.'

89. 'That was with floures swete embrouded al;' Prol. to Legend of Good Women, l. 119.

97. *nightertale*, night-time, time (or reckoning) of night. So also *wit nighter-tale*, lit. with night-time, Cursor Mundi, l. 2783; *on nighter-tale*,

id. 2991. The word is used by Holinshed in his account of Joan of Arc (under the date 1429).

98. *sleep*, also written *slep, slepte.* Cf. *weep, wepte ; leep, lepte,* &c. ; such verbs, once strong, became weak. See l. 148 ; and Kn. Ta. 1829.

100. *carf*, the past tense of *kerven*, to carve (pp. *corven*).

101. *Yeman*, yeoman. ' As a title of service, it denoted a servant of the next degree above a *garson* or groom .... The title of *yeoman* was given in a secondary sense to people of middling rank not in service. The appropriation of the word to signify a small landholder is more modern.'—Tyrwhitt.

102. *him liste*, it pleased him. *liste* is past tense ; *list* = pleaseth. See note on l. 37.

104. *a sheef of pecok-arwes*, a sheaf of arrows with peacocks' feathers. Ascham, in his Toxophilus, ed. Arber, p. 129, does not say much in favour of 'pecock fethers' ; for 'there is no fether but onely of a goose that hath all commodities in it. And trewelye at a short but, which some man doth vse, the *pecock fether* doth seldome kepe vp the shaft eyther ryght or level, it is so roughe and heuy, so that many men which haue taken them vp for gaynesse, hathe layde them downe agayne for profyte ; thus for our purpose, the goose is best fether for the best shoter.' In the Geste of Robyn Hode, pr. by W. Copland, we read—

> 'And every arrowe an ell longe
>   With *peacocke* well ydight,
> And nocked they were with white silk,
>   It was a semely syght.'

In the Liber Compotis Garderobæ, sub anno 4 Edw. II, p. 53, is this entry—Pro duodecim flecchiis cum pennis de pauone emptis pro rege, de 12 den. ; that is, For 12 arrows plumed with peacock's feathers, bought for the king, 12*d.* (MS. Cotton, Nero c. viii).—Strutt, Sports and Pastimes, bk. ii. ch. 1, § 12. Cf. Warton, Hist. Eng. Poetry, ed. 1840, ii. 211.

106. *takel*, lit. 'implement' or 'implements'; here (perhaps) the set of arrows. Strutt, Sports, bk. ii. ch. 1, § 16, quotes a ballad in which Robin Hood proposes that each man who misses the mark shall lose 'his *takell*'; and one of the losers says—'Syr abbot, I deliver thee myne *arrowe*.' In the Cursor Mundi, l. 3600, Isaac sends Esau to hunt, saying :—

> 'Ga lok thi *tacle* be puruaid.'

Fairholt (s.v. *tackle*) quotes from A Lytel Geste of Robyn Hood—

> 'When they had theyr *bowes* ibent,
>   Their *takles* fedred fre.'

109. *not-heed.* Tyrwhitt badly explains this as *a head like a nut*, from the hair probably being cut short ; but *not-heed* = crop-head. Cf. 'To *Notte*

his haire, *comas recidere*;' Baret's Alvearie, 1580. Cf. '*notted* heare,' Jack Juggler, p. 22; where Hazlitt's edition of Dodsley's Plays, vol. ii. p. 135, has the inferior reading '*knotted* hair.' Shakespeare has *not-pated*, i.e. crop-headed, 1 Henry IV, ii. 4. 78. Cooper's Thesaurus, 1565, has:—'*Tondere*, to cause his heare to be *notted* or polled of a barbour;' also, 'to *notte* his heare shorte;' also, '*Tonsus homo*, a man rounded, polled, or *notted*.' Cotgrave explains the F. *tonsure* as 'a sheering, clipping, powling, *notting*, cutting, or paring round.' Florio, ed. 1598, explains the Ital. *Zucconare* as 'to poule, to *nott*, to shaue, or cut off ones haire,' and *zuccone* as 'a shauen pate, a *notted* poule, a pouled pate, a gull, a ninnie, a ioult-head.' Gouldman's Lat. and E. Dict., 1664, has—'To *nott* or cut the hair away, *Tondeo*. *Notted* or clipped, *Tonsus*.' In later days the name of Roundhead came into use for a like reason.

111. *bracer*, a guard for the arm used by archers to prevent the friction of the bow-string on the coat. It was made like a glove with a long leathern top, covering the fore-arm (Fairholt). Fr. *bras*, the arm, whence *bracelet*.

'*Phi.* Which be instrumentes [of shotynge]?

Tox. Bracer, shotyng-glove, stryng, bowe and shafte. . . . . . A *bracer* serueth for two causes, one to saue his arme from the strype of the strynge, and his doublet from wearynge, and the other is, that the strynge glydynge sharpelye and quicklye of the bracer, may make the sharper shoote. . . . . . . In a *bracer* a man muste take hede of .iii. thinges, that it haue no nayles in it, that it haue no bucles, that it be fast on with laces wythout agglettes.'—Ascham's Toxophilus, ed. Arber, pp. 107, 108.

114. *Harneised*, equipped. The word *harness* signifies equipage, furniture, tackling for sea or land. 'A certain girdle, *harnessed* with silver' is spoken of in Riley's Memorials of London, p. 399, with reference to the year 1376; cf. Riley's tr. of Liber Albus, p. 521.

115. *Cristofre*. 'A figure of St. Christopher, used as a brooch. . . . The figure of St. Christopher was looked upon with particular reverence among the middle and lower classes; and was supposed to possess the power of shielding the person who looked on it from hidden dangers;' note in Wright's Chaucer. St. Christopher's day is July 25. There is a well-known early woodcut which is supposed to exhibit one of the earliest specimens of printing from a wooden block, engraved at p. 123 of the second volume of Chambers, Book of Days, and frequently elsewhere. The inscription beneath the figure of the saint runs as follows:

'Christofori faciem die quacunque tueris,
    Illa nempe die morte mala non morieris.'

Hence the Yeoman wore his brooch for good luck. See also, for the legend, Mrs. Jameson's Sacred and Legendary Art, ii. 48–59; and compare Brand's Popular Antiquities, ed. Ellis, i. 359, 364; Butler's Lives of the Saints, July 25.

116. Riley, in his Memorials of London, p. 115, explains *baldric* as 'a belt passing mostly round one side of the neck, and under the opposite arm.' See Spenser, F. Q. i. 7. 29.

120. *seynt Loy.* Tyrwhitt says that *Loy* is from *Eloy*, i. e. St. *Eligius*, whose day is Dec. 1; see the long account of him in Butler's Lives of the Saints. He was a goldsmith, and master of the mint to Clotaire II, Dagobert I, and Clovis II of France; and was also bishop of Noyon. He became the patron saint of goldsmiths, farriers, smiths, and carters. The Lat. *Eligius* necessarily became *Eloy* in O. French, and is *Eloy* or *Loy* in English, the latter form being the commoner. The Catholicon Anglicum (A.D. 1483) gives: '*Loye*, elegius (*sic*), nomen proprium.' Sir T. More, Works, ed. 1577, p. 194, says: '*St. Loy* we make an horse-leche.' Barnaby Googe, as cited in Brand, Pop. Antiq. i. 364 (ed. Ellis), says:—

'And *Loye* the smith doth looke to horse, and smithes of all degree,
   If they with iron meddle here, or if they goldesmithes bee.'

Dr. Oliver, in his Ecclesiastical Antiquities in Devon, speaks of St. Eligius's Chapel or St. Eloy's Chapel; it is the half-ruined chapel near Exeter commonly called *St. Loyes* (see The Academy, June 5, 1880, p. 122; and the same, May 29, June 5, 12 and 19, 1880). There is a district called *St. Loye's* in Bedford. There was a *St. Loy's house* in Wedon-Pinckney, Northamptonshire, mentioned in Bridges' History of that county (Brand). Churchyard mentions 'sweete *Saynct Loy*;' Siege of Leith, st. 50. In Lyndesay's Monarchè, bk. ii. lines 2299 and 2367, he is called 'sanct *Eloy.*' Much more might be added; see, e.g. *St. Eligius* in the Index to the Parker Society's publications. In the Cant. Tales, 7146, the carter prays to God and Saint Loy, joining the names according to a common formula; but the Prioress dropped the divine name. Perhaps she invoked *St. Loy* as being the patron saint of goldsmiths; for she seems to have been a little given to a love of gold and corals; see ll. 158–162. Guillaume de Machault (ed. 1849, p. 120), in his *Confort d'Ami*, near the end, uses the expression:—'Car je te jur, *par saint Eloy.*' '*By St. Loy*, that draws deep;' Nash's Lenten Stuff, p. xiv. ed. Hindley.

'We use to call her at home, dame Coye,
   A pretie gingerlie piece, God save her and *Saint Loye.*'

Jack Juggler, ed. Roxb. Club, p. 9.

See also Mrs. Jameson's Sacred and Legendary Art, p. 728. The Harl. MS. has *nas*, which is merely a shorter form of *ne was*. Mr. A. J. Ellis thinks that *nas* should stand, and that *seynt* should be pronounced as a word of two syllables.

123. *nose*. This is the reading of the best MSS. Speght reads *voice* (wrongly).

semely is in some MSS. written *semily*. The *e* is here to be distinctly sounded; *hertily* is sometimes written for *hertely*. See l. 136.

125. *scole*, school; here used for *style* or pronunciation.

126. *Frensh*. 'The French taught in England was the debased form of the Old Anglo-Norman, somewhat similar to that used at a later period in the courts of law; and it was this at which Chaucer and some of his contemporaries sneered. The writer of the Vision of Piers Plowman speaks of French of Norfolk, l. 2949;' Wright. 'Chaucer thought but meanly of the English-French spoken in his time. It was proper, however, that the Prioress should speak some sort of French; not only as a woman of fashion, a character which she is represented to affect (ll. 139, 140), but as a religious person;' Tyrwhitt.

'It is necessary to quote the above rather odd criticisms by Wright and Tyrwhitt because they have been too often repeated. There is nothing to shew that Chaucer intended a sneer; he merely states a *fact*, viz. that the Prioress spoke the usual Anglo-French of the English court, of the English law-courts, and of the English ecclesiastics of the higher rank. The poet, however, had been himself in France, and knew precisely the difference between the two dialects; yet there is no proof that he thought *more highly* of the Parisian than of the Anglo-French. He merely states that the French which the Prioress spoke was, *naturally*, such as was spoken in England. She had never travelled, and was therefore quite satisfied with the French which she had learnt at home. The language of the King of England was quite as good, in the esteem of Chaucer's hearers, as that of the King of France. Warton's note on the line is quite sane. He shews that queen Philippa wrote business letters in French (doubtless Anglo-French) with "great propriety." What Mr. Wright means by saying that "it was similar to that used *at a later period* in the courts of law" is somewhat puzzling. It was, of course, not *similar to*, but the *very same* language as was used *at the very same period* in the courts of law. In fact, he and Tyrwhitt have unconsciously given us the view entertained, not by Chaucer, but by unthinking readers of the present age; a view which is *not* expressed, and was probably not intended. At the modern Stratford we may find Parisian French inefficiently taught; but at the ancient Stratford, the very important Anglo-French was taught efficiently enough. There is no parallel between the cases, nor any such jest as the modern journalist is never weary of. The "French of Norfolk" as spoken of in P. Plowman (B. v. 239) was no French at all, but *English*; and the alleged parallel is misleading, as the reader who cares to refer to that passage will easily see.'—Skeat.

127. *At mete*. These simple conditions of good breeding are to be found in most of the mediæval tracts on *Curtesy* and *Nurture*, written for

the purpose of teaching manners at table. See The Babees Book, Early Eng. Text Society.

It is, however, of much more importance to observe that Tyrwhitt has acutely pointed out how Chaucer, throughout this passage, merely reproduces what he had found in his favourite book, viz. *Le Roman de la Rose*, l. 13612, &c.

> 'Et bien se gart qu'ele ne moile
> Ses dois es broez jusqu'as jointes,
> Ne qu'el n'ait pas ses levres ointes
> De sopes, d'aulx, ne de char grasse,
> Ne que trop de morsiaus n'entasse,
> Ne trop gros, nes mete en sa bouche.
> Du bout des dois le morsel touche
> Qu'el devra moillier en la sauce,
> Soit vert, ou cameline, ou jauce,
> Et sagement port sa bouchée
> Que sus son piz goute n'en chée
> De sope, de savor, de poivre.
> Et si gentement redoit boivre,
> Que sor soi n'en espande goute.'

I.e. 'and takes good care not to wet her fingers up to the joints in broth, nor to have her lips anointed with soups, or garlic, or fat flesh, nor to heap up too many or too large morsels and put them in her mouth. She touches with the tips of her fingers the morsel which she has to moisten with the sauce (be it green, or brown, or yellow), and lifts her mouthful warily, so that no drop of the soup, or relish or pepper may fall on her breast. And so daintily she contrives to drink, as not to sprinkle a drop upon herself.'

Again, a few lines below :—

> 'Si doit si bien sa bouche terdre,
> Qu'el n'i lest nule gresse aerdre,
> Au mains en la levre desseure.'

I.e. 'she ought to wipe her lip so well, as not to permit any grease to stay there, at least upon her upper lip.' Cf. also Ovid, Ars Amatoria, iii. 755, 756.

132. *lest* = *list*, pleasure, delight.

134. *ferthing* signifies literally a fourth part, and hence a small portion.

> 'Embrewe not youre vesselle ne youre napery
> Ouer mesure and maner, but saue them clene :
> Ensoyle not youre cuppe, but kepe hit clenely,
> Lete no fatte *ferthyng* of youre lippe be sen ;
> For that is foule ; wotte you what I mene ?
> Or than ye drincke, for youre owne honesté,
> Youre lippis wepe [wipe], and klenly loke they be.

> Blowe not in youre drincke ne in youre potage,
> Ne farsith not youre disshe to full of brede,
> Ne bere not youre knyf towarde youre vysage,
> For there-in is parell and mekell drede.
> Clawe not youre face ne touche not youre hede
> Wyth youre bare hande, sittyng at the table,
> For in norture that is reprouable.'
>
> Caxton's Book of Curtesye, p. 20.

139. *peyned hir*, took pains, endeavoured.

139, 140. *to countrefete chere Of court*, to imitate courtly behaviour.

141. *to ben holden*, &c., to be esteemed worthy of reverence.

147. *wastel breed.* Horses and dogs were not usually fed on *wastel breed* or cake bread (bread made of the best flour), but on coarse lentil bread baked for that purpose. 'The domestic baker prepared several kinds and qualities of bread, suitable to the various departments of the household; the *manchet* loaf of wheaten flour was for the master's table, the fine *chete* for the side-tables, and the brown bread for the board's end. The finer quality was made of flour passed through a sieve or boulting-cloth, and sometimes called boulted bread; the chete was of unboulted flour, and the household was made of a mixture of flour and rye-meal, called mystelon or maslin; the latter was the quality usually made in the houses of the middle class; the poor ate bread made of rye, lentils, and oatmeal. Fancy bread, such as paynepuff and marchpane, was prepared for company; the latter was in old times a favourite delicacy, made of flour, sugar, and almonds; originally it was used especially at Easter, and called mass-pane, or mass-bread, and sometimes payne-mayne.' — Our English Home, pp. 79, 80. Cf. Riley, Memorials of London, p. 108; tr. of Liber Albus, p. 305. In l. 334 we read that the Frankeleyn loved a '*sop* in wyn.' In the Anturs of Arther at the Tarnewathelan, st. 37, we read that

> 'Thre soppus of demayn (i. e. paindemayne)
> Wos broghte to Sir Gauan
> For to cumford his brayne.'

And in Harl. MS. 279, fol. 10, we have the necessary instruction for the making of these sops. 'Take mylke and boyle it, and thanne (then) tak (take) yolkys (yolks) of eyroun (eggs), ytryid (separated) fro (from) the whyte, and hete it, but let it nowt boyle, and stere (stir) it wyl tyl it be somwhat thikke; thenne cast therto salt and sugre, and kytte (cut) fayre paynemaynnys in round soppys, and caste the soppys theron, and serue it forth for a potage.' — Way, in Promptorium Parvulorum, p. 378.

148. *But sore weep she if oon*, &c. Read *But so / re weep / shif oon*, &c.

149. *men smoot.* If *men* were the ordinary plural of *man*, *smoot* ought

to be *smiten* (pl. past); but *men*, M.E. *me*, is used like the Ger. *man*, French *on*, with the singular verb.

yerde, stick, rod. Cf. *yard*-measure, and *yard* as a nautical term; a *gird* of land (about seven acres of ploughland, and pasture for two oxen, one cow, and six sheep).

151. *wimpel.* The *wimple* or *gorger* is stated first to have appeared in Edward the First's reign. It was a covering for the neck, and was used by nuns and elderly ladies. See Gloss. to Spec. of English, Part I; Reliq. Antiquae, ii. 15; Fairholt's Costume, 1885, ii. 413.

pinched. 'But though I olde and hore be, sone myne,
      And poore by my clothing and aray,
      And not so wyde a gown have as is thyne
      So small *ypynched* and so gay,
      My rede in happe yit the profit may.'
                        Occleve, De Reg. Principum, p. 15.

152. *eyen greye.* This seems to have been the favourite colour of ladies' eyes in Chaucer's time. Cf. C. T. 3972; Rom. Rose, 546, 862; also—

                'Hyr forheed lely whyht,
      Hyr bent browys blake, and hyr *grey eyne*,
      Hyr chyry chekes, *hyr nose streyt* and ryht,
      Hyr lyppys rody.'—Lives of Saints, Roxb. Club, p. 14.

      ' Her eyes are *grey as glass.*'—Two Gent. of Verona, iv. 4. 197.

156. *hardily* is here used for *sikerly*, certainly; see CH. 2, Gloss.

157. *fetis* literally signifies 'made artistically,' and hence well-made, *feat*, neat, handsome. See Glossary.

war, aware; 'I was *war*' = I perceived.

159. *bedes.* The word *bede* signifies, (1) a prayer; (2) a string of grains upon which the prayers were counted, or the grains themselves. See Glossary, s. v. *Bede.* *A pair* here means 'a set.' 'A *peire of bedis* eke she bere;' Rom. Rose, 7372.

      'Sumtyme with a portas, sumtyme with a *payre of bedes.*'
                Bale's King John, p. 27; Camden Soc.
In the year 1399, Eleanor of Gloucester in her last will left her mother 'a pair of paternosters of coral.'—Nicolas, Test. Vet. i. 147. In 1412, Roger de Kyrkly had *unum par de bedes et unus agnus dei.*—Wills and Inventories, p. 56; Surtees Soc.

gauded al with grene, having the *gawdies* green. Some were of silver gilt. The *gawdies* or *gaudees* were the larger beads in the set. 'A peyre bedys of jeete [*get*], gaudied with corall;' Bury Wills, p. 82, l. 16. The note says that every eleventh bead, or *gaud*, stood for a Paternoster; the smaller beads, each for an Ave Maria. The full number was 55 or 165. ' *Gaudye* of beedes, *signeau de paternoster.*'—Palsgrave.

'A paire of bedes blacke as sable
   She toke and hyng my necke about;
Upon the *gaudees* all without
   Was wryte of gold, *pur reposer.*'
         Gower, Confessio Amantis, f. 190; ed. Pauli, iii. 372.

160. *broche = brooch*, signified, (1) a pin; (2) a breast-pin; (3) a buckle or clasp; (4) a jewel or ornament. It was an ornament common to both sexes. The brooch seems to have been made in the shape of a capital A, surmounted by a crown. See the figure of a silver-gilt brooch in the shape of an A in the Glossary to Fairholt's Costume in England. The 'crowned A' is supposed to represent *Amor* or *Charity*, the greatest of all the Christian graces. 'Omnia uincit amor;' Vergil, Eclog. x. 69.

163. *Another Nonne.* It was not common for Prioresses to have female chaplains; but Littré gives *chapelaine*, fem., as an old title of dignity in a nunnery. Moreover, it is an office still held in most Benedictine convents, as is fully explained in a letter written by a modern Nun-Chaplain, and printed in Anglia, iv. 238.

164. The mention of *three priests* presents some difficulty. To make up the twenty-nine mentioned in l. 24, we only want *one* priest, and it is afterwards assumed that there was but *one* priest, viz. the Nonnes Preest, who tells the tale of the Cock and Fox. Chaucer also, in all other cases, supposes that there was but *one* representative of each class.

The most likely solution is that Chaucer wrote a character of the Second Nun, beginning—

'Another Nonne with hir hadde she
   That was hir chapeleyne'—

and that, for some reason, he afterwards suppressed the description. The line left imperfect, as above, may have been filled up, to stop a gap, either by himself (temporarily), or indeed by some one else.

If we are to keep the text (which stands alike in all MSS.), we must take 'wel nyne and twenty' to mean 'at least nine and twenty.'

The letter from the Nun-Chaplain mentioned in the last note shews that an Abbess might have as many as *five* priests, as well as a chaplain. The difficulty is, merely, how to reconcile this line with l. 24.

165. *a fair*, i. e. a fair one.

for the maistrie is equivalent to the French phrase *pour la maistrie*, which in old medical books 'is applied to such medicines as we usually call sovereign, excellent above all others;' Tyrwhitt. In the Promptorium Parvulorum we find 'maystrye, or soverenté, and heyare (higher) honde yn stryfe or werre (war): Dextre, pl., victoria, triumphus.' Another copy reads, 'maistri or worchip (honour) or the heyer hond,' &c. The phrase *vor the maistre* is in Rob. of Glouc. l. 11554.

166. *venerye,* hunting. 'The monks of the middle ages were extremely attached to hunting and field-sports; and this was a frequent subject of complaint with the more austere ecclesiastics, and of satire with the laity.'—Wright.

168. *deyntee,* dainty, is frequently used by Chaucer in the sense of precious, valuable, rare.

170. *Ginglen,* jingle. Fashionable riders were in the habit of hanging small bells on the bridles and harness of their horses. 'Wycliffe, in his Triloge, inveighs against the priests [of his time] for their "fair hors, and joly and gay sadeles and bridles ringing by the way;" Lewes' Wycliffe, p. 121;' cited by Warton, ed. 1840, i. 167. At a much later period Spenser (F. Q. i. 2. 13) makes mention of these 'bells' in his description of a lady's steed :—

> 'Her wanton palfrey all was overspred
> With tinsell trappings, woven like a wave,
> Whose bridle rung with golden bels and bosses brave.'

See also Warton, as above; and C. T. 14800.

172. *Ther as* = where that.

173. *The reule* (rule) *of seint Maure* (St. Maur) and that of *seint Beneyt* (St. Benet or Benedict) were the oldest forms of monastic discipline in the Romish Church. St. Maur (Jan. 15) was a disciple of St. Benet (Dec. 4).

175. Harl. MS. reads, 'This ilke monk leet forby hem pace' (leet hem forby him pace?), 'This same monk let them pass by him unobserved.' *hem* refers to the rules of St. Maur and St. Benet, which were too *streit* (strict) for this 'lord' or superior of the house, who seems to have preferred a milder sort of discipline. *Forby* is still used in Scotland for *by* or *past,* and occurs frequently in the North English literature of the fourteenth century in the sense of by, past, near.

176. *space.* Lansd. MS. reads *pace* (steps). Tyrwhitt reads *trace,* path.

177. *a pulled hen,* lit. a plucked hen; hence, the value of a hen without its feathers; see l. 652. In C.T. 6694, the phrase is 'not worth *a hen.*' Mr. Earle suggests that *pulled* = pullet; but the later phrase is also *polled hen*; (see below). Tyrwhitt says, 'I do not see much force in the epithet *pulled;*' but adds, in his Glossary—'I have been told since, that a hen whose feathers are pulled, or plucked off, will not lay any eggs.' Becon speaks of a 'polled hen,' i.e. pulled hen, as one unable to fly. 'But to pray at the shrines of his canonized saints, or in places of pilgrimage, where the devil worketh stiracles, I would say miracles, but namely at Rome, at Compostella, at Jerusalem, &c., this passeth all. Prayers made in those places with this confidence, that they be the sooner heard and the better accepted by the reason of the places, fly to heaven as it were *a polled hen.*'—Becon's Works, p. 533; Parker Soc. Another explanation is to

suppose *pulled* to be put for *pilled* ; though these words are properly
distinct. *Pilled* means bald, or scurfy ; and hence, perhaps 'moulting.'
'*Pylld*, or scallyd, depilatus, glabellus ;' Prompt. Parv. Cf. *peeled* in
Isaiah xviii. 2, 7 (also 'plucked off the hair' in Isa. l. 6) ; Ezek. xxix.
18 ; Shakespeare, 1 Hen. VI. i. 3. 30.

179. *reccheles* (in MS. E.) means careless ; but, as Professor Ten
Brink says, 'a careless monk' is not necessarily 'a monk out of his
cloister.' He proposes to read *reset-les*, without a resting-place or place
of retreat ; *reset* is a common word in M.E. writers for resting-place,
abode. Cf. Allit. Poems (ed. Morris), A. 1067 :—'Ther entrez non to
take *reset* ;' 'No one enters to take up (their) abode there.' But the
reading *cloisterlees* (in MS. Harl.) solves the difficulty ; being a coined
word, Chaucer goes on to explain it.

179–181. This passage is a literal translation of one from the Decretal
of Gratian : '*Sicut piscis sine aqua caret vita, ita sine monasterio monachus.*'
Joinville says, 'The Scriptures do say that a monk cannot live out of
his cloister without falling into deadly sins, any more than a fish can
live out of water without dying.' Cf. P. Plowm. B. x. 292. Moreover,
the poet here imitates a passage in Le Testament de Jehan de Meung,
ed. Méon, l. 1166 :—

'Qui les voldra trover, si les quiere en leur cloistre . . .
Car ne prisent le munde la montance d'une oistre.'

182. *held*, esteemed. Some MSS. read *hild* or *huld*.

184. *what* has here its earliest sense of *wherefore*, or *why*.

wood, mad, foolish, is frequently employed by Spenser.

186. *swinken*, to toil ; whence '*swinked* hedger,' used by Milton (Comus,
l. 293). But *swinken* is, properly, a strong verb.

187. *bit*, the 3rd pers. sing. pres. of *bidden*, to command.

187, 188. *Austyn.* St. Augustine made his cathedral clergy, as far as
their duties permitted it, live as strictly as the monkish orders.

189. *a pricasour*, a hard rider.

192. *for no cost*, &c., for in no way would he abstain from these
sports. Cf. 'Of my nede gyfe þou no *coost.*'—The Sowdone of Babyloyne, l. 1721. See note on Knightes Tale, l. 619.

193. *purfiled.* The M.E. *purfil* signifies the embroidered or furred
hem of a garment, so that *purfile* is to work upon the edge. *Purfiled*
has also a more extended meaning, and is applied to garments overlaid
with gems or other ornaments. '*Pourfiler d'or*, to *purfle*, tinsell, or
overcast with gold thread, &c. *Pourfileure*, *purfling*, a purfling lace or
work, bodkin work, tinselling ;' Cotgrave.

194. *grys*, a sort of costly fur, formerly very much esteemed ; but
what species of fur it was is not clear ; O. F. *gris*, Rom. de la Rose,
9121, 9307. Some suppose it to be that of the *grey* squirrel. Such a

dress as is here described must have been very expensive. Occleve
refers to the fashion in the following lines :—

> 'But this me thynkethe a grete abusioun,
> To see one walke in gownes of scarlet
> Twelve yerdes wide, with pendaunt sleves doune
> On the grounde, and the furre therin set,
> Amountyng unto twenty pound and bet.'
> >> *De Regimine Principum*, p. 16, ed. Wright.

> 'His armes two han right ynoughe to done,
> And somwhat more, his sleves up to holde.
> The taillours, I trowe, mote hereafter sone
> Shape in the felde, they shalle not sprede and folde
> On her bord, though they never so fayne wolde,
> The clothe that shall be in a gowne wrought.'—Ib. p. 18.

The fur of the grey rabbit was used up to a very late period. ' After
him followed two pert apple-squires ; the one had a murrey cloth gown
on, faced down before with *grey coney*, and laid thick on the sleeves
with lace, which he quaintly bare up, to show his white taffata hose
and black silk stockings.'—1592. A Quip for an Upstart Courtier, p. 83,
ed. Hindley.

198. *balled*, bald. See Specimens of Early English, pt. ii. p. 15,
l. 408.

200. *in good point* = Fr. *embonpoint*, i. e. in good case.

201. *stepe*, M. E. *steap*, does not here mean *sunken*, but *bright*, burning, fiery. Mr. Cockayne has illustrated the use of this word in his
Seinte Marherete, pp. 9, 108 : 'His twa ehnen [semden] *steappre* þene
steorren,' his two eyes seemed *brighter* than stars. So also : 'schininde
and schenre, of ʒimstanes *steapre* then is eni steorre,' shining and clearer,
brighter with gems than is any star ; St. Katherine, l. 1647.

202. *stemed as a forneys of a leed*, shone like the fire under a cauldron.

203. *botes souple*. 'This is part of the description of a smart abbot,
by an anonymous writer of the thirteenth century : "Ocreas habebat in
cruribus quasi innatæ essent, sine plicâ porrectas."—Bod. MS. James,
n. 6, p. 121.'—Tyrwhitt.

205. *for-pyned*, tormented, and hence wasted away ; from *pine*, torment,
pain ; *pined* also signifies wasted, as in the modern verb *pine*. The *for-*
is intensive, as in Eng. *forswear*.

208. *Frere*, friar. The four orders of mendicant friars mentioned in
l. 210 were :—(1) The Dominicans, or friars-preachers, who took up
their abode in Oxford in 1221, known as the Black Friars. (2) The
Franciscans, founded by St. Francis of Assisi in 1209, and known by the
name of Grey Friars. They made their first appearance in England in
1224. (3) The Carmelites, or White Friars. (4) The Augustin (or
Austin) Friars. The friar was popular with the mercantile classes on

account of his varied attainments and experience. 'Who else so welcome at the houses of men to whom scientific skill and information, scanty as they might be, were yet of no inconsiderable service and attraction. He alone of learned and unlearned possessed some knowledge of foreign countries and their productions; he alone was acquainted with the composition and decomposition of bodies, with the art of distillation, with the construction of machinery, and with the use of the laboratory.' See Professor Brewer's Preface to Monumenta Franciscana, p. xlv.

wantown, sometimes written *wantowen*, literally signifies untrained, and hence wild, brisk, lively. *wan-* is a common M. E. prefix, equivalent to our *un-* or *dis-*, as *wanhope*, despair; *wanbeleve*, unbelief; *wantruste*, distrust: *towen* or *town* occurs in M. E. writers for well-behaved, well taught. See Glossary.

merye, pleasant; cf. M. E. *merry wether*, pleasant weather.

209. *limitour* was a begging friar to whom was assigned a certain district or *limit*, within which he was permitted to solicit alms. Hence in later times the verb *limit* signifies to beg.

> 'Ther walketh noon but the *limitour* hymself,
> In undermeles and in morweninges;
> And saith his matins and his holy thinges
> As he goth in his *limitacioun*.'
>
> Wife of Bath's Tale; C. T. 6456.

210. *can* here signifies *knows*. See Glossary.

211. *daliaunce and fair langage*, gossip and flattery. *daliaunce* in M. E. signifies tittle-tattle, gossip. The verb *dally* signifies not only to loiter or idle, but to play, sport; cf. *daly*, a die, plaything; Prov. Eng. *dallybones*, sheep's trotters. See Glossary.

214. *post*, pillar or support. See Gal. ii. 9.

220. *licentiat*. He had a licence from the Pope to give absolution for all sins without being obliged to refer to his bishop. The *curate*, or parish priest, could not grant absolution in all cases, some of which were reserved for the bishop's decision.

224. *pitaunce* here signifies a mess of victuals. It originally signified an extraordinary allowance of victuals given to monastics, in addition to their usual commons, and was afterwards applied to the whole allowance of food for a single person, or to a small portion of anything.

226. *y-shrive = y-shriven*, confessed, *shriven*. The final *n* is dropped.

233. *tipet*, hood, cuculla, or cowl, which seems to have been used as a pocket. 'When the Order [of Franciscans] degenerated, the friar combined with the spiritual functions the occupation of pedlar, huxter, mountebank, and quack doctor.' (Brewer.) In an old poem printed in Professor Brewer's Monumenta Franciscana, we have the following allusion to the dealings of the friars:—

'For thai have noght to lyve by, they wandren here and there,
  And dele with dyvers marche, right as thai pedlers were.
  Thei dele with pynnes and knyves,   ) Ther thai are haunted
  With gyrdles, gloves for wenches and wyves,) till.'

See the chapter on *Bride-knives* in Brand's Popular Antiquities.

236. *rote* is a kind of fiddle or 'crowd,' not a hurdy-gurdy.

237. *yeddynges*, songs embodying some popular tales or romances.

239. *champioun.*

> 'The regent was there that daye a lion,
>   And faught in armes like any *champion*.'

Hardyng, p. 393.

241. *tappestere*, a female tapster. In olden times the retailers of beer,
and for the most part the brewers also, appear to have been females.
Cf. 'the *tapper* of Taystocke,' and 'the *tapsters* potte' (Thyrsytes, ed.
Roxb. Club, p. 68). The *-stere* or *-ster* as a feminine affix (though in
the fourteenth century it is not always or regularly used as such) occurs
in M.E. *brewstere*, *webbestere*; Eng. *spinster*. In *huckster*, *maltster*,
songster, this affix has acquired the meaning of an agent; and in *young-
ster*, *gamester*, *punster*, &c., it implies contempt. See Skeat, Principles
of Etymology, § 238.

242. *lazar*, a leper; from *Lazarus*, in the parable of Dives and
Lazarus; hence *lazarette*, a hospital for lepers, a lazar-house.

246. 'It is not becoming, it may not advance (profit) to deal with
(associate with) such poor people.'

248. *riche*, i.e. rich people.

250. 'Courteous he was, and humble in offering his services.'

252, 253. Between these two lines the Hengwrt MS. inserts the following two lines, which are omitted by the Harl., Corpus, Cambridge,
Petworth, Ellesmere, and Lansdowne MSS.:—

> 'And yaf a certeyn ferme for the graunt
>   Noon of his bretheren cam ther in his haunt.'

Tyrwhitt inserts these two lines; hence a slight difference in the methods
of numbering the lines after this line.

253. *sho.* It has been proposed to read *sou* (a halfpenny, as we now
should say), but the best MSS. do not countenance any such reading;
which would (in fact) give *a false rime.* The friars do not seem to have
been above taking small articles. 'Ever be giving of somewhat, though
it be but a cheese or a piece of bacon, to the holy order of St. Francis,
or to any other of my [Antichrist's] friars, monks, canons, &c. Holy
Church refuseth nothing, but gladly taketh whatsoever cometh.'—Becon's
Acts of Christ and of Antichrist, p. 531; Parker Society. So also 'not
worth his olde *sho*;' C.T. 6290. Cf.

> 'For had a man slayne al his kynne,
>   Go shryve him at a frere,

> And for lesse then *a payre of shone,*
> He wyl assoil him clene and sone.'
>
> Polit. Poems, ed. Wright, i. 266.

254. *In principio.* 'Tyrwhitt, in his note on the line, leaves it doubtful whether these words refer to the beginning of St. John's Gospel, the beginning of Genesis, or some passage in the conclusion of the Mass. (He notes that the words are also used in l. 15169.) The following passage from Tyndale sets the question at rest: " And where he [the priest] should cross himself, to be armed and to make himself strong to bear the cross with Christ, he crosseth himself to drive the cross from him ; and blesseth himself with a cross from the cross.   And if he leave it undone, he thinketh it no small sin, and that God is highly displeased with him, and if any misfortune chance, thinketh it is therefore ; which is also idolatry, and not God's word. . . . Such is the limiter's saying of ' *In principio erat verbum,*' from house to house."—Tyndale, vol. iii. pp. 61, 62, in his Answer to Sir T. More's Dialogue, 1530, edited for the Parker Society, by the Rev. H. Walter, B.D.'—F. J. Furnivall, in Temp. Pref. to the Six-Text edit. of Chaucer, p. 93. Hence the reference is to John i. 1.

256. *purchas* = proceeds of his begging. What he acquired in this way was greater than his *rent* or income.

We find also : 'My purchas is theffect of al my rente ;' C. T. 7033.

> 'To wynnen is always myn entente,
> *My purchace is bettir than my rente.*'
>
> Romaunt of the Rose, l. 6840.

Here the F. original has (l. 11760)—'Miex vaut mes porchas que ma rente.'

257. *as it were right* (Elles. &c.) ; *and pleyen as* (Harl.).

258. *love-dayes.* 'Love-days (*dies amoris*) were days fixed for settling differences by umpire, without having recourse to law or violence.   The ecclesiastics seem generally to have had the principal share in the management of these transactions, which, throughout the Vision of Piers Ploughman, appear to be censured as the means of hindering justice and of enriching the clergy.'—Wright's Vision of Piers Ploughman, vol. ii. p. 535.

> 'Ac now is Religion a rydere, and a rennere aboute,
> A ledere of *love-dayes,*' &c.

Piers Ploughman, A. xi. 208, ed. Skeat ; see also note to P. Pl. ed. Skeat, B. iii. 196. (Mr. Kitchin suggests that these private days of peace are analogous to the *Treuga Dei,* truce of God, so often proclaimed by bishops between A. D. 1000 and 1300.   This truce lasted from 3 p.m. on Saturday to 6 a.m. on Monday.   But all the evidence shews that the *love-day* was a totally different thing.)

260. *cope,* a priest's vestment; a cloak forming a semicircle when laid flat; the *semi-cope* (l. 264) was a short cloak or cape.

270. *a forked berd.* In the time of Edward III *forked beards* were the fashion among the franklins and bourgeoisie, according to the old custom before the Conquest. See Fairholt's Costume in England, fig. 30.

276. *were kept,* should be guarded; so that he should not suffer from *pirates* or privateers. The old subsidy of tonnage and poundage was given to the king for the safeguard and custody of the sea.

'The *see* wel *kept,* it must bee doo for drede.'

Hakluyt, i. 206 [marked 204]; cited from A Libell of English Policie.

for any thing, i.e. for fear of anything; *for* = for fear of. 'Lyons folde up their nailes when they are in their dennes *for* wearing them in the earth and neede not. Eagles draw in their tallants as they sit in their nestes, *for* blunting them there amonge drosse: And I will caste Ancor in these abuses, rest my Barke in the simple roade, *for* grating my wits upon needelesse shelues.'—Gosson, The Schoole of Abuse, p. 54, ed. Arber.

277. *Middleburgh and Orewelle.* '*Middleburgh* is still a well-known port of the island of Walcheren, in the Netherlands, almost immediately opposite Harwich, beside which are the estuaries of the rivers Stoure and *Orwell.* This spot was formerly known as the port of *Orwell* or *Orewelle.*'—Saunders, p. 229.

278. He well knew how to make a profit by the exchange of his crowns in the different money-markets of Europe. *Sheeldes* are French crowns (*écus*), from their having on one side the figure of a shield.

279. *his wit bisette,* employed his knowledge to the best advantage. *bisette* = used, employed. Cf. Piers Plowman, ed. Skeat, B. v. 297:—

'And if thow wite (know) nevere to whiche, ne whom to restitue
  [the goods gotten wrongfully]
Bere it to the bisschop, and bidde hym of his grace,
  Bisette it hymselue, as best is for thi soule.'

281, 282. 'So respectably did he order his bargains and agreements in borrowing money.'

284. *noot* = *ne* + *wot,* know not; so *nost* = *ne* + *wost,* (thou) knowest not.

285. *Clerk,* a university student, a scholar preparing for the priesthood. It also signifies a man of learning, a man in holy orders. See Anstey's Munimenta Academica for much interesting information on early Oxford life and studies.

Oxenford, Oxford, as if the ford of the oxen (A.S. *Oxnaford*); and it has not been proved that this etymology is wrong.

287. *As . . . as.* Some MSS. read *also . . . as* = as . . . as.

290. 'His uppermost short cloak of coarse cloth.'

297. *philosophre* is used in a double sense; it sometimes meant an

alchemist, as in C. T. Group G, l. 1427. The clerk knew philosophy, but he was no alchemist, and so had but little gold.

301. Chaucer often imitates his own lines. He here imitates Troil. iv. 1174—'And pitously gan for the soule preye.'

302. *yaf him.* An allusion to the common practice, at this period, of poor scholars in the Universities, who wandered about the country begging, to raise money to support them in their studies. In a poem in MS. Lansd. 762, the husbandman, complaining of the many burdens he supports in taxes to the court, payments to the church, and charitable contributions of different kinds, enumerates among the latter the alms to scholars :—

> 'Than commeth clerkys of Oxford, and make their mone,
> To her scole-hire they most have money.'

See God spede the Plough, p. 71, in Pierce the Ploughman's Crede, ed. Skeat.

scoleye, to attend school. It is used in the same sense by Lydgate.

307. *Sowninge in,* tending to. Cf. our phrase, 'it *sounds* bad.'

> 'That day (Domesday) sal (shall) na man be excused
> Of nathyng that he wrang (wrong) here used,
> That *sounes in* ille on any manere,
> Of whilk (which) he was never delyverd here.'
>
> Pricke of Conscience, p. 164, l. 6079.

Ascham evidently plays upon the word in the following passage:—'Some siren shall sing him a song sweete in tune, but *sounding in* the ende to his utter destruction.'—The Scholemaster, p. 72, ed. Mayor, 1863; or ed. Arber, p. 74.

310. *at the parvys,* at the *church-porch,* or portico of St. Paul's, where the lawyers were wont to meet for consultation. Cf. *Parvisum,* the church-porch of St. Mary's, Oxford, where the examinations used to be held. See Warton, ed. 1871, ii. 377; Todd, Illustrations, p. 245; Saunders, p. 164.

320. *Purchasing,* conveyancing; *infect,* invalid. 'The learned Sergeant was clever enough to untie any entail, and pass the property as estate in fee simple.'—W. H. H. Kelke, in N. and Q. 5 S. vi. 487.

323, 324. 'He was well acquainted with all the legal cases and decisions (or decrees) which had been ruled in the courts of law since the time of William the Conqueror.' The Harl. MS. reads, *of King Will were falle* (=*were fallen,* had befallen or occurred).

326. *pinche at,* find fault with. Its original meaning was to act in a niggardly manner (as in the modern verb *pinch*), to deny oneself common necessaries; from which sprang a secondary meaning, to deny or refuse the courtesy or praise due to another, and hence to blame. Palsgrave uses the phrase, 'I *pynche courtaysye* (as one that doth that is nyce of condyscions, *Ie fays le nyce*).'

328. *medlee cote*, a coat of mixed stuff or colour.

329. *Gird*, which is the reading in the Harl. MS., is the same as *girt*, girded. The past tense would be *girde*.

ceint of silk, &c., a girdle of silk with small ornaments. The *barres* were called *cloux* in French, and were the usual ornaments of a girdle (Lat. *clavus*). They were perforated to allow the tongue of the buckle to pass through them. 'Originally they were attached transversely to the wide tissue of which the girdle was formed, but subsequently were round or square, or fashioned like the heads of lions, and similar devices, the name of *barre* being still retained, though improperly.'—Way, in Promptorium Parvulorum; s.v. *barre*.

331. Fortescue describes a franklin to be a *pater familias—magnis ditatus possessionibus*. The following extract from John Russell's Boke of Nurture (p. 170, ed. Furnivall) gives us a good idea of a franklin's feast :—

'A Franklen may make a feste Improberabille, ⎱ bakoun serued with
brawne with mustard is concordable, ⎰　 pesoun,
Beef or motoun stewed seruysable, ⎱ convenyent for þe se-
Boyled Chykoun or capoun agreable, ⎰　 soun ;

Rosted goose & pygge fulle profitable, ⎱ whenne eggis &
Capoun / Bakemete, or Custade Costable, ⎰　 crayme be gesoun
　　　　　　　　　　　　　　　　　　　 (scarce).

þerfore stuffe of household is behoveable, ⎱ for the second course
Mortrowes or Iusselle ar delectable ⎰　 by resoun.
Thanne veel, lambe, kyd, or cony, ⎱ bakemetes or dow-
Chykoun or pigeoun rosted tendurly, ⎰　 cettes with alle.
þenne followynge frytowrs, & a leche lovely ; ⎱ to serue with bothe
Suche seruyse in sesoun is fulle semely ⎰　 chambur and halle.
Thenne appuls & peris with spices delicately ⎱ with bred and chese
Aftur þe terme of þe yere fulle deynteithly, ⎰　 to calle.
Spised cakes and wafurs worthily, ⎱ plese welle bothe gret
With bragot & methe, þus men may meryly ⎰　 & smalle.'

334. *a sop in wyn.* See note to l. 147.

340. 'St. *Julian* was eminent for providing his votaries with good lodgings and accommodation of all sorts. [See Chambers' Book of Days, ii. 388.] In the title of his legend, Bodl. MS. 1596, fol. 4, he is called "St. Julian the gode herberjour" (St. Julian the good harbourer). It ends thus :—

"Therfore yet to this day thei that over lond wende (go),
　Thei biddeth (pray) Seint Julian anon that gode herborw (lodging)
　　　he hem sende,
　And Seint Julianes Paternoster ofte seggeth (say) also
　For his fader soule and his moderes, that he hem bringe therto."
Of the virtue of St. Julian's Paternoster see the Decameron, Day 2,

nov. 2.'—Tyrwhitt. His day is Jan. 9. See also Gesta Romanorum, ed. Swan; tale 18.

342. *envyned*, stored with wine. 'Cotgrave has preserved the French word *enviné* in the same sense.'—Tyrwhitt.

343. *bake mete = baked meat;* the old past participle of *bake* was *baken*. Baked meats = meats baked in *coffins* (pies).

345. The verb *snewed* is usually explained as a metaphor from snowing; but the M. E. *snewe*, like the Prov. Eng. *snie* or *snive*, also signifies *to abound, swarm.* Camb. MS. reads 'It snowede in his mouth of mete and drynk.' Cf. 'He was with yiftes [presents] all *bisnewed*;' Gower, C. A. iii. 51.

349. *mewe*. The *mewe* was the place where the hawks were kept while moulting; it was afterwards applied to the *coop* wherein fowl were fattened, and lastly to a place of confinement or secrecy.

350. *stewe*, fish-pond. 'To insure a supply of fish, stew-ponds were attached to the manors, and few monasteries were without them; the moat around the castle was often converted into a fish-pond, and well stored with luce, carp, or tench.'—Our English Home, p. 65.

351. *Wo was his cook*, woeful or sad was his cook. We only use *wo* or *woe* as a substantive. Cf. 'Who was *woo* but Olyvere then.'—Sowdone of Babyloyne, l. 1271. 'I am *woe* for 't;' Tempest, v. 1. 139. Rob. of Brunne (Handling Synne, 7250) says that a rich man's cook 'may no day Greythe hym hys mete to pay.'

351, 352. *sauce—Poynaunt* is like the modern phrase *sauce piquant*. 'Our forefathers were great lovers of "piquant sauce." They made it of expensive condiments and rare spices. . . In the statute of Henry III to restrain high living, the use of sauce is prohibited unless it could be procured at a very moderate cost.'—Our English Home, p. 62.

353. *table dormant*. 'Previous to the fourteenth century a pair of common wooden trestles and a rough plank was deemed a table sufficient for the great hall. . . . . Tables, with a board attached to a frame, were introduced about the time of Chaucer, and, from remaining in the hall, were regarded as indications of a ready hospitality.'—Our English Home, p. 29.

355. *sessiouns*. At the Sessions of the Peace. Cf. '*At Sessions* and at Sises we bare the stroke and swaye.'—Higgins's Mirrour for Magistrates, ed. 1571, p. 2.

357. *anlas* or *anelace*. Speght defines this word as a *falchion*, or wood-knife. It was, however, a short two-edged knife or dagger usually worn at the girdle, broad at the hilt and tapering to a point. See Murray's New Eng. Dictionary; Liber Albus, p. 75; Knight, Pict. Hist. of England, i. 872.

gipser was properly a pouch or budget used in hawking, &c., but commonly worn by the merchant, or with any secular attire.—(Way.)

358. *Heng* (or *Hing* in some MSS.), the past tense of *hongen* or *hangen*, to hang.

   morne mylk = morning milk.

359. *schirreve*, the *reve* of a *shire*, governor of a county; our modern word *sheriff*.

   countour, O. Fr. *comptour*, an accountant, a person who audited accounts or received money in charge, &c.; ranked with pleaders in Riley's Memorials of London, p. 58. It occurs in Rob. of Gloucester, l. 11153. In the Book of the Duch. 435, it simply means 'accountant.'

360. *vavasour*, or *vavaser*, originally a sub-vassal or tenant of a vassal or tenant of the king's, one who held his lands in fealty. Tyrwhitt says 'it should be understood to mean the whole class of middling land-holders.' See Lacroix, Military Life of Middle Ages, p. 9. Spelt *favasour* in King Alisaunder, ed. Weber, l. 3827.

361. *Haberdassher*. Haberdashers were of two kinds: haberdashers of small wares—sellers of needles, tapes, buttons, &c.; and haberdashers of hats.

362. *Webbe*, properly a male weaver; *webstere* was the female weaver, but there appears to have been some confusion in the use of the suffixes *-e* and *-stere* (see Piers Plowman, ed. Skeat, B. v. 215), 'mi *wyf* was a *webbe*.'

363. *liveree*, livery. Under the term 'livery' was included whatever was dispensed (*delivered*) by the lord to his officials or domestics annually or at certain seasons, whether money, victuals, or garments. The term chiefly denoted external marks of distinction, such as the *roba estivalis* and *hiemalis*, given to the officers and retainers of the court, as appears by the Wardrobe Book, 28 Edw. I, p. 310, and the Household Ordinances. The practice of distributing such tokens of general adherence to the service or interests of the individual who granted them, for the maintenance of any private quarrel, was carried to an injurious extent during the reigns of Edward III and Richard II, and was forbidden by several statutes, which allowed liveries to be borne only by menials, or the members of guilds. (See Stat. of Realm, ii. pp. 3, 74, 93, 156, 167.) The '*liverée des chaperons*,' often mentioned in these documents, was a hood or tippet, which being of a colour strongly contrasted to that of the garment, was a kind of livery much in fashion, and well adapted to serve as a distinctive mark. This, in later times, assumed the form of a round cap, to which was appended the long *liripipium*, which might be rolled around the head, but more commonly was worn hanging over the arm; and vestiges of it may still be traced in the dress of civic liverymen. The Stat. 7 Hen. IV expressly permits the adoption of such distinctive dress by fraternities and '*les gentz de mestere*,' the trades of the cities of the realm, being ordained

with good intent; and to this prevalent usage Chaucer alludes when he describes five artificers of various callings, who joined the pilgrimage, clothed all '*in o lyveré of a solempne and greet fraternité.*' (All from Way, note to Prompt. Parv., p. 308.)

And they were clothed alle (Elles. &c.); *Weren with us eeke clothed* (Harl.).

365. *apyked* signifies cleaned, trimmed. Bullinger, in his fortieth sermon on the Apocalypse, inveighing against the Roman clergy, says, 'They be commed, and *piked*, and very finely apparelled.'

366. *y-chaped*, having *chapes* (i. e. plates or *caps* of metal at the point of the sheath or scabbard). Tradesmen and mechanics were prohibited from using knives adorned with silver, gold, or precious stones. So that Chaucer's pilgrims were of a superior estate, as is indicated in l. 369.

370. *deys, dese,* or *dais* (Fr. *deis* or *daix,* whence Low Lat. *dasium*), is used to denote the raised platform which was always found at the upper end of a hall, the table or seat of distinction placed thereon; it also meant the tester (Lat. *discus*) with hanging drapery, called also *seler*, cloth of estate, and in French *ciel,* suspended over it.

371. *that he can,* that he knows; *as he couthe,* as he knew how. See l. 390.

372. *shaply,* adapted, fit. It sometimes signifies comely, of good *shape* or form.

373. 'For they had sufficient property and income' (to entitle them to undertake the office of alderman).

377. *And gon to vigilyes al bifore.* 'It was the manner in times past, upon festival evens, called *vigiliæ,* for parishioners to meet in their church-houses, or church-yards, and there to have a drinking-fit for the time. Here they used to end many quarrels betwixt neighbour and neighbour. Hither came the wives in comely manner, and they which were of the better sort had their mantles carried with them, as well for show as to keep them from cold at table.'—Speght.

379. *for the nones=for the nonce;* this expression, if grammatically written, would be *for then once,* M. E. *for þan anes,* for the once, i. e. for the occasion; where the adv. *anes* (orig. a gen. form) is used as if it were a sb. in the dat. case. Such phrases as *at the nale, at the noke*=at the ale, at the oak, contain also a remnant of the dative case (*then*) of the article: *for then* or *for þan* was originally *for þam.* Cf. M. E. *atte=atten =at þan=at þam.*

381. *poudre-marchaunt tart* is a sharp (tart) kind of flavouring powder, twice mentioned in Household Ordinances and Receipts (Soc. Antiq. 1790) at pp. 425, 434: 'Do therto *pouder marchant,*' and 'do thi flessh therto, and gode herbes and *poudre marchaunt,* and let hit well stew.'— Notes and Queries, Fourth Series, iii. 180.

In the Boke of Nurture (Harl. MS. 4011), l. 533, we read that
'Mustard is meete for brawne, beef, or powdred motoun;
Verdius to boyled capoun, veel, chiken, or bakoun;

.   .   .   .   .   .

Roost beeff and goos with garlek, vinegre, or pepur; . . .
Gynger sawce to lambe, to kyd, pigge, or fawn; . . .
To feysand (pheasant), partriche, or cony, mustard with the sugure.'

'*Tart* and *galingale*, which Chaucer, pre-eminentest, economioniseth above all junquetries or confectionaries whatsoever.'—Nash's Lenten Stuff, p. 36, ed. Hindley. *galyngale* is the root of sweet cyperus. Harman (ed. Strother) notices three varieties: *Cyperus rotundus, Galanga major, Galanga minor*; Babees Book, ed. Furnivall, pp. 152, 216. See Beaumont and Fletcher's Bloody Brother, ii. 2 (near the end); Marco Polo, ed. Yule, ii. 181; Prompt. Parv., p. 185, note 4; and Rogers, Hist. of Agriculture and Prices, i. 629.

382. *London ale.* London ale was famous as early as the time of Henry III, and much higher priced than any other ale; cf. C. T. 3142.

384. *mortreux* or *mortrewes.* There were two kinds of 'mortrews,' '*mortrewes de chare*' and '*mortrewes of fysshe.*' The first was a kind of soup in which chickens, fresh pork, crumbs of bread, yolks of eggs, and saffron formed the chief ingredients; the second kind was a soup containing the roe (or milt) and liver of fish, bread, pepper, ale. The ingredients were first stamped or brayed in a *mortar*, whence it probably derived its name. Lord Bacon (Nat. Hist. i. 48) speaks of 'a *mortresse* made with the brawne of capons stamped and strained.' See Babees Book, pp. 151, 170, 172.

386. *mormal*, a cancer or gangrene. Ben Jonson, in imitation of this passage, has described a cook with an 'old *mortmal* on his skin;' Sad Shepherd, act ii. sc. 2. Palsgrave gives—'*Mormall*, a sore.' In MS. Oo. i. 20, last leaf, in the Camb. Univ. Library, are notices of remedies 'Por la maladie que est apele *malum mortuum.*' It says that it comes from melancholy, and shows a broad hard scurf or crust. Lydgate speaks of 'Goutes, *mormalles*, horrible to the sight;' Fall of Princes, bk. vii. c. 10.

388. *by weste = westward.* A good old expression, which was once very common as late as the 16th century. Cf.

'And made hym kyng agayne *by north* and *south.*'
Hardyng's Chronicle, p. 69.

389. Dartmouth was once a very considerable port; see Essays on Chaucer, p. 456.

390. *rouncy*, a common hackney horse, a nag. Cf. *Rozinante.* '*Rocin-ante*—significativo de lo que habia sido cuando fué *rocin, antes* de lo que ahora era.'—Don Quijote, cap. 1. 'From *Rozin*, a drudge-horse, and

ante, before.'—Jarvis's note. 'A *Runcina* cost £5 10s. at Burton in 1262.' (Rogers.)

391. *a gowne of falding*, a gown (robe) of coarse cloth. The term *falding* signifies 'a kind of frieze or rough-napped cloth,' which was probably 'supplied from the North of Europe, and identical with the woollen wrappers of which Hermoldus speaks, "*quos nos appellamus Faldones*."'—Way. '*Falding* was a coarse serge cloth, very rough and durable,' &c.; Essays on Chaucer, p. 458.

394. *the hote somer*. 'Perhaps this is a reference to the summer of the year 1351, which was long remembered as the dry and hot summer.' —Wright. There was another such summer in 1370, much nearer the date of this Prologue.

396–398. 'Very many a draught of wine had he drawn (stolen away or carried off from Bordeaux, cask and all) while the chapman (merchant or supercargo to whom the wine belonged) was asleep; for he paid no regard to any conscientious scruples.'

399. *hyer hond*, upper hand.

400. 'He sent them home to wherever they came from *by water*,' i.e. he made them 'walk the plank,' as it used to be called; or, in plain English, threw them overboard, to sink or swim. However cruel this may seem now, it was probably a common practice. 'This battle (the sea-fight off Sluys) was very murderous and horrible. Combats at sea are more destructive and obstinate than upon land;' Froissart's Chron. bk. i. c. 50.

'Fone (*few*) left þai oliue (*alive*), bot did tham to lepe (*made them leap overboard*) . . .

'To wade war tho wrecches casten in the brim,
  The kaitefs come out of France at lere tham to swim;'

i.e. those wretches were cast into the surf to wade (if they could); the caitiffs came out of France, to teach themselves to swim.—Minot's Poems, ed. Hall, p. 16. And see Essays on Chaucer, p. 460.

403. *lodemenage*, pilotage. A pilot was called a *lodesman*; see Way's note in Prompt. Parv. p. 310; Riley's Memorials of London, p. 655; Chaucer's Legend of Good Women, 1486; Furnivall's Temporary Preface, p. 98; Essays on Chaucer, pp. 480, 481, 484. At a later period *lodesman* meant any guide; Monk of Evesham, ed. Arber, p. 106.

409. *cryke*, creek, harbour, port.

410. We find actual mention of a vessel called the *Mandelayne* belonging to the port of Dartmouth, in the years 1379 and 1386; see Essays on Chaucer, p. 484. See also N. & Q. 6 S. xii. 47.

411. *With us ther was* (Elles. &c.); *Ther was also* (Harl.).

414. *astronomye*, (really) astrology. See Saunders on Chaucer, p. 175.

415, 416. *kepte*, watched. The *houres* are the astrological hours. He carefully watched for a favourable star in the ascendant. 'A great portion of the medical science of the middle ages depended upon astrological and other superstitious observances.'—Wright. Cf. Nonne Preestes Tale, l. 135.

416. *magik naturel*. Chaucer alludes to the same practices in the House of Fame, bk. iii. ll. 169–180:—

> 'Ther saugh I pleyen jugelours
>
> . . . .
>
> And clerkes eek, which conne wel
> Al this *magyke naturel*,
> That craftely doon her ententes
> To make, *in certeyn ascendentes*,
> Images, lo! through which magyke,
> To make a man ben hool or syke.'

417. The *ascendent* is the point of the zodiacal circle which happens to be ascending above the horizon at a given moment, such as the moment of birth. Upon it depended the drawing out of a man's horoscope, which represented the aspect of the heavens at some given critical moment. The moment, in the present case, is that for making images. It was believed that images of men and animals could be made of certain substances and *at certain times,* and could be so treated as to cause good or evil to a patient, by means of magical and planetary influences. See Cornelius Agrippa, De Occulta Philosophia, lib. ii. capp. 35–47. Cf. Horace, *Sat.* i. 8. 30; Ovid, *Heroid.* vi. 91. In Norton's Ordinall, printed in Ashmole's Theatrum Chemicum, p. 60, it is said that astrologers

> 'With Astrologie joyne Elements also,
> To *fortune*[n] their Workings as theie goe;' &c.

Cf. Notes to Man of Law's Tale, 312; Squire's Tale, 352.

420. These are the *four* elementary qualities, hot, cold, dry, moist. Milton, Par. Lost, ii. 898. Diseases were supposed to be caused by an undue excess of some one quality.

424. *his bote*, his remedy.

426. *drogges*. MS. Harl. *dragges;* the rest *drogges, drugges*, drugs. The Promptorium Parvulorum has *dragge*, dragetum; and Cotgrave defines *dragée* (the French form of the word *dragge*) as 'a kind of digestive powder prescribed unto weak stomachs after meat, and hence any jonkets, comfits, or sweetmeats served in the last course for stomach-closers.' Old English writers occasionally employ *dragy* in the sense of a small comfit, and *dragoir, dragenall*, a vessel for *dragges*.

429–434. Read *th'oldë*. 'The authors mentioned here wrote the chief medical text-books of the middle ages. Rufus was a Greek physician

of Ephesus, of the age of Trajan; Haly, Serapion, and Avicen were
Arabian physicians and astronomers of the eleventh century; Rhasis was
a Spanish Arab of the tenth century; and Averroes was a Moorish
scholar who flourished in Morocco in the twelfth century. Johannes
Damascenus was also an Arabian physician, but of a much earlier date
(probably of the ninth century); Constanti[n]us Afer, a native of
Carthage, and afterwards a monk of Monte Cassino, was one of the
founders of the school of Salerno—he lived at the end of the eleventh
century; Bernardus Gordonius, professor of medicine at Montpellier,
appears to have been Chaucer's contemporary; John Gatisden was a distinguished physician of Oxford in the earlier half of the fourteenth
century; Gilbertyn is supposed by Warton to be the celebrated Gilbertus
Anglicus. The names of Hippocrates and Galen were, in the middle
ages, always (or nearly always) spelt Ypocras and Galienus.'—Wright.
Æsculapius, god of medicine, was fabled to be the son of Apollo.
Dioscorides was a Greek physician of the second century. Cf. Book of
the Duchess, 572. Cf. 'Ippocrate, Avicenna, e Galieno, Averrois,' &c.;
Dante, *Inf.* iv. 143. And see the long note in Warton, 1871, ii. 368.

439. 'In cloth of a blood-red colour and of a blueish-grey.' Cf. 'robes
de *pers*,' Rom. de la Rose, 9116.

> 'And where ben my gownes of *scarlet*,
>   *Sangweyn, murrey,* and *blewes* sadde and light,
>   *Grenes* also, and the *faire* vyolet,
>   Hors and harneys, fresshe and lusty in sight?'
>   Occleve, De Reg. Principum, p. 26.

440. *taffata* (or *taffety*), a sort of thin silk.

sendal (or *cendal*), a kind of rich thin silk used for lining, very highly
esteemed. Thynne says—'a thynne stuffe lyke sarcenett.' Palsgrave
however has '*cendell*, thynne lynnen, *sendal*.' See Piers Plowman, B. vi.
11; Marco Polo, ed. Yule (see the index).

441. *esy of dispence*, moderate in his expenditure.

442. *wan in pestilence*, acquired during the pestilence. This is an
allusion to the great pestilence of the years 1348, 1349; or to the later
pestilences in 1362, 1369, and 1376. See Introd. to Piers Plowman
(Clarendon Press Series); table at end of Preface.

443. *For* = because, seeing that. It was supposed that *aurum potabile*
was a remedy in some cases. '*Aurum potabile* est auri oleum vel in
liquorem redactum;' Ducange. The actual reference is, probably, to
Les Remonstrances de Nature, by Jean de Meun, ll. 979, 980, &c.;
'C'est le fin et bon or potable, L'humide radical notable; C'est souve-
raine medicine;' and the author goes on to refer us to Ecclus. xxxviii. 4—
'The Lord hath created medicines out of the earth; and he that is wise
will not abhor them.' Hence the Doctor would not abhor gold. And
further—'C'est medicine *cordiale*;' ib. 1029.

445. *of bisyde* &c., from (a place) near Bath.

446. 'But she was somewhat deaf, and that was her misfortune.'

447. *cloth-makyng.* 'The West of England, and especially the neigh-bourhood of Bath, from which the "good wif" came, was celebrated, till a comparatively recent period, as the district of cloth-making. Ypres and Ghent were the great clothing-marts on the Continent.'—Wright. 'Edward the third brought clothing first into this Island, transporting some families of artificers from *Gaunt* hither.'—Burton's Anat. of Mel. p. 51.

450. *to the offring.* We have here an allusion to the offering on Relic-Sunday, when the congregation went up to the altar in succession to kiss the relics. 'But the relics we must kiss and offer unto, especially on Relic-Sunday.'—Book of Homilies.

453. *coverchief (keverchef, or kerchere, kerché).* The *kerchief*, or covering for the head, was, until the fourteenth century, almost an indispensable portion of female attire.

> 'Upon hir hed a *kerché* of Valence.'
>
> Lydgate's Minor Poems, p. 47.

ful fyne of ground, of a very fine texture. See Pierce the Ploughman's Crede, l. 230, which means 'it was of fine enough texture to take dye in grain.'

454. *ten pound.* 'Ornaments of golden net-work were worn at this time at the side of the face, thickest just beside the eyes, which formed, in reality, part of the caul.'—Pierce the Ploughman's Crede, note to l. 84, ed. Skeat. Cf. the following amusing description of the head-dress of Elizabethan dames from 'The Anatomy of Abuses,' 1585: 'They have also other ornamentes besides these to furnishe forthe their ingenious heades, whiche they call (as I remember) cawles, made netwise, to the ende, as I think, that the clothe of golde, clothe of silver, or els tinsell, (for that is the worst wherewith their heads are covered and attired withall underneath their caules), may the better appeare, and shew itselfe in the bravest maner; so that a man that seeth them (their heades glister and shine in such sorte) would thinke them to have golden heades . . . Then have they *petticoates* (see Prol., ll. 455, 472) of the beste clothe that can be made. And sometimes they are not of clothe neither, for that is thought too base, but of scarlet, grograine, taffatie, silke and such like, fringed about the skirtes, with silke fringe, of chaungeable colour. But whiche is more vayne, of whatsoever their petticoates be, yet must they have kirtles (for so they call them) either of silke, velvett, grograine, taffatie, satten or scarlet, bordered with gardes, lace, fringes, and I cannot tell what besides . . . Their nether-stockes, in like maner, are either of silke, iearnsey, worsted, crewell, or, at least, of as fine yearne, thread or cloth as is possible to be hadde; yea, they are not ashamed to weare *hoase* all *kinde of chaungeable colours*, as green, red,

white, russet, tawny and elswhat.'—pp. 63, 70, 72—(or ed. Furnivall, pp. 69, 74, 76). And see Fairholt's Costume, figs. 125, 129, 130, 151.

457. *moiste*, soft—not 'as hard as old boots.'

460. *chirche-dore.* The priest married the couple at the church-porch, and immediately afterwards proceeded to the altar to celebrate mass, at which the newly-married persons communicated. See Warton, Hist. E. Poetry, 1871, ii. 366, note 1; Anglia, vi. 106; cf. C. T. 5588.

461. *Withouten* = besides. *Other campaignie*, other lovers. This expression (copied from Le Rom. de la Rose, l. 12985—'autre companie') makes it quite certain that the character of the Wife of Bath is copied, in some respects, from that of *La Vieille* in the Roman de la Rose.

465. *Boloigne.* Cf. 'I will have you swear by our dear Lady of Boulogne;' Gammer Gurton's Needle, Act 2, sc. 2. An image of the virgin was preserved at Boulogne. See Heylin's Survey of France, p. 193, ed. 1656 (quoted in the above, ed. Hazlitt).

466. *In Galice* (Galicia), at the shrine of St. James of Compostella, a famous resort of pilgrims in the fourteenth and fifteenth centuries. As the legend goes, the body of St. James the Apostle was supposed to have been carried in a ship without a rudder to Galicia, and preserved at Compostella. See Piers Plowman, A. iv. 109, 110, and note to B. Prol. 47.

Coloigne. At Cologne, where the bones of the Three Kings or Wise Men of the East, *Gaspar, Melchior,* and *Balthazar,* are said to be preserved. See Coryat's Crudities; Chambers, Book of Days, ii. 751.

468. *Gat-tothed* = gat-toothed, meaning gap-toothed, having teeth wide apart or separated from one another. A *gat* is an opening, and is allied to E. *gate.* Cf. Icel. *gat,* a hole, as in *skrár-gat,* a key-hole; O. Sax. *gat,* an opening, as in *nádlon gat,* the eye of a needle. Hexham's Dutch Dict. has: '*een Gat,* a hole; *het Gat van een Net,* the hole of a net; also *een Gat,* a dore, or a gate.' The Friesic *gat,* Dan. *gat,* and Norweg. *gat* all mean a hole, or a gap. Very similar is the use of the Shropshire *glat,* a gap in a hedge, also a gap in the mouth caused by loss of teeth. Example: 'Dick, yo' bin a flirt; I thought yo' wun (*were*) gwein to marry the cook at the paas'n's. Aye, but 'er 'd gotten too many *glats* i' the mouth for me;' Miss Jackson's Shropshire Word-book. Speght reads *cat-tothed. Gat-toothed* has also been explained as *goat-toothed,* lascivious, but the word *goat* appears as *goot* in Chaucer. 'Famine—the *gap-toothed* elf;' Golding's Ovid, b. 8; leaf 105. Holland uses it for *tut-mouthed* = having the lower jaw projecting beyond the upper. See Trench's 'On some Deficiencies in our Eng. Dictionaries,' p. 42. It occurs again, C. T. 6185.

472. *foot-mantel.* Tyrwhitt supposes this to be a sort of *riding-petticoat,* such as is now used by market-women. It is clearly shewn, as a blue

outer skirt, in the drawing in the Ellesmere MS. At a later time it was called a *safe-guard*, and its use was to keep the gown clean.

475. *remedyes.* An allusion to the title and subject of Ovid's book, Remedia Amoris.

476. *the olde daunce*, the old game, or custom. Cotgrave has the French phrase, '*Elle sçait asses de la vieille danse.*' Cf. *wrechit dans*, Launcelot of the Laik, l. 1321, and *loves daunce*, Chaucer (Aldine), vol. iv. p. 198, l. 4. The phrase is borrowed from Le Roman de la Rose, l. 3946—'Qu'el scet toute la vielle dance;' E. version, l. 4300—'For she knew alle the olde daunce.' It occurs again; Troil. iii. 695.

478. *Persoun of a toun*, the parson or parish priest. Chaucer, in his description of the parson, contrasts the piety and industry of the secular clergy with the wickedness and laziness of the religious orders or monks. See Dryden's 'Character of a Good Parson.'

486. 'He was very loath to excommunicate those who failed to pay the tithes that were due to him.' 'Refusal to pay tithes was punishable with the lesser excommunication;' Bell.

489. *offring*, the voluntary contributions of his parishioners.

substaunce, income derived from his benefice.

492. *lafte not*, left not, ceased not.

502. *lewed*, unlearned, ignorant. *Lewed* or *lewd* originally signified the people, laity, as opposed to the clergy; the modern sense of the word is not common in Middle English.

503–504. St. John Chrysostom also saith, 'It is a great shame for priests, when laymen be found faithfuller and more righteous than they.' —Becon's Invective against Swearing, p. 336.

507. *to hyre.* The parson did not leave his parish duties to be performed by a strange curate, that he might have leisure to seek a chantry in St. Paul's. See Piers Plowman, B-text, Prol. l. 83: and cf. the following:—

> 'Fulle many men knowe I that yane and gape
> After some fatte and riche benefice;
> Chirche ne prebende unnethe hem may escape,
> But they as blive it hent up and trice.

> Adayes now, my sone, as men may see,
> O (one) chirche to o man may nat suffise,
> But algate he mote have pluralitee,
> Elles he kan not lyve[n] in no wise.
> Ententyfly he kepeth his servise
> In court, ther his labour shall not moule,
> But to his cure loketh he fulle foule.

> Though that his chauncelle roof be alle to-torne,
> And on hye awtere reyne or snewe,

> He rekkethe not, the cost may be forborne
> Cristes hous to repaire or make newe ;
> And thoughe ther be fulle many a vicious hewe
> Undir his cure, he takethe of it no kepe :
> He rekkethe never how rusty ben his shepe.'
>
> Occleve, De Reg. Principium, pp. 51, 52.

510. *chaunterie*, chantry, an endowment for the payment of a priest to sing mass agreeably to the appointment of the founder.

517. *daungerous*, not affable, difficult to approach. *digne*, full of dignity ; hence, repellent. 'She was as *digne* as water in a ditch ;' C. T. 3962 ; because stagnant water keeps people at a distance.

519. *fairnesse*, i. e. by leading a fair or good life. The Harleian MS. has *clennesse*, that is, a life of purity.

525. *wayted after*, looked for. See line 571. Cf. Knightes Tale, line 364.

526. *spyced conscience* ; so also in C. T. 6017. *Spiced* here seems to signify, says Tyrwhitt, nice, scrupulous. It occurs in the Mad Lover, act iii. sc. 1, by Beaumont and Fletcher. When Cleanthe offers a purse, the priestess says,—

> 'Fy ! no corruption . . . .
>   *Cle.* Take it, it is yours ;
> Be not so *spiced ;* 'tis good gold ;
> And goodness is no gall to th' conscience.'

'Under pretence of *spiced* holinesse.'—Tract dated 1594, ap. Todd's Illustrations of Gower, p. 380.

534. *though him gamed or smerte*, though it was pleasant or unpleasant to him.

541. *mere.* People of quality would not ride upon a mare.

548. *the ram.* This was the usual prize at wrestling-matches. See Ch. II., note to Group B, l. 1931.

549. *a thikke knarre*, a thickly knotted (fellow), i.e. a muscular fellow.

550. *of harre*, off its hinges, lit. hinge. 'I horle at the notes, and heve hem al of herre ;' Poem on Singing, in Reliq. Antiquæ, ii. 292. Gower has *out of herre*, off its hinges, out of use, out of joint ; Conf. Amant. bk. ii, ed. Pauli, i. 259 ; bk. iii, i. 318.

553. Todd cites from Lilly's *Midas*—' How, sir, will you be trimmed ? Will you have your beard like a *spade* or a bodkin ?'—Illust. of Gower, p. 258.

559. *forneys.* 'Why, asks Mr. Earle, should Chaucer so readily fall on the simile of a *furnace* ? What, in the uses of the time, made it come so ready to hand? The weald of Kent was then, like our "black country" now, a great smelting district, its wood answering to our coal ; and Chaucer was Knight of the Shire, or M.P. for Kent.'—Temporary Preface to the Six-Text edition of Chaucer's Canterbury Tales, p. 99.

560. *golyardeys,* one who gains his living by following rich men's tables, and telling tales and making sport for the guests. Tyrwhitt says, 'This jovial sect seems to have been so called from *Golias,* the real or assumed name of a man of wit, towards the end of the twelfth century, who wrote the Apocalypsis Goliæ, and other pieces in burlesque Latin rhymes, some of which have been falsely attributed to Walter Map. In several authors of the thirteenth century, quoted by Du Cange, the *goliardi* are classed with the *joculatores et buffones.*' But Mr. Skeat thinks that *Golias* is the sole invention of Walter Map, the probable author of the 'Golias' poems. See Piers Plowman, ed. Skeat, p. 101 (Clarendon Press Series); Morley's Eng. Writers, 1866, i. 586.

562. 'Besides the usual payment in money for grinding corn, millers are always allowed what is called "toll," amounting to 4 lbs. out of every sack of flour.'—Bell.

563. *a thombe of gold.* 'An explanation of this proverb is given on the authority of Mr. Constable, the Royal Academician, by Mr. Yarrell in his History of British Fishes, who says, when speaking of the Bullhead or *Miller's Thumb,* "The head of the fish is smooth, broad, and rounded, and is said to resemble exactly the form of the thumb of a miller, as produced by a peculiar and constant action of the muscles in the exercise of a particular and most important part of his occupation. It is well known that all the science and tact of a miller is directed so to regulate the machinery of his mill that the meal produced shall be of the most valuable description that the operation of grinding will permit, when performed under the most advantageous circumstances. His profit or his loss, even his fortune or his ruin, depend upon the exact adjustment of all the various parts of the machinery in operation. The miller's ear is constantly directed to the note made by the running-stone in its circular course over the bed-stone, the exact parallelism of their two surfaces, indicated by a particular sound, being a matter of the first consequence; and his hand is as constantly placed under the meal-spout, to ascertain by actual contact the character and qualities of the meal produced. The thumb, by a particular movement, spreads the sample over the fingers; the thumb is the gauge of the value of the produce, and hence have arisen the sayings of *worth a miller's thumb,* and *an honest miller hath a golden thumb,* in reference to the amount of the profit that is the reward of his skill. By this incessant action of the miller's thumb, a peculiarity in its form is produced, which is said to resemble exactly the shape of the head of the fish, constantly found in the mill-stream, and has obtained for it the name of the Miller's Thumb, which occurs in the comedy of Wit at several Weapons by Beaumont and Fletcher, act v. sc. 1; and also in Merrett's Pinax. Although the improved machinery of the present time has diminished the necessity for the miller's skill in the mechanical department, the thumb is still

constantly resorted to as the best test for the quality of flour." After all, is not the old proverb satirical, inferring that all millers who *have not golden* thumbs are rogues—argal, as Shakspeare says, that all millers are rogues?' See Notes and Queries, Fourth Series, iii. May 1, 1869, p. 407. The latter is Tyrwhitt's explanation. Cf.

> 'When millers toll not with a golden thumbe.'
> > Gascoigne's Steel Glass, l. 1080.

Ray's Proverbs give us—'An honest miller has a golden thumb;' ed. 1768, p. 136. Brand, in his Pop. Antiquities, ed. Ellis, iii. 387, quotes from an old play—'Oh the mooter-dish, *the miller's thumbe!*'

567. *Maunciple* or *manciple*, an officer who had the care of purchasing provisions for a college, an inn of court, &c. (Still in use.)

570. *took by taille*, took on credit. Cf. Piers Plowman, ed. Wright, vol. i. p. 68, and ed. Skeat (Clarendon Press Series), B. iv. 58:—

> 'And (he) bereth awey my whete,
> And taketh me but a *taille*
> For ten quarters of otes.'

572. *ay biforn*, ever before (others).

584. *al a*, a whole. Cf. '*al a* summer's day' (Milton, P. L. i. 449).

586. *hir aller cappe*, the caps of them all. *Hir aller* = eorum omnium. '*To sette*' a man's '*cappe*' is to overreach him, to cheat him, or to befool him. Cf. C. T. 3145.

587. *Reve.* See Mr. Thorold Rogers' capital sketch of Robert Oldman, the Cuxham bailiff, a serf of the manor (as reeves always were), in his Agriculture and Prices in England, i. 506–510.

609. *astored* (Elles. &c.); *istored* (Harl.).

612. *and yet a gowne and hood* (Elles.); *a cote and eek an hood* (Harl.).

615. *Stot*, probably what we should now call a cob. Mr. J. E. T. Rogers, in his Hist. of Agriculture, i. 36, supposes that a stot was a low-bred undersized stallion.

616. *Scot.* 'The name given to the horse of the reeve (who lived at Bawdeswell, in Norfolk) is a curious instance of Chaucer's accuracy; for to this day there is scarcely a farm in Norfolk or Suffolk, in which one of the horses is not called Scot;' note in Bell's Chaucer.

617. *pers.* Some MSS. read *blew.* See note on l. 439.

621. *Tukked aboute,* with his long coat tucked up round him by help of a girdle. In the pictures in the Ellesmere MS., both the reeve and the friar have girdles, and rather long coats. See *Tuck* in Skeat, Etym. Dict.

624. *cherubinnes face.* H. Stephens, Apologie for Herodotus, i. c. 30, quotes the same thought from a French epigram—'Nos grands docteurs *au cherubin visage.*'—T. 'His face was red as any *cherubyn*;' Thynne, Debate between Pride and Lowliness.

625. *sawceflem* or *sawsfleam*, having a red pimpled face. 'Tyrwhitt has a note upon the word, which proves that *sawceflem* was a special kind of malady. He quotes from an old French physic-book, and from the Thousand Notable Things: " Oignement magistrel *pur sausefleme* et pur chescune manere de *roigne*. . . . A *sawsfleame* or red pimpled face is helped with this medicine following." In his Glossary, however, he gives a quotation from " MS. Bodl. 2463," which seems to settle the etymology of the word—"Unguentum contra *salsum flegma*, scabiem, &c. See Galen in Hippoc. de Aliment. Comment. iii. p. 277 : ὁ λάχην . . . γίνεται ἀπὸ φλέγματος ἀλμυροῦ καὶ τῆς ξανθῆς χόλης. And again : ὁ ἀλφὸς . . . ὑπὸ τοῦ φλέγματος, οὐκ ἀλυκοῦ." See also Halliwell under " Sauseflemed." In John Russell's Boke of Nurture, l. 776 (Manners and Meals in Olden Time), we have " a *flewische* countenance " given as the sign of the phlegmatic temperament, and a note refers us to Promptorium Parvulorum, where we find *flew* and *flewme*=*flegma*. (In some MSS. of Chaucer we get *sawceflewm* and *sauseflewme*.) The four humours of the blood, and the four consequent temperaments, are constantly referred to in various ways by early writers—by Chaucer as much as by any. In the Ayenbite of Inwyt, p. 157, we are told how the Devil tempts men through the four complexions—" þane *fleumatike* mid glotonye and be sleauþe." As to imposthumes, &c. arising from disorders of the four humours, I find an apposite fragment in the Retrospective Review (New Series, ii. p. 411, August, 1854): " It is to wit atte begynny[n]g that all empostimes withoutforth, that be hoven and swollen, eythir thei ben litill or grett. If thei be grett, thei ben sprongen of iiij humers synnynge. Wherfor empostume off *blode* and yer-off engendred is callyd *fflegmon ; empostume sprungen off flewme* is callyd baas, that is to say law, empostume ; of rede *coleryk* is called hersipula. Empostume sprungen off *malancoli* is called sclyros."'—John Addis, M.A.; in Notes and Queries, Fourth Series, iv. 64, July 17, 1869.

632. Cf. ' Such *whelkes* [on the head] haue small hoales, out of the which matter commeth. . . And this euill commeth of vicious and gleymie [viscous] humour, which commeth to the skin of their head, and breedeth therein pimples and *whelks*.'—Batman on Bartholome, lib. 7. c. 3. In the same, lib. 7. c. 67, we read that ' A *sauce flume* face is a priuye signe of leprosie.' Cf. Shak. Hen. V. iii. 6. 108.

643. *Can clepen Watte*, i. e. can call Walter (Wat) by his name ; just as parrots are taught to say ' Poll.' In Political Songs, ed. Wright, p. 328, an ignorant priest is likened to a jay in a cage, to which is added : ' God Engelish he speketh, ac [*but*] he wot nevere what.'

646. *Questio quid iuris.* ' This kind of question occurs frequently in Ralph de Hengham. After having stated a case, he adds, *quid juris*, and then proceeds to give an answer to it.'—T. It means—' the question is, what law (is there)?' i. e. what is the law on this point?

654-657. 'He would teach his friend to stand in no awe of the archdeacon's curse (excommunication), unless he supposed that his soul resided in his purse; for in his purse [not in his soul] he should be punished' (i.e. by paying a good round sum he could release himself from the archdeacon's curse).

662. *war him of,* i.e. let him beware of.

significavit, i.e. of a writ *de excommunicato capiendo,* which usually began, 'Significavit nobis venerabilis frater,' &c.—T.

663. *In daunger,* in his jurisdiction, within the reach or control of his office; the true sense of M. E. *daunger* is 'power to harm.' For *gyse* (Elles. &c.) Harl. alone has *assise.*

665. *and was al hir reed,* and was wholly their adviser.

666, 667. *gerland.* The *garland* here spoken of was distinct from the *bush.* The latter was made of ivy-leaves; and every tavern had an ivy-bush hanging in front as its sign; hence the phrase, 'Good wine needs no bush,' &c. See Becon's works, 'The Acts of Christ,' p. 524. But the *garland,* often used in addition to the *bush,* was made of three equal hoops, at right angles to each other, and decorated with ribands. It was also called a *hoop.* The sompnour wore only a *single* hoop. In Riley's Memorials of London, p. 133, *garland* means a metal circlet worn on the head.

667. *ale-stake,* a support for a garland in front of an ale-house. For a picture of an ale-stake with a garland, see Hotten's Book of Sign-boards. Chatterton, in his poem of Aella, st. 30, has the line
'Around the ale-stake minstrels sing the song.'
On this Mr. Skeat remarks, in his edition of Chatterton, vol. ii. p. xix—
'The very use of the prep. *around* shews that the line was written long after ale-stakes had ceased to exist, by a person who had never seen one. It is true that Speght wrongly explains an *ale-stake* by a May-pole, in which he is, as usual, carefully copied by Kersey and Bailey; but it is, in reality, nothing of the sort, nor would minstrels be able to gather *around* it, unless they possessed the unusual qualification of being able to walk like flies up and down the side of a house. The position of it was such that it did not stand upright, but projected *horizontally* from the side of a tavern at some height from the ground, as shewn in Lar-wood and Hotten's Book of Signboards. Hence the enactments made that it should never extend above the roadway for more than seven feet; see Liber Albus, ed. H. T. Riley, 1861, pp. 292, 389. . . . The right expression is "*at* this ale-stake," Cant. Tales, 12255.'

670. *Of Rouncivale.* 'I can hardly think that Chaucer meant to bring his Pardoner from Roncevaux, in Navarre, and yet I cannot find any place of that name in England. An hospital, Beatæ Mariæ de Rouncyvalle, in Charing, London, is mentioned in the Monast. tom. ii. p. 443; and there was a Runceval-Hall in Oxford. (Stevens, vol. ii.

p. 262.) So that perhaps it was the name of some fraternity.'—Tyrwhitt.

672. *Com hider, love, to me.* 'This, I suppose, was the beginning, or the burthen of some known song.'—Tyrwhitt.

673. *bar ... a stif burdoun,* sang the bass. Cf. Fr. *bourdon,* the name of a deep organ-stop.

682. *the newe Iet,* the new fashion, which is described in ll. 680–683.

> 'Also, there is another newe *gette,*
> A foule waste of clothe and excessyfe,
> There goth no lesse in a mannes typette
> Than of brode clothe a yerd, by my lyfe.'—Occleve.

685. *vernicle,* 'a diminutive of *Veronike* (Veronica), a copy in miniature of the picture of Christ, which is supposed to have been miraculously imprinted upon a handkerchief preserved in the church of St. Peter at Rome. . . It was usual for persons returning from pilgrimages to bring with them certain tokens of the several places which they had visited; and therefore the Pardoner, who is just arrived from Rome, is represented with a *vernicle sowed on his cappe.*'—Tyrwhitt. See Piers Plowman, ed. Skeat, B. v. 526 :—

> 'A bolle and a bagge he bare by his syde;
> An hundreth of ampulles on his hatt seten,
> Signes of Synay, and shelles of Galice,
> And many a cruche on his cloke and keyes of Rome,
> And the *vernicle* bifore, for men shulde knowe
> And se bi his signes, whom he sought hadde.'

687. *Bret-ful of pardoun,* brim-full (top-full, full to the top) of indulgences.

692. *Fro Berwik,* from Berwick to Ware (in Hertfordshire), from North to South of England. See the similar phrase—'From Barwick to Dover, three hundred miles over'—in Pegge's Kenticisms (E.D.S.), p. 70.

701. Heywood in the following lines has borrowed, with some alterations, the preamble to Chaucer's Pardoner's Tale (see 'A Dialogue of Wit and Folly,' ed. Fairholt, pp. liii–lvi):—

> '*The pardoner.* God and saynte Leonarde sende ye
>   all his grace
> As many as ben assembled in this place.
>   Good devout people that here do assemble,
> I pray God that ye may all well resemble
> The ymage, after whiche you are wrought;
> And that ye save that Chryst in you bought.
>   Devout chrysten people, ye shall all wytte
> That I am comen hyther ye to vysytte,
> Wherfore let us pray thus or I begynne,

Our sauyoure preserue ye all from synne!
And enable ye to receyue this blessed pardon,
Whiche is the greatest vndor the son,
Graunted by the pope in his bulles under lede,
Whiche pardon ye shall fynde whan ye are dede,
That offereth outher grotes er els pens,
To these holy relyques, whiche or I go hens
I shall here shewe, in open audyence,
Exortynge ye all to do to them reuerence.
　　But first ye shall know well, y^t I com fro Rome,
Lo here my bulles, all and some,
Our lyege lorde seale here on my patent
I bere with me, my body to warant;
That no man be so bolde, be he preest or clarke,
Me to dysturbe of Chrystes holy warke;
Nor haue no dysdayne, nor yet scorne,
Of these holy reliques whiche sayntes haue worne.
　　Fyrst, here I shewe ye, of a holy Jewes shepe
A bone, I pray you take good kepe
To my wordes, and marke them well:—
Yf any of your bestes belyes do swell,
Dyppe this bone in the water that he dothe take
Into his body, and the swellynge shall slake.
And yf any worme haue your beestes stonge,
Take of this water, and wasshe his tonge,
And it wyll be hole anon; and furthermore
Of pockes, and scabbes, and every sore,
He shall be quyte hole that drynketh of the well
That this bone is dipped in; it is treuth that I tell!
And yf any man that any beste oweth
Ones in the weke, or that the cocke croweth,
Fastynge wyll drynke of this well a draughte,
As that holy Jew hath vs taught,
His beestes and his store shall multeply.
And maysters all, it helpeth well;
Thoughe a man be foule in ielous rage,
Let a man with this water make his potage,
And neuermore shall he his wyfe mystryst.
　　Here is a mytten eke, as ye may se;
He that his hande wyll put in this myttayn,
He shall haue encrease of his grayn,
That he hath sowne, be it w[h]ete or otys,
So that he offer pens, or els grotes.
And another holy relyke eke here se ye may;

The blessed arme of swete Saynt Sondaye!
And who so euer is blessyd with this ryght hande,
Can not spede amysse by se nor by lande;
And if he offereth eke with good deuocyon,
He shall not fayle to come to hyghe promocyon.
    And another holy relyke here may ye see,
The great too of the Holy Trynyte.
And who so euer ones doth it in his mouthe take,
He shall neuer be dysseasyd with the tothe-ake!
Canker nor pockys shall there none brede!
This that I shewe ye is matter indede!
    And here is of our Lady, a relyke full good,
Her bongrace which she ware with her French hode*
Whan she wente oute, al-wayes for sonne-bornynge;
.   .   .   .
And if this bongrace they do deuoutly kys,
And offer therto, as theyre deuocyon is.
    Here is another relyke, eke a precyous one,
Of all helowes [All Saints] the blessyd jaw-bone,
Which relyke, without any fayle,
Agaynst poyson chefely dothe preuayle.
For whom so euer it toucheth, without dout,
All maner venym from hym shall issue out;
So that it shall hurt no maner wyghte;
Lo, of this relyke the great power and myght,
Which preseruyth from poyson euery man.
Lo of Saynt Myghell, eke the brayn-pan!
Which for the hed-ake is a preseruatyfe,
To every man or beste that beryth lyfe.
And further it shall stande hym in better stede,
For his hede shall neuer ake whan that he is dede.
Nor he shall fele no maner grefe nor payn,
Though with a sworde one cleue it than a-twayn!
But be as one that lay in a dede slepe,
Wherfore to these relykes now come crouche and crepe.
But loke that ye offerynge to them make
Or els can ye no maner profyte take.'
Cf. Pardoner's Prol. 336–340, 350–376; see CH. 3, pp. 40, 41.

---

* The French hood was the close coif, fashionable among ladies at
this period; the bongrace was a frontlet attached to the hood, and
standing up round the forehead; as may be particularly seen in the
portraits of Queen Anne Bullen. See History of Costume in England,
p. 243, and Glossary, p. 441 (vol. i. p. 232, vol. ii. p. 57, ed. 1885).

716. *Thestat, tharray* = the estate, the array: the coalescence of the article with the noun is very common in Old English writers.

726. 'That ye ascribe it not to my ill-breeding.'

727. *pleynly speke* (Elles. &c.); *speke al pleyn* (Harl.).

734. *Al speke he,* although he speak. See *al have I,* l. 744.

741, 742. This saying of Plato is taken from Boethius, De Consolatione, lib. iii. pr. 12. 'Thou hast lerned by the sentence of Plato, that nedes the wordes moten ben cosynes to the thinges of whiche thei speken;' see Boeth., ed. Morris, p. 106, ll. 16, 17. In Le Roman de la Rose, 7131, Jean de Meun says that Plato tells us speech was given us to express our wishes and thoughts, and proceeds to argue that men ought to use coarse language. Chaucer was thinking of this singular argument. We also find in Le Roman (l. 15372) the very words of the present passage :—

> 'Li dis doit le fait resembler ;
> Car les vois as choses voisines
> Doivent estre à lor faiz cosines.'

764. *I saugh nat* (Elles. &c.); *I ne saugh* (Harl.). To scan the line, read *I n' saugh,* dropping the *e* in *ne.*

770. 'May the blessed martyr reward you!'

772. *talen* = to tell tales.

785. *to make it wys,* to make it a matter of wisdom or deliberation; so also *made it straunge* = made it a matter of difficulty, C. T. 3978.

810. *and our othes swore,* and *we* our oaths swore; see next line.

817. *In heigh and lowe.* 'Lat. *In,* or *de alto et basso,* Fr. *de haut en bas,* were expressions of entire submission on one side, and sovereignty on the other.'—Tyrwhitt. It here means—'under all circumstances.'

822. *day.* It is the morning of the 17th of April. See CH. 2, p. xi.

826. *St. Thomas a Waterings* was a place for watering horses, at a brook beside the second mile-stone on the road to St. Thomas's shrine, i. e. to Canterbury. See Nares.

838. *draweth cut,* draw lots, lit. draw the *short* straw. In the Gloss. to Allan Ramsay's poems, ed. 1721, he explains—'*cutts,* lots. These cuts are usually made of straws unequally cut, which one hides between his finger and thumb, whilst another draws his fate.' See Brand, Pop. Antiq., iii. 337. The one who drew the shortest (or else the longest) straw was the one who drew the lot. Cf. '*Sors,* a kut, or a lotte ;' Reliquiæ Antiquæ, i. 7. 'Froissart calls it *tirer à longue paille,* to draw the *long* straw,' vol. i. c. 294.—T. 'After supper, we drew *cuttes* for a score of apricoks, the longest *cut* stil to draw an apricoke ;' Marston, Induction to *The Malcontent.*

847. *as was resoun,* as was reasonable or right.

THE KNIGHTES TALE.

It is only possible to give here a mere general idea of the way in which the Knightes Tale is related to the Teseide of Boccaccio. The following table gives a sketch of it, but includes very many lines wherein Chaucer is quite original. The reference to the Knightes Tale are to the lines; those to the Teseide are to the books and stanzas.

Kn. Tale.	Tes.	Kn. Tale.	Tes.
7–25	I. and II.	1244–1348	VI. 71, 14–22, 65–70, 8.
35–169	II. 2–5, 25–95.		
172–416	III. 1–11, 14–20, 47, 51–54, 75.	1364–1735	VII. 40–49, 68–93, 23–41, 67, 95–99, 7–13, 131, 132, 14, 100–102, 113–118, 19.
503–590	IV. 26–29, 59.		
593–621	V. 1–3, 24–27, 33.		
687–707	IV. 13, 14, 31, 85, 84, 17, 82.	1742–1825	VIII. 2–131.
		1826–1876	IX. 4–61.
780–783	VII. 106, 109.	1877–1881	XII. 80, 83.
810–881	V. 77–91.	1885–1950	X. 12–112.
954–1002	V. 92–98.	1951–2104	XI. 1–67.
1029–1164	VII. 108–110, 50–64, 29–37.	2109–2244	XII. 3–19, 69–83.

The MSS. quote a line and a half from Statius, *Thebaid*, xii. 519, 520, because Chaucer is referring to that passage in his introductory lines to this tale; see particularly ll. 9, 11, 12.

Lines 1–24 and 106–123 should be compared with Chaucer's Anelida and Arcite, ll. 22–46. Lines 24 and 114 are borrowed from that poem, with but slight alteration.

3. *governour.* It should be observed that Chaucer continually accents words in the Anglo-French manner, on the *last* syllable. Thus we have here *governóur*; again in the next line, *conqueróur*; in l. 7, *chivalrýe*; in l. 11, *contrée*; in l. 18, *manére*, &c. &c. The most remarkable examples are when the words end in -*oun* (ll. 35, 77).

6. *contree* is here accented on the *first* syllable; in l. 11, on the *last*. This is a good example of the unsettled state of the accents of such words in Chaucer's time, which afforded him an opportunity of licence, which he freely uses. In fact, *cóntree* shews the *English*, and *contrée* the *French* accent.

7. *chivalrye*, knightly exploits. In l. 20, *chivalrye*=knights; Eng. *chivalry.* So also in l. 124.

8. *regne of Femenye.* The kingdom (Lat. *regnum*) of the Amazons. *Femenye* is from Lat. *fœmina*, a woman. Cf. Statius, *Theb.* xii. 578.

9. *Scithia,* Scythia   Cf. *Scythicæ* in the quotation from Statius; p. 31.

10. *Ipolita,* Shakespeare's *Hippolyta,* in Mids. Night's Dream.   The name is in Statius, *Theb.* xii. 534, spelt *Hippolyte.*

27. *as now,* at present, at this time.   Cf. the M.E. adverbs *as-swithe, as-sone,* immediately.

31. *I wol nat letten eek noon of this route,* I desire not to hinder eke (also) none of all this company.   *Wol* = desire; cf. 'I *will* have mercy,' &c.

43. *crëature* is here a word of three syllables.   In l. 248 it has *four* syllables.

45. *nolde,* would not: *ne wolde* was no doubt pronounced *nolde,* would not; so *ne hath,* hath not, was pronounced *nath.*

  stenten, stop.   'It *stinted,* and said aye.'—Romeo and Juliet, i. 3. 48.

50. *that thus,* i. e. *ye* that thus.

53. *clothed thus* (Elles.); *clad thus al* (Harl.).

54. *alle* is to be pronounced *al-lè.*   Tyrwhitt inserts *than,* then, after *alle,* against the authority of the best MSS.

Statius (*Theb.* xii. 545) calls this lady *Capaneia coniux;* see l. 74, below. He says all the ladies were from Argos, and their husbands were kings.

55. *a deedly chere,* a deathly countenance.

60. *we biseken,* we beseech, ask for.   For such double forms as *beseken* and *besechen,* cf. mod. Eng. *dike* and *ditch, kirk* and *chirch, sack* and *satchel, stick* and *stitch.*   In the Early Eng. period the harder forms with *k* were very frequently employed by *Northern* writers, who preferred them to the palatalised *Southern* forms (perhaps influenced by Anglo-French) with *ch.*   Cf. M. E. *brig* and *rigg* with *bridge* and *ridge.*

68. This line means 'that ensureth no estate to be (always) good.'

70. *Clemence,* Clemency, Pity.   Suggested by 'il tempio . . . di Clemenza,' *Tes.* ii. 17; which again is from ' mitis posuit Clementia sedem,' *Theb.* xii. 482.

74. *Capaneus,* one of the seven heroes who besieged Thebes: struck dead by lightning as he was scaling the walls of the city, because he had defied Zeus; *Theb.* x. 927.   See note to l. 54, above.

83. *for despyt,* out of vexation; mod. E. 'for spite.'

84. *To do the dede bodyes vileinye,* to treat the dead bodies shamefully.

90. *withouten more respyt,* without longer delay.

91. *they fillen gruf,* they fell flat with the face to the ground.   In M.E. we find the phrase *to fall grovelinge*s, or *to fall groveling.*

96. *Him thoughte,* it seemed to him; cf. *methinks,* it seems to me.   In M. E. the verbs *like, list, seem, rue* (pity), are used impersonally, and take the dative case of the pronoun.   Cf. the modern expression ' if you please' = if it be pleasing to you.

97. *mat,* dejected.   'Ententyfly, not feynt, wery ne *mate.*'—Hardyng, p. 129.

102. *ferforthly*, i. e. *far-forth-like*, to such an extent, as far as.

107. *abood*, delay, awaiting, abiding.

108. *His baner he desplayeth*, i. e. he summons his troops to assemble for military service.

110. *No neer*, no nearer.

112. *lay*, lodged for the night.

117. *statue*, the image, as depicted on the banner.

119. *feeldes*, field, is an heraldic term for the ground upon which the various charges, as they are called, are emblazoned. Some of this description was suggested by the Thebais, lib. xii. 665, &c.; but the resemblance is very slight.

120. *penoun*, pennon. *y-bete*, beaten; the gold being hammered out into a thin foil in the shape of the Minotaur; see Marco Polo, ed. Yule, i. 344. But, in the *Thebais*, the Minotaur is upon Theseus' shield.

130. *In pleyn bataille*, in open or fair fight.

135. *obséquies* (Elles., &c.); *exéquies* (Harl.); accented on the *second* syllable.

146. *as him leste*, as it pleased him.

147. *tas*, heap, collection. Some MSS. read *cas* (*caas*), which might =downfall, ruin, Lat. *casus*; but, as *c* and *t* are constantly confused, this reading is really due to a mere blunder. Gower speaks of gathering a *tasse* of sticks; Conf. Amant. bk. v. ed. Pauli, ii. 293. Palsgrave has— 'On a heape, *en vng tas*;' p. 840. Hexham's Dutch Dict. (1658) has— ' *een Tas*, a Shock, a Pile, or a Heape.'

148. *harneys*. 'And *arma* be not taken onely for the instruments of al maner of crafts, but also for *harneys* and weapon; also standards and banners, and sometimes battels.'—Bossewell's Armorie, p. 1, ed. 1597. Cf. l. 755.

152. *Thurgh-girt*, pierced through. This line occurs again in Troilus, iv. 599 [or 627]: 'Thorwgh-gyrt with many wyde and blody wounde.'

153. *liggyng by and by*, lying separately. In later English, *by and by* signifies presently, immediately, as 'the end is not *by and by*.'

154. *in oon armes*, in one (kind of) arms or armour, shewing that they belonged to the same house. Chaucer adapts ancient history to medieval times.

157. *Nat fully quike*, not wholly alive.

158. *by her cote-armures*, by their coat-armour, by the devices on the armour covering the breast. Cf. l. 154.

by hir gere, by their *gear*, i. e. equipments.

160. *they*. Tyrwhitt reads *tho*, those; but the seven best MSS. have *they*.

165. *Tathenes*, to Athens; Harl. MS. Cf. *tallegge*, l. 2142 (footnote).

166. *he nolde no raunsoun*, he would accept of no ransom.

171. *Terme of his lyf*, the remainder of his life. Cf. 'The end and

term of natural philosophy.'—Bacon's Advancement of Learning, Bk. ii. p. 129, ed. Aldis Wright.

177. Cf. Leg. of Good Women, 2422, 2423.

180. *strof hir hewe*, strove her hue, i. e. her complexion contested the superiority with the rose's colour.

181. *I noot*, I know not; *noot = ne wot*.

189. *May.* 'Against Maie, every parishe, towne, and village, assembled themselves together, bothe men, women, and children, olde and yonge, even all indifferently, and either going all together or devidyng themselves into companies, they goe, some to the woodes and groves, some to the hills and mountaines, some to one place, some to another, where they spend all the night in pastimes; in the morninge they return, bringing with them birche, bowes and branches of trees, to deck their assemblies withalle.'—Stubbs, Anatomy of Abuses, ed. 1585, leaf 94 (ed. Furnivall, p. 149). Cf. Midsummer Night's Dream, i. 1. 167 :—

> ' To do observance to a morn of May.'

See also l. 642, and the note.

191. *Hir yelow heer was broyded*, her yellow hair was braided. Yellow hair was esteemed a beauty ; see Seven Sages, 477, ed. Weber ; King Alisaunder, 207. Boccaccio has here—' Co' biondi crini avvolti alla sua testa ;' *Tes.* iii. 10.

193. *the sonne upriste*, the sun's uprising ; the *-e* in *sonne* represents the old genitive inflexion. *Upriste* is here the dat. of the sb. *uprist*. It occurs also in Gower, Conf. Amantis, bk. i. ed. Pauli, i. 116.

194. *as hir liste*, as it pleased her.

195. *party*, partly ; Fr. *en partie*.

196. *sotil gerland*, a subtle garland ; *subtle* has here the exact force of the Lat. *subtilis*, finely woven.

197. Cf. 'Con angelica voce ;' *Tes.* iii. 10.

202. *even-Ioynant*, closely joining, or adjoining.

203. *Ther as this Emelye hadde hir pleyinge*, i. e. where she was amusing herself.

205. In the *Teseide* (iii. 11) it is Arcite who first sees Emily.

216. *by aventure or cas*, by adventure or hap.

218. *sparre*, a square wooden bolt ; the bars, which were of iron, were as thick as they must have been if wooden. See l. 132.

220. *bleynte*, the past tense of *blenche*, or *blenke* (to blench), to start, draw back suddenly. Cf. *dreynte*, pt. t. of *drenchen*. 'Tutto stordito, Gridò, Omè !' *Tes.* iii. 17.

229. *Som wikke aspect.* 'Cf. "wykked planete, as Saturne or Mars," Astrolabe, ii. 4. 21 ; notes in Wright's edition, ll. 2453, 2457 ; and Piers the Plowman, B. vi. 327. Add to these the description of Saturn, "Significat in *quartanis, lepra, scabie*, in mania, *carcere, submersione*, &c.

Est infortuna."—Johannis Hispalensis, Isagoge in Astrologiam, cap. xv.
See Knightes Tale, ll. 470, 1576, 1611.'—Skeat's Astrolabe, p. xlviii.

231. *al-though*, &c., although we had sworn to the contrary. Cf. 'And
can nought flee, *if I had it sworn*;' Lydgate, Dance of Machabre, *The
Sergeaunt*. Also—'he may himselfe not sustene Upon his feet, *though
he had it sworne*;' Lydgate, Siege of Thebes (The Sphinx), pt. i.

233. *the short and pleyn*, the brief and manifest statement of the case.

243. *wher*, a very common form for *whether*. This line is also in
Troilus, i. 425, with slight alteration.

247. *Yow* (used reflexively), yourself.

248. *wrecche*, wretched, is a word of two syllables, like *wikke*, wicked,
where the *d* is a later and unnecessary addition.

250. *shapen*, shaped, determined. '*Shapes* our ends.'— Shakespeare,
Hamlet, v. 2. 10.

262. 'And except I have her pity and her favour.'

263. *atte leste weye*, at the least. Cf. *leastwise* = *at the leastwise*; '*at
leastwise*;' Bacon's Advancement of Learning, ed. Wright, p. 147, l. 23.
See English Bible (Preface of 'The Translators to the Reader').

264. 'I am not but (no better than) dead, there is no more to say.'
Chaucer uses *ne—but* much in the same way as the Fr. *ne—que*. Cf.
North English 'I'm *nobbut* clemmed' = I am almost dead of hunger.

268. *by my fey*, by my faith, in good faith.

269. *me list ful evele pleye*, it pleaseth me very badly to play.

270. This debate is an imitation of the longer debate (in the *Teseide*),
where Palamon and Arcite meet in the grove; cf. l. 722 below.

271. *It nere* = *it were not*, it would not be.

275. 'That never, even though it cost us a miserable death, a death
by torture.' So in Troilus, i. 674: 'That certein, for to dyen in the
peyne.' Also in the E. version of The Romaunt of the Rose, 3326.

276. 'Till that death shall part us two.' Cf. the ingenious alteration
in the Marriage Service, where the phrase 'till death us depart' was
altered into 'do part' in 1661.

278. *cas*, case. It properly means event, hap. See l. 216.
    my leve brother, my dear brother.

283. *out of doute*, without doubt, doubtless.

289. *to my counseil*, to my adviser. See l. 303.

293. *I dar wel seyn*, I dare maintain.

295. *Thou shalt be.* Chaucer occasionally uses *shall* in the sense of
owe, so that the true sense of *I shall* is *I owe* (Lat. *debeo*); it expresses a
strong obligation. So here it is not so much the sign of a future tense
as a separate verb, and the sense is 'Thou art sure to be false sooner
than I am.'

297. *par amour*, with love, in the way of love. To love *par amour* is
an old phrase for to love excessively.

300. *affeccioun of holynesse*, a sacred affection, or aspiration after.

304. *I pose*, I put the case, I will suppose.

305. 'Knowest thou not well the old writer's saying?' The *olde clerk* is Boethius, from whose book, De Consolatione Philosophiæ, Chaucer has borrowed largely in many places. The passage alluded to is in lib. iii. met. 12 :—

> 'Quis legem det amantibus?
> Major lex amor est sibi.'

Chaucer's translation (ed. Morris, p. 108) has—'But what is he that may yeue a lawe to loueres. Loue is a gretter lawe ... than any lawe that men may yeuen.'

309. *and swich decree*, and (all) such ordinances.

310. *in ech degree*, in every rank of life.

314. *And eek it is*, &c., 'and moreover it is not likely that ever in all thy life thou wilt stand in her favour.'

319. This fable is not in any of the usual collections.

328. *everich of us*, each of us, every one of us.

331. *to theffect*, to the result, or end.

342. *in helle.* An allusion to Theseus accompanying Pirithous in his expedition to carry off Proserpina, daughter of Aidoneus, king of the Molossians, when both were taken prisoner, and Pirithous torn in pieces by the dog Cerberus. At least, such is the story in Plutarch; see Shakespeare's Plutarch, ed. Skeat, p. 289. Chaucer found the mention of Pirithous' visit to Athens in Boccaccio's Teseide, iii. 47–51. The rest he found in Le Roman de la Rose, 8186—

> 'Si cum vesquist, ce dist l'istoire,
> Pyrithous apres sa mort,
> Que Theseus tant ama mort, ...
> Que vis en enfer l'ala querre.'

354. Most MSS. read *or stounde.* The Harl. MS. has *o stound*, one moment, any short interval of time.

> 'The storme sesed within a stownde.'
> Ywaine and Gawin, l. 384.

360. *his nekke lyth to wedde*, his neck is in jeopardy.

364. *To sleen himself he wayteth prively*, he watches for an opportunity to slay himself unperceived.

365. This line, slightly altered, occurs also in the Legend of Good Women, 658.

367. *Now is me shape*, now am I destined; literally, now is it *shapen* (or appointed) for me.

389. It was supposed that all things were made of the four elements mentioned in l. 388. 'Does not our life consist of the four elements?'— Shakespeare, Twelfth Night, ii. 3. 10.

397. Cf. P. Plowman, C. xiii. 236.

399. 'And another man would fain (get) out of his prison.'

401. *matere*, in the *matter* of thinking to excel God's providence.

402. 'We never know what thing it is that we pray for here below.'
See Romans viii. 26.

403. *dronke is as a mous.* The phrase seems to have given way to
'drunk as a rat.' 'Thus satte they swilling and carousyng, one to
another, till they were both *as dronke as rattes*.'—Stubbes, Anatomie of
Abuses ; ed Furnivall, p. 113.

> 'I am a Flemyng, what for all that,
> Although I wyll be *dronken* otherwhyles *as a rat*.'
>
> Andrew Boorde, ed. Furnivall, p. 147.

Cf. 'When that he is *dronke as a dreynt mous ;*' Ritson, Ancient Songs,
i. 70. 'And I will pledge Tom Tosspot, till I be *drunk as a mouse-a ;*'
Old Plays, ed. Hazlitt, iii. 339.

404. This is from Boethius, De Consolatione, lib. iii. pr. 2 : 'But I
retourne ayeyne to the studies of men, of which men the corage alwey
rehersith and seeketh the sovereyne good of alle, be it so that it be with a
derke memorie ; but he not by whiche path, *ryght as a dronke man not
nat by whiche pathe he may retourne home to hys house*.'—Chaucer's Translation of Boethius ; ed. Morris, pp. 66, 67.

406. *slider*, slippery ; as in the Legend of Good Women, l. 648. Cf.
the gloss—'*Lubricum*, slidere ;' Reliquiæ Antiquæ, i. 7.

421. *pure fettres*, the very fetters. 'So in the Duchesse, l. 583, *the
pure deth*. The Greeks used καθαρός in the same sense.'—Tyrwhitt.

425. *at thy large*, at large.

444. 'White like box-wood, or ashen-gray ;' cf. l. 506. Cf. 'And pale
as box she wex ;' Legend of Good Women, l. 866. Also 'asshen pale
and dede ;' Troil. ii. 539.

459. *to letten of his wille*, to refrain from his will (or lusts).

475. Cf. the phrase 'paurosa gelosia ;' Tes. v. 2.

486. *upon his heed*, on pain of losing his head. Froissart has *sur sa
teste, sur la teste*, and *sur peine de la teste*.—T.

489. *this questioun.* 'An implied allusion to the medieval courts of
love, in which questions of this kind were seriously discussed.'—Wright.

508. *making his mone*, making his complaint or *moan*.

514–517. 'And in his manner, for all the world, he conducted himself
not merely like one suffering from the lover's disease of Eros, but
rather (his disease was) like *mania* engendered of melancholy humour.'
This is one of the numerous allusions to the four humours, viz. the
choleric, phlegmatic, sanguine, and melancholic. An excess of the
latter was supposed to produce 'melancholy madness.'

518. *in his celle fantastyk.* Tyrwhitt reads *Beforne his hed in his celle
fantastike*. Elles. has *Biforn his owene celle fantastik*. 'The division of
the brain into cells, according to the different sensitive faculties, is very

ancient, and is found depicted in medieval manuscripts. The *fantastic cell* (*fantasia*) was in front of the head.'—Wright. Hence *Biforen* means 'in the front part of his head.'

'Madnesse is infection of the formost cel of the head, with priuation of imagination, lyke as melancholye is the infection of the middle cell of the head, with priuation of reason, as Constant saith in *libro de Melancolia*. Melancolia (saith he) is an infection that hath mastry of the soule, the which commeth of dread and of sorrow. And these passions be diuerse after the diuersity of the hurt of their workings; for by madnesse that is called *Mania*, principally imagination is hurted; and in the other reson is hurted.'—Batman upon Bartholome, lib. vii. c. 6. Vincent of Beauvais, bk. xxviii. c. 41, cites a similar statement from the *Liber de Anatomia*.

532. *Argus*, Argus of the hundred eyes, whom Mercury charmed to sleep before slaying him. Ovid, *Met.* i. 714.

543. Cf. 'Her face ... Was al ychaunged in another kind;' Troil. iv. 864.

547. *bar him lowe*, conducted himself as one of low estate.

551. Cf. 'in maniera di pover valletto ;' *Tes.* iv. 22.

570. In the *Teseide*, iv. 3, he takes the name of *Penteo*. *Philostrato* is the name of another work by Boccaccio, answering to Chaucer's Troilus.

586. *slyly*, prudently, wisely. The M. E. *sleigh*, *sly* = wise, knowing; and *sleight* = wisdom, knowledge. (For change of meaning compare *cunning*, originally knowledge; *craft*, originally power; *art*, &c.)

> 'Ne swa *sleygh* payntur never nan was,
> Thogh his *sleght* mught alle other pas,
> That couthe ymagyn of þair [devils'] gryslynes.'
>   Hampole's Pricke of Consc., ll. 2308, 2309.

605. 'The third night is followed by the fourth day; so Palamon and Arcite meet on the 4th of May (l. 715), which was a Friday (l. 676); the first hour of which was dedicated to Venus (l. 678) and to lovers' vows (l. 643).'—Skeat. The 4th of May was a Friday in 1386.

613. *clarree*. 'The French term *claré* seems simply to have denoted a clear transparent wine, but in its most usual sense a compound drink of wine with honey and spices, so delicious as to be comparable to the nectar of the gods. In Sloan MS. 2584, f. 173, the following directions are found for making *clarré* :—"Take a galoun of honi, and skome (skim) it wel, and loke whanne it is isoden (boiled) that ther be a galoun ; thanne take viii galouns of red wyn, than take a pounde of pouder canel (cinnamon), and half a pounde of pouder gynger, and a quarter of a pounde of pouder pepper, and medle (mix) alle these thynges togeder and (with) the wyn ; and do hym in a clene barelle, and stoppe it fast, and rolle it wel ofte sithes, as men don verious, iii dayes."'—Way; note to Prompt. Parv., p. 79.

619. *nedes-cost*, for *needes coste*, by the force of necessity. It seems to be equivalent to M. E. *needes-wyse*, of necessity. *Alre-coste* (Icelandic *alls-kostar*, in all respects) signifies 'in every wise.' It occurs in Old English Homilies (ed. Morris), part i. p. 21 : 'We ne maȝen *alre-coste* halden Crist(es) bibode,' we are not able in every wise to keep Christ's behests. The right reading in Leg. Good Women, 2694, is :—

> 'And nedes cost this thing moot have an ende.'

636. A beautiful line; but copied from Dante, Purg. i. 20—'Faceva tutto rider l'oriente.'

642. See note to l. 189, where the parallel line from Shakespeare is quoted. See the interesting article on May-day Customs in Brand's Popular Antiquities (where the quotation from Stubbes will be found); also Chambers, Book of Days, i. 577, where numerous passages relating to May are cited from old poems. An early passage relative to the 1st of May occurs in the Orologium Sapientiæ, printed in Anglia, x. 387 :—
'And thanne is the custome of dyuerse contrees that yonge folke gone on the nyghte or erely on the morow to Medowes and woddes, and there they kutten downe bowes that haue fayre grene leves, and arayen hem with flowres; and after they setten hem byfore the dores where they trowe to haue amykes [friends?] in her lovers, in token of frendschip and trewe loue.'

650. *Were it* = if it were only.

651. So in Troilus, ii. 920:

> 'Ful lowde song ayein the moone shene.'

664. 'Veld haueð hege, and wude haueð heare,' i. e. 'Field hath eyes, and wood hath ears.'

> 'Campus habet lumen, et habet nemus auris acumen.'

This old proverb, with Latin version, occurs in MS. Trin. Coll. Cam. O. 2. 45, and is quoted by Mr. T. Wright in his Essays on England in the Middle Ages, vol. i. p. 168. Cf. Cotgrave's F. Dict. s. v. *Oeillet*.

666. *at unset stevene*, at a meeting not previously fixed upon, an unexpected meeting or appointment.

> 'Wee may chance to meet with Robin Hood
> Here *att some unsett steven*.'

Robin Hood and Guy of Gisborne; in Percy's *Reliques of Eng. Poetry*.

> 'And ther they *setten steven* for to mete;' C. T. 4381.

673. *hir queynte geres*, their strange behaviours.

674. Now in the top (i. e. elevated, in high spirits), now down in the briars (i. e. depressed, in low spirits).

> 'Allas! where is this worldes stabilnesse?
> *Here up, here doune;* here honour, here repreef;
> Now hale, now sike; now bounté, now myscheef.'
>
> Occleve, De Reg. Princip. p. 2.

675. *boket in a welle*. Cf. Shakespeare's Richard II. iv. 1. 184. 'Like

so many buckets in a well; as one riseth another falleth, one's empty, another's full.'—Burton's Anat. of Mel. p. 33.

678. *gery*, changeable; so also *gerful* in l. 680. Observe also the sb. *gere*, a changeable manner, in ll. 514, 673, and Book of the Duchesse, 1257. This very scarce word deserves illustration. Mätzner's Dictionary gives us some examples.

> 'By revolucion and turning of the yere
> A *gery* March his stondis doth disclose,
> Nowe reyne, nowe storme, nowe Phebus bright and clere.'
> *Lydgate, Minor Poems, p. 25.*

'Her *gery* Iaces,' their changeful ribands; Richard Redeless, iii. 130.

> 'Now *gerysshe*, glad and anoon aftir wrothe.'
> *Lydgate, Minor Poems, p. 245.*

' *Gerysshe*, wylde or lyght-headed ;' Palsgrave's *Dict.*, p. 313. In Skelton's poem of Ware the Hauke (ed. Dyce, i. 157) we find :—

> 'His seconde hawke wexid *gery*,
> And was with flying wery.'

Dyce, in his note upon the word, quotes two passages from Lydgate's *Fall of Princes*, B. iii. c. 10. leaf 77, and B. vi. c. 1. leaf 134.

> 'Howe *gery* fortune, furyous and wode.'

> 'And, as a swalowe *geryshe* of her flyghte,
> Twene slowe and swyfte, now croked, now upright.'

Two more occur in the same, B. iii. c. 8, and B. iv. c. 8.

> 'The *gery* Romayns, stormy and unstable.'

> 'The *geryshe* quene, of chere and face double.'

681. A writer in Notes and Queries quotes the following Devonshire proverb: 'Fridays in the week are never aleek,' i.e. Fridays are unlike other days.

> 'Vendredy de la semaine est
> Le plus beau ou le plus laid ;'
> Recueil des Contes, par A. Jubinal, p. 375.

708. Compare Legend of Goode Women, 2626 :—

> 'Sens first that day that *schapen was my sherte*,
> Or by the *fatal suster* had my dome.'

735. *I drede not*, I have no fear, I doubt not.

735, 736. *outher . . . or*=either . . . or.

764. *to borwe.* This expression has the same force as *to wedde*, in pledge. See l. 360.

768, 1249. *hir thankes*, willingly, with their good-will. Cf. M. E. *myn unthonkes*= ingratis. 'He faught with them in batayle their *unthankes*.' —Hardyng's Chronicle, p. 112.

780–4. Cf. *Teseide*, vii. 106, 119 ; Statius, *Theb.* iv. 494–9.

807. *hath seyn biforn*, hath seen before, hath foreseen.

810, 811. From the *Teseide*, v. 77.

818. *ther daweth him no day*, no day dawns upon him.

840. Similarly, Adrastus stopped the fight between Tydeus and Polynices; Statius, *Theb.* i.

848. *Ho*, an exclamation made by heralds, to stop the fight. It was also used to enjoin silence. See ll. 1675, 1798.

849. *Up peine* is the old phrase; as in '*up peyne* of emprisonement of 40 days;' Riley's Memorials of London, p. 580.

878. *it am I.* This is the regular construction in early English. In modern English the pronoun *it* is regarded as the direct nominative, and *I* as forming part of the predicate.

881. 'Therefore I ask my death and my doom.'

889. *Mars the rede.* Boccaccio uses the same epithet in the opening of his Teseide, i. 3: '*O Marte rubicondo.*' *Rede* refers to the colour of the planet.

903. This line occurs again three times; Squire's Tale, 479; Cant. Tales, 9860; Legend of Good Women, 503.

922. *can no divisoun*, knows no distinction.

923. *after oon* = after one mode, according to the same rule.

925. *eyen lighte*, cheerful looks.

941. 'Amare et Sapere vix Deo conceditur.'—Publius Syrus, Sent. 15. Cf. Adv. of Learning, ii. proem. § 15—'It is not granted to man to love and to be wise;' ed. Wright, p. 84. So also in Bacon's 10th Essay.

949. *jolitee*, joyfulness—said of course ironically.

950. *Can . . . thank*, acknowledges an obligation, owes thanks.

957, 960. Cf. the *Teseide*, v. 92.

979. *Looth or leef*, displeasing or pleasing.

980. *pypen in an ivy leef* is an expression like 'blow the buck's-horn,' to console oneself with any useless or frivolous employment; it occurs again in Troilus, v. 1434. Cf. the expression 'to go and whistle.' Cf. 'farwel the gardiner; he may pipe with an yue-leafe; his fruite is failed;' Test. of Love, bk. iii; ed. 1561, fol. 316. Boys still blow against a leaf, and produce a squeak. Lydgate uses similar expressions:—

> 'But let his brother blowe in an horn,
> Where that him list, or pipe in a reede.'
> Destruction of Thebes, part ii.

992. *fer ne neer*, farther nor nearer, neither more nor less. 'After some little trouble, I have arrived at the conclusion that Chaucer has given us sufficient *data* for ascertaining both the days of the month and of the week of many of the principal events of the "Knightes Tale." The following scheme will explain many things hitherto unnoticed.

'On Friday, May 4, before 1 A.M., Palamon breaks out of prison. For (l. 605) it was during the "third night of May, but (l. 609) a little *after* midnight." That it was Friday is evident also, from observing that Palamon hides himself at day's approach, whilst Arcite rises "for

to doon his observance to May, remembering on the *poynt of his desire.*"
To do this best, he would go into the fields at *sunrise* (l. 633), during
the hour dedicated to *Venus,* i.e. during the hour after sunrise *on a
Friday.* If however this seem for a moment doubtful, all doubt is
removed by the following lines :—

> "Right as the *Friday,* sothly for to telle,
> Now it shyneth, now it reyneth faste,
> Right so gan gery *Venus* overcaste
> The hertes of hir folke ; right as *hir day*
> Is gerful, right so chaungeth she array.
> Selde is the *Friday* al the wyke ylyke."

'All this is very little to the point unless we suppose Friday to be the
day. Or, if the reader have *still* any doubt about this, let him observe
the curious accumulation of evidence which is to follow.

'Palamon and Arcite meet, and a duel is arranged for an early hour
on the *day following.* That is, they meet on Saturday, May 5. But, as
Saturday is presided over by the inauspicious planet Saturn, it is no
wonder that they are both unfortunate enough to have their duel inter-
rupted by Theseus, and to find themselves threatened with death. Still,
at the intercession of the queen and Emily, a day of assembly for a
tournament is fixed for "*this day fyfty weekes*" (l. 992). Now we must
understand "fyfty wekes" to be a poetical expression for *a year.* This
is not mere supposition, however, but a *certainty ;* because the appointed
day was in the month of *May,* whereas fifty weeks and no more would
land us in *April.* Then "this day fyfty wekes" means "this day year,"
viz. on May 5. [In fact, Boccaccio has 'un anno intero;' Tes. v. 98.]

'Now, in the year following (supposed not a leap-year), the 5th of
May would be *Sunday.* But this we are expressly told in l. 1330. It
must be noted, however, that this is not the day of the *tournament*[1], but
of the *muster* for it, as may be gleaned from ll. 992–995 and 1238. The
eleventh hour "inequal" of Sunday night, or the second hour before sunrise of Monday, is dedicated to *Venus,* as explained by Tyrwhitt (l. 1359) ;
and therefore Palamon then goes to the temple of Venus. The third
hour after this, the first after sunrise on Monday, is dedicated to Luna
or Diana, and during this Emily goes to Diana's temple. The third
hour after this again, the fourth after sunrise, is dedicated to Mars, and
therefore Arcite then goes to the temple of Mars. But the rest of the
day is spent merely in jousting and preparations—

> "Al the *Monday* jousten they and daunce." (l. 1628.)

The tournament therefore takes place on Tuesday, May 7, on the day

---

[1] 'It has been objected, that this makes the tournament to take place,
not on the *anniversary* of the duel, but two days later. I cannot help it.
It is Chaucer's doing, not mine. Let the reader judge. See l. 1237.'

of the week presided over by *Mars,* as was very fitting; and this perhaps helps to explain Saturn's exclamation in l. 1811, "Mars hath his wille."' —Walter W. Skeat, in Notes and Queries, Fourth Series, ii. 2, 3; Sept. 12, 1868.

To this was added the observation, that May 5 was on a Saturday in 1386, and on a Sunday in 1387. But Ten Brink (*Studien,* p. 189) thinks it is of no value.

1008. 'That one of you shall be either slain or taken prisoner;' i.e. one of you must be fairly conquered.

1031. The various parts of this round theatre are subsequently described. On the North was the turret of Diana, with an oratory; on the East the gate of Venus, with altar and oratory above; on the West the gate of Mars, similarly provided.

1032. *Ful of degrees,* full of steps (placed one above another, as in an amphitheatre). 'But now they have gone a nearer way to the wood, for with wooden galleries in the church that they have, and *stairy degrees of seats* in them, they make as much room to sit and hear, as a new west end would have done.'—Nash's Red Herring, p. 21. See Shakespeare, Julius Cæsar, ii. 126, and also 2 Kings xx. 9. Cf. 'While she stey up from *gre* to *gre.*'—Lives of Saints, Roxb. Club, p. 59. Lines 1029-1036 are more or less imitated from the *Teseide,* vii. 108-110.

1061. *on the wal,* viz. on the walls *within* the oratory. The description is loosely imitated from Boccaccio's *Teseide,* vii. 55-59. It is remarkable that there is a much closer imitation of the same passage in Chaucer's Parl. of Foules, ll. 183-294. Thus at l. 246 of that poem we find:—

> 'Within the temple, of syghes hote as fyr,
> I herde a swogh, that gan aboute renne
> Which syghes were engendred with desyr
> That maden every auter for to brenne
> Of newe flaume; and wel aspyed I thenne
> That al the cause of sorwes that they drye
> Com of the bitter goddesse Ielosye.'

There is yet another description of the temple of Venus in the House of Fame, 119-139, where we have the very line 'Naked fleting in a see' (cf. l. 1098 below), and a mention of the 'rose garlond' (cf. l. 1103), and of 'Hir dowves and dan Cupido' (cf. ll. 1104-5).

1071. *golde,* a *gold* or turnsol. '*Goolde,* herbe. Solsequium, quia sequitur solem, elitropium, calendula;' Prompt. Parv. The corn-mari-gold in the North is called *goulans, guilde,* or *goles,* and in the South, *golds* (Way). Gower says that Leucothea was changed

> 'Into a floure was named *golde,*
> Which stant governed of the sonne.'

> Conf. Am., ed. Pauli, ii. 356.

1078. *Citheroun* = Cithaeron, sacred to Venus.

1082. In the Romaunt of the Rose, *Idleness* is the *porter* of the garden in which the rose (Beauty) is kept. In the Parl. of Foules, 261, the porter's name is *Richesse.* Cf. ll. 2, 3 of the Second Nonnes Tale.

1083. *of yore agon,* of years gone by. Cf. Ovid, *Met.* iii. 407.

1113. *estres,* the inner parts of a building; as also in C. T. 4293, and Leg. of Good Women, 1711.

> 'For thow knowest better then I
>   Al the *estris* of this house.'

Pardoner and Tapster, 556; pr. with Tale of Beryn (below). 'His sportis [portes?] and his *estris;*' Tale of Beryn, ed. Furnivall, 837. Cf. 'Qu'il set bien de l'ostel les *estres;*' Rom. de la Rose, 12720.

By mistaking the long *s* (f) for *f,* this word has been misprinted as *eftures* in the following. 'Pleaseth it you to see the *eftures* of this castle?'—Sir Thomas Malory, *Mort Arthure,* b. xix. c. 7.

1121. *a rumbel in a swough,* a rumbling in a gust of wind.

1124. *Mars armypotente.*

> 'O thou rede Marz armypotente,
> That in the trende baye hase made thy throne;
> That God arte of bataile and regent,
> And rulist all that alone;
> To whom I profre precious present,
> To the makande my moone
> With herte, body and alle myn entente,
>
> .   .   .   .   .   .
>
> In worshipe of thy reverence
> On thyn owen Tewesdaye.'

Sowdone of Babyloyne, ll. 939–953.

The word *armipotent* is borrowed from Boccaccio's *armipotente,* in the *Teseide,* vii. 32. Other similar borrowings occur hereabouts, too numerous for mention.

Let the reader take particular notice that the temple here described (ll. 1124–1136) is merely a *painted* temple, depicted on one of the walls *inside* the oratory of Mars. The other walls had paintings similar to those inside the temple of which the outside is thus depicted. Chaucer describes the painted temple as if it were real, which is somewhat confusing. Inconsistent additions were made in revision.

1126. *Streit,* narrow; 'la stretta entrata;' *Tes.* vii. 32.

1127. *vese* is glossed *impetus* in the Ellesmere MS. See the Glossary. Copied from 'salit Impetus amens E foribus;' *Theb.* vii. 47, 48.

1128. *rese* = to shake, quake. 'þe eorðe gon *to-rusien,*' 'the earth gan to shake.'—Laȝamon, l. 15946. *To resye,* to shake, occurs in Ayenbite of Inwyt, pp. 23, 116. Cf. also—'The tre *aresede* as hit wold falle;' Seven Sages, ed. Weber, l. 915.

1129. 'I suppose the *northern light* is the aurora borealis, but this phenomenon is so rarely mentioned by mediæval writers, that it may be questioned whether Chaucer meant anything more than the faint and cold illumination received by reflexion through the door of an apartment fronting the north.' (Marsh.) The fact is, however, that Chaucer here copies Statius, *Theb.* vii. 40–58; see the translation in the note to l. 1159 below. The 'northern light' seems to be an incorrect rendering of 'adversum Phœbi iubar;' l. 45.

1132. 'E le porte eran d'eterno diamante;' *Teseide,* vii. 32. Such is the reading given by Warton. However, the true source is the phrase in Statius—'adamante perenni ... fores;' *Theb.* vii. 68.

1139–40. Cf. the *Teseide,* vii. 33 :—

> 'Videvi l' Ire rosse, come fuoco,
>   E le Paure pallide in quel loco.'

But Chaucer follows Statius still more closely. Ll. 1137–1154 answer to *Theb.* vii. 48–53.

> —'cæcumque Nefas, Iræque rubentes,
> Exsanguesque Metus, occultisque ensibus astant
> Insidiæ, geminumque tenens Discordia ferrum.
> Innumeris strepit aula minis ; tristissima Virtus
> Stat medio, lætusque Furor, vultuque cruento
> Mars armata sedet.'

1143. See Chaucer's Legend of Hypermestre.

1146. *chirkyng* is properly the cry of birds. The Lansd. MS. has *schrikeinge* (shrieking). See House of Fame, iii. 853 (or 1943). In Batman upon Bartholome, lib. viii. c. 29, the music of the spheres is attributed to the '*cherkyng* of the mouing of the circles, and of the roundnes of heauen.'

1149. This line contains an allusion to the death of Sisera, Judges iv. But Dr. Koch has pointed out (Essays on Chaucer, Chaucer Soc. iv. 371) that we have here some proof that Chaucer may have altered his first draft of the poem without taking sufficient heed to what he was about. The original line may have stood—

> 'The sleer of *her husband* saw I there'—

or something of that kind; for the reason that no suicide has ever yet been known to drive a nail into his own head. That a wife might do so to her husband is *Chaucer's own* statement; for, in the Cant. Tales, 6347–52, we find—

> 'Of later date of wives hath he red,
>   That somme han slain hir husbonds in hir bed ...
>   And somme han driven nailes in hir brain,
>   Whyl that they slepe, and thus they han hem slain.'

Of course it may be said that l. 1148 is entirely *independent* of l. 1149; but the suggestion is worth notice.

1159. *hoppesteres.* Speght explains this word by pilots (*gubernaculum tenentes*); Tyrwhitt, female dancers (Ital. *ballatrice*). Others explain it *hopposteres = opposteres =* opposing, hostile, so that *schippes hoppesteres = bellatrices carinae* (Statius). As, however, it is impossible to suppose that even *opposteres* without the *h* can ever have been formed from the verb to *oppose*, the most likely solution is that Chaucer mistook the word *bellatrices* in Statius (vii. 57) or the corresponding Ital. word *bellatrici* in the *Teseide*, vii. 37, for *ballatrices* or *ballatrici*, which might be supposed to mean 'female dancers'; an expression which would exactly correspond to a M. E. form *hoppesteres*, from the A. S. *hoppestre*, a female dancer. Herodias' daughter is mentioned (in the dative case) as *þære lyðran hoppystran* (better spelt *hoppestran*) in Ælfric's A. S. Homilies, ed. Thorpe, i. 484. Hence *shippes hoppesteres* simply means 'dancing ships.' Shakespeare likens the English fleet to 'A city on the inconstant billows *dancing*;' Hen. V. iii. prol. 15.

The following extract from Lewis' translation of Statius' Thebaid, bk. vii. is of some interest.

> 'Beneath the fronting height of Æmus stood
> The fane of Mars, encompass'd by a wood.
> The mansion, rear'd by more than mortal hands,
> On columns fram'd of polish'd iron stands;
> The well-compacted walls are plated o'er
> With the same metal; just without the door
> A thousand Furies frown. The dreadful gleam,
> That issues from the sides, reflects the beam
> Of adverse Phœbus, and with cheerless light
> Saddens the day, and starry host of night.
> Well his attendants suit the dreary place;
> First frantic Passion, Wrath with redd'ning face,
> And Mischief blind from forth the threshold start;
> Within lurks pallid Fear with quiv'ring heart,
> Discord, a two-edged falchion in her hand,
> And Treach'ry, striving to conceal the brand.'

1162. *for al*, notwithstanding. Cf. Piers the Plowman, B. xix. 274.

1163. *infortune of Marte.* 'Tyrwhitt thinks that Chaucer might intend to be satirical in these lines; but the introduction of such apparently undignified incidents arose from the confusion already mentioned of the god of war with the planet to which his name was given, and the influence of which was supposed to produce all the disasters here mentioned. The following extract from the Compost of Ptolemeus gives some of the supposed effects of Mars :—" Under Mars is borne theves and robbers that kepe hye wayes, and do hurte to true men, and nyght-walkers, and quarell-pykers, bosters, mockers, and skoffers, and these men of Mars causeth warre and murther, and batayle; they wyll

be gladly *smythes* or workers of yron, lyght-fyngred, and lyers, gret
swerers of othes in vengeable wyse, and a great surmyler and crafty.
He is red and angry, with blacke heer, and lytell iyen; he shall be a
great walker, and a maker of swordes and knyves, and a sheder of
mannes blode, and a fornycatour, and a speker of rybawdry . . . . and
good to be a *barboure* and a blode-letter, and to drawe tethe, and is
peryllous of his handes." The following extract is from an old astrological book of the sixteenth century:—"Mars denoteth men with red
faces and the skinne redde, the face round, the eyes yellow, horrible to
behold, furious men, cruell, desperate, proude, sedicious, souldiers,
captaines, *smythes*, colliers, bakers, alcumistes, armourers, furnishers,
butchers, chirurgions, *barbers*, sargiants, and hangmen, according as they
shal be well or evill disposed."'—Wright. Chaucer has 'cruel Mars'
in The Man of Lawes Tale, 301; and cf. note to l. 229.

1164. From Statius, *Theb.* vii. 58:—

> 'Et uacui currus, protritaque curribus ora.'

1171. For the story of Damocles see Cicero, Tuscul. 5. 61; cf. Horace,
Od. iii. 1. 17.

1179, *sterres* (Harl.) Elles. &c. have *certres* (*sertres*); but this strange
reading can hardly be other than a mistake for *sterres*, which is proved
to be the right word by the parallel passage in The Man of Lawes Tale,
194–6.

1187. 'The names of two figures in geomancy, representing two constellations in heaven. Puella signifieth Mars retrograde, and Rubeus
Mars direct.' (Speght.)

1198. *Calistopee* = *Callisto*, a daughter of Lycaon, King of Arcadia,
and companion of Diana. See Ovid's Fasti, ii. 153; Gower, Conf.
Amantis, ed. Pauli, ii. 336.

1201, 1203. 'Cf. Ovid's Fasti, ii. 153–192; especially 189, 190,

> "Signa propinqua micant. Prior est, quam dicimus Arcton,
>   Arctophylax formam terga sequentis habet."

The nymph Callisto was changed into *Arctos* or the Great Bear. This
was sometimes confused with the other Arctos or Lesser Bear, in which
was situate the *lodestar* or Polestar. Chaucer has followed this error.
Callisto's son, Arcas, was changed into Arctophylax or Boötes: here
again Chaucer says a *sterre*, when he means a whole constellation;
as, perhaps, he does in other passages.'—Skeat's Astrolabe, pp. xlviii,
xlix.

1204, 1206. *Dane* = *Daphne*, a girl beloved by Apollo, and changed
into a laurel. See Ovid's Metamorph. i. 450; Gower, Conf. Amantis,
ed. Pauli, i. 336.

1207. *Attheon* = *Actaeon*. See Ovid's Metamorph. iii. 138.

1212. *Athalante* = *Atalanta*. See Ovid's Metamorph. x. 560.

1216. *nat drawen to memorie* = *not draw to memory*, not call to mind.

1228. *thou mayst best,* art best able to help, thou hast most power. Lucina was a title both of Juno and Diana; see Vergil, *Ecl.* iv. 10.

1257. *benedicite* is here pronounced as a trisyllable, viz. *ben'dic'te.* It *is* so sometimes, though five syllables in l. 927. Cf. *benste* in Towneley Myst. p. 85.

1267. This line seems to mean that there is nothing new under the sun.

1271. This is the 're Licurgo' of the *Teseide,* vi. 14; and the Lycurgus of the *Thebaid,* iv. 386, and of Homer, *Il.* vi. 130. But the description of him is partly taken from that of another warrior, *Tes.* vi. 21, 22.

1276. *kempe heres,* shaggy, rough hairs. Tyrwhitt and subsequent editors have taken for granted that *kempe = kemped,* combed (an impossible equation); but *kempe* is rather the reverse of this, and instead of smoothly combed, means bristly, rough, or shaggy. In an Early English poem it is said of Nebuchadnezzar that

'Holghe (hollow) were his *yghen* anunder (under) *campe hores.*'

Early Eng. Alliterative Poems, p. 85, l. 1695.

Campe hores = shaggy hairs (about the eyebrows), and corresponds exactly in form and meaning to *kempe heres.* See Glossary.

1284. *for-old,* very old. See next note.

1286. *for-blak* is generally explained as *for blackness;* it means *very black.*

1294. *Colers of,* having collars of. Some MSS. read *Colerd of. Colerd* is not an improbable form: cf. 'as they (the Jews) were tied up with girdles .... so were they *collared* about the neck.' (Fuller's Pisgah Sight of Palestine, p. 524, ed. 1869.)

torets, 'probably eyes in which rings will turn round, because each eye is a little larger than the thickness of the ring.'—Skeat. This appears from Chaucer's Astrolabe, ed. Skeat, i. 2. 1—'This ring renneth in a maner turet,' i.e. in a kind of eye. Warton, in his Hist. E. Poet. ed. 1871, ii. 314, gives several instances. It also meant a small loose ring. Cotgrave gives: '*Touret,* the annulet, or little ring whereby a hawk's lune is fastened unto the jesses.'

1297. *Emetrius* is not mentioned either by Statius or by Boccaccio; cf. *Tes.* vi. 29, 17, 16, 41.

1302. *cloth of Tars,* 'a kind of silk, said to be the same as in other places is called *Tartarine* (*tartarinum*), but the exact derivation of which appears to be somewhat uncertain.'—Wright. Cf. Piers the Plowman, B. xv. 224, and Skeat's note to the same, C. xvii. 299.

1329. *alle and some,* 'all and singular,' 'one and all.'

1347. See the *Teseide,* vi. 8.

1359. *And in hire houre.* 'I cannot better illustrate Chaucer's astrology than by a quotation from the old Kalendrier de Bergiers, edit. 1500,

Sign. K. ii. b :—" Qui veult savoir comme bergiers scevent quel planete regne chascune heure du jour et de la nuit, doit savoir la planete du jour qui veult s'enquerir ; et la premiere heure temporelle du soleil levant ce jour est pour celluy planete, la seconde heure est pour la planete en-suivant, et la tierce pour l'autre," &c., in the following order: viz. Saturn, Jupiter, Mars, Sol, Venus, Mercury, Luna. To apply this doctrine to the present case, the first hour of the Sunday, reckoning from sunrise, belonged to the Sun, the planet of the day ; the second to Venus, the third to Mercury, &c. ; and continuing this method of allotment, we shall find that the twenty-second hour also belonged to the Sun, and the twenty-third to Venus ; so that the hour of Venus really was, as Chaucer says, two hours before the sunrise of the following day. Accordingly, we are told in l. 1413, that the third hour after Palamon set out for the temple of Venus, the Sun rose, and Emily began to go to the temple of Diane. It is not said that this was the hour of Diane, or the Moon, but it really was ; for, as we have just seen, the twenty-third hour of Sunday belonging to Venus, the twenty-fourth must be given to Mercury, and the first hour of Monday falls in course to the Moon, the presiding planet of that day. After this Arcite is described as walking to the temple of Mars, l. 1509, in *the nexte houre of Mars,* that is, the *fourth* hour of the day. It is necessary to take these words together, for *the nexte houre,* singly, would signify the *second* hour of the day ; but that, according to the rule of rotation mentioned above, belonged to Saturn, as the *third* did to Jupiter. The *fourth* was *the nexte houre of Mars* that occurred after the hour last named.'—Tyrwhitt. 'In fact, just as Emily is three hours later than Palamon, so Arcite is three hours later than Emily.'—Skeat.

1363–1406. To be compared with the *Teseide,* vii. 43–49, and vii. 68.

1366. *Adoun,* Adonis. See Ovid, Met. x. 503.

1380. 'I care not to boast of arms (success in arms).'

1381. *Ne I ne axe,* &c., are to be pronounced as *ni naxe,* &c. So in l. 1772 of this tale, *Ne in* must be pronounced as *nin.*

1394. *wher I ryde or go,* whether I ride or walk.

1395. *fyres bete,* kindle or light fires. *Bete* also signifies to mend or make up the fire ; see l. 1434.

1413. *The thridde hour inequal.* 'In the astrological system, the day, from sunrise to sunset, and the night, from sunset to sunrise, being each divided into twelve hours, it is plain that the hours of the day and night were never equal except just at the equinoxes. The hours attributed to the planets were of this *unequal* sort. See Kalendrier de Berg. loc. cit., and our author's treatise on the Astrolabe.'—Tyrwhitt.

1417–1502. Cf. the *Teseide,* vii. 71–92.

1428. *a game,* a pleasure.

1432. 'E coronò di quercia cereale ;' *Tes.* vii. 74.

1436. *In Stace of Thebes*, in the Thebaid of Statius, where the reader will *not* find it. Cf. the *Teseide*, vii. 72.

1445. *aboghte*, atoned for. Cf. the phrase 'to *buy* dearly.'

1455. *thre formes*. Diana is called *Diva Triformis;*—in heaven, Luna; on earth, Diana and Lucina, and in hell, Proserpina.

1507. *the nexte waye*, the nearest way. Cf. the *Teseide*, vii. 93.

1510. *walked is*, has walked.

1513–1576. Cf. the *Teseide*, vii. 23–28, 39–41.

1537. *lyves creature*, creature alive, living creature.

1547. *do*, bring it about, cause it to come to pass.

1579. 'As joyful as the bird is of the bright sun.' So in Piers Pl., B. x. 153.

1580–3. Cf. the *Teseide*, vii. 67.

1591. 'Men may outrun old age, but not outwit (surpass its counsel).' Cf. 'Men may the wise at-renne, and nought at-rede.'—Troilus, iv. 1428, ed. Morris; (or iv. 1456).

> 'For of him (the old man) þu migt leren
> Listes and fele þewes,
> þe baldure þu migt ben:
> Ne for-lere þu his redes,
> For þe elder mon me mai of-riden
> Betere þenne of-reden.'

> 'For of him thou mayest learn
> Arts and many good habits,
> The bolder thou mayest be.
> Despise not thou his counsels,
> For one may out-ride the old man
> Better than out-wit.'

The Proverbs of Alfred, ed. Morris, in an Old Eng. Miscellany, p. 136.

1593. *agayn his kynde*. According to the Compost of Ptolemeus, Saturn was influential in producing strife: 'And the children of the sayd Saturne shall be great jangeleres and chyders .... and they will never forgyve tyll they be revenged of theyr quarell.'—Wright.

1596. *My cours.* 'The course of the planet *Saturn*. This refers to the orbit of Saturn, supposed to be the largest of all. So it was, till Uranus and Neptune were discovered.'—Skeat.

1597. *more power.* The Compost of Ptolemeus says of Saturn, 'He is mighty of hymself. ... It is more than xxx yere or he may ronne his course. ... Whan he doth reygne, there is moche debate.'—Wright.

1604. In astrology, Leo is the 'mansion' of the Sun; but the first 10 degrees of the sign are called 'the face of Saturn.'

1611. 'Er ffyue ȝer ben folfult, such ffamyn schal aryse,
> þorw fflodes and foul weder, ffruites schul fayle,
> And so seiþ Saturne, and sent vs to warne.'

Specimens of Early English, 2nd ed. vol. ii. p. 202.

1633–1667. Cf. the *Teseide*, vii. 95–99.

1646. In Sir Bevis, ed. Kölbing, p. 134, we find—

> 'Sir Beues was ful glad, iwis,
> Hise *laynerys* [printed *layueres*] he took anon,
> And fastenyd his hawberk hym upon.'

1653. Cf. House of Fame, 1239, 1240 :—

> 'Of hem that maken blody soun
> In trumpe, beme, and clarioun.'

Also *Tes*. viii. 5 :—'D'armi, di corni, nacchere e trombette.'
'The *Nakkárah* or *Naqárah* was a great kettle-drum, formed like a
brazen cauldron, tapering to the bottom, and covered with buffalo-hide,
often 3½ or 4 feet in diameter . . . The crusades naturalised the word in
some form or other in most European languages, but in our own apparently with a transfer of meaning. Wright defines *naker* as "a cornet
or horn of brass," and Chaucer's use seems to countenance this.'—Marco
Polo, ed. Yule, i. 303–4 ; where more is added. But Wright's explanation is a mere guess, and should be rejected. There is no reason for
assigning to the word *naker* any other sense than 'kettle-drum.' Minot
(Songs, iv. 80) is explicit :—

> 'The princes, that war riche on raw,
> Gert *nakers* strike, and trumpes blaw.'

Hence a *naker* had to be struck, not blown. See also *Naker* in Halliwell's Dictionary. Boccaccio has the pl. *nacchere* ; see above. Cf. Hous
of Fame, 1239, 1240.

1679. As to the regulations for tournaments, see Strutt's Sports and
Pastimes, book iii. c. 1. §§ 16–24 ; the passages are far too long for
quotation. We may, however, compare the following extract, given by
Strutt, from MS. Harl. 326. 'All these thinges donne, thei were em-
batailed eche ageynste the othir, and the corde drawen before eche
partie ; and whan the tyme was, the cordes were cutt, and the trum-
pettes blew up for every man to do his devoir [*duty*]. And for to asser-
tayne the more of the tourney, there was on eche side a stake ; and at
eche stake two kyngs of armes, with penne, and inke, and paper, to
write the names of all them that were yolden, for they shold no more
tournay.' And, from MS. Harl. 69, he quotes that—'no one shall bear
a sword, pointed knife, mace, or other weapon, except the sword for the
tournament.'

1682–1735. Cf. the *Teseide*, vii. 12, 131–2, 12, 14, 100–2, 113–4,
118, 19.

1688. 'Nor short sword having a *biting* (sharp) point to stab with.'

1707. Cf. Legend of Good Women, 635 :—'Up goth the trompe.'

1742–66. Cf. the *Teseide*, viii. 5, 7, 14, 12, &c.

1744. 'In go the spears full firmly into the *rest*,'—i. e. the spears were
couched ready for the attack.

> 'Thai layden here speres in *areeste,*
> Togeder thai ronnen as fire of thondere,
> That both here launces to-braste;
> That they seten, it was grete wonder,
> So harde it was that they gan threste;
> Tho drowen thai oute here swordes kene,
> And smyten togeder by one assente.'
>
> The Sowdone of Babyloyne, l. 1166.

See Glossary, s.v. *Arest.*

1756-7. *he ... he* = one ... another. See Historical Outlines of English Accidence, p. 282. Cf. the parallel passage in the Legend of Good Women, 642-8.

1757. *feet.* Some MSS. read *foot.* Tyrwhitt proposed to read *foo,* foe, enemy; but see l. 1692.

1766. *wrought . . . wo,* done harm to his opponent.

1768. *Galgopheye.* 'This word is variously written *Colaphey, Galgaphey, Galapey.* There was a town called *Galapha* in Mauritania Tingitana, upon the river Malva (Cellar. Geog. Ant. v. ii. p. 935), which perhaps may have given name to the vale here meant.'—Tyrwhitt. But doubtless Chaucer was thinking of the Vale of Gargaphie, where Actæon was turned into a stag:—

> 'Vallis erat, piceis et acutâ densa cupressu,
> Nomine *Gargaphie,* succinctae sacra Dianae.'
>
> Ovid, Met. iii. 155, 156.

1769. Cf. the *Teseide,* viii. 26.

1788. *swerdes lengthe.* Cf.

> 'And then he bar me sone bi strenkith
> Out of my sadel my speres lenkith.'
>
> Ywaine and Gawin, ll. 421, 2.

1817. *Which a,* what a, how great a.

1818-22. Cf. the *Teseide,* viii. 131, 124-6.

1825. *al his chere* may mean 'all his delight, as regarded his heart.' All the MSS. insert *in* before *his chere.*

1826. Elles. reads *furie,* as noted; so in the *Teseide,* ix. 4.

1828-1848. Cf. the *Teseide,* ix. 7, 8, 47, 48, 38, 26.

1831. The following is a very remarkable account of a contemporary occurrence, which took place at the time when a parliament was held at Cambridge, A. D. 1388, as told by Walsingham, ed. Riley, ii. 177.

'Tempore Parliamenti, cum Dominus Thomas Tryvet cum Rege sublimis equitaret ad Regis hospitium, quod fuit apud Bernewelle [Barnwell], dum nimis urget equum calcaribus, equus cadit, et omnia pene interiora sessoris dirumpit [cf. l. 1833]; protelavit tamen vitam in crastinum.' The *saddle-bow* or *arsoun* was the 'name given to two curved pieces of wood or metal, one of which was fixed to the front of the saddle, and

another behind, to give the rider greater security in his seat;' Murray's
Eng. Dict. s.v. *Arson.* Violent collision against the front saddle-bow
produced very serious results. Cf. the *Teseide,* ix. 8—'E 'l forte arcione
gli premette il petto.'

1838. 'Then was he cut out of his armour.' I.e. the laces were cut,
to spare the patient trouble.

1840. *in memorie,* conscious.

1853. 'As a remedy *for* other wounds,' &c.

1854, 1855. *charmes . . . save.* 'It may be observed that the salves,
charms, and pharmacies of herbs were the principal remedies of the
physician in the age of Chaucer. *Save* (*salvia,* the herb sage) was considered one of the most universally efficient mediæval remedies.'—
Wright. Hence the proverb of the school of Salerno, 'Cur moriatur
homo, dum salvia crescit in horto?'

1864. *nis nat but* = is only. *aventure,* accident.

1867. *O persone,* one person.

1875. *Gree,* preëminence, superiority; lit. rank, or a step; answering
to Lat. *gradus* (not *gratus*). The phrases *to win the gree,* i.e. to get
the first place, and *to bear the gree,* i.e. to keep the first place, are still
in common use in Scotland. See note to the Allit. Destruction of Troy,
ed. Panton and Donaldson, l. 1353, and Jamieson's Dictionary.

1878. *dayes thre.* Wright says the period of three days was the usual
duration of a feast among our early forefathers. As far back as the
seventh century, when Wilfred consecrated his church at Ripon, he held
'magnum convivium trium dierum et noctium reges cum omni populo
laetificantes.'—Eddius, Vit. S. Wilf. c. 17.

1903. *This al and som,* i.e. *this* (is) *the al and som,* this is the short
and long of it. With ll. 1903–50 compare the *Teseide,* x. 12, 37, 51, 54,
55, 64, 102–3, 60–3, 111–2.

1942. *overcome.* Tyrwhitt reads *overnome,* overtaken, the pp. of *over-
nimen;* but none of the seven best MSS. have this reading.

1952. The *real* reason why Chaucer could not here describe the
passage of Arcite's soul to heaven is because he had already copied
Boccaccio's description, and had used it with respect to the death of
Troilus; see Troil. V (Stanzas 7, 8, 9 from the end).

1957. *ther Mars,* &c., where I hope that Mars will, &c.; may
Mars, &c.

1964. *swich sorwe,* so great sorrow.

1969–1988. Cf. the *Teseide,* xi. 8, 7, 9–11, xii. 6.

1995–2104. Cf. the *Teseide,* xi. 13–16, 30, 31, 35, 38, 40, 37, 18, 26–7,
22–5, 21, 27–9, 39–67.

2005–2104. The whole of this description should be compared with
the funeral rites at the burial of Archemorus, as described in Statius,
Thebaid, bk. vi; which Chaucer probably consulted, as well as the

imitation of the same in Boccaccio's *Teseide.* For example, the 'tree-list' in ll. 2063–5 is not a little remarkable. The first hint of it is in Vergil, *Æn.* vi. 180; Statius took the hint, and amplified it. After which, it reappears in Boccaccio, *Teseide,* xi. 22; in Chaucer, Parl. of Foules, 176; in the present passage; in Tasso, Gier. Lib. iii. 75; and in Spenser, F. Q. i. 1. 8. Again, we may just compare ll. 2093–2097 with the following lines in Lewis's translation of Statius:—

> 'Around the pile an hundred horsemen ride,
> With arms reversed, and compass every side;
> They faced the left (for so the rites require);
> Bent with the dust, the flames no more aspire.
> Thrice, thus disposed, they wheel in circles round
> The hallow'd corse: their clashing weapons sound.
> Four times their arms a crash tremendous yield,
> And female shrieks re-echo through the field.'

Moreover, Statius imitates the whole from Vergil, *Æn.* xi. 185–196. And Lydgate copies it all from Chaucer in his Sege of Thebes, part 3 (near the end).

2006. *Funeral he myghte al accomplice* (Elles.); *Funeral he mighte hem all complise* (Corp., Pet.).

2027. 'And surpassing others in weeping came Emily.'

2037. Cf. 'deux ars Turquois,' i. e. two Turkish bows; Rom. de la Rose, 913.

2070. *Amadrides*; i. e. *Hamadryades*; see Ovid, *Met.* i. 192, 193, 690.

2085. *men made the fyr* (Heng.); *maad was the fire* (Corp. Pet.).

2095. *loud* (Elles.); *heih* (Harl.); *bowe* (Corp.).

2100. 'Chaucer seems to have confounded the *wake-plays* of his own time with the funeral games of the antients.'—Tyrwhitt. Cf. Troil. v. 304; and see 'Funeral Entertainments' in Brand's Popular Antiquities.

2104. *in no disioynt,* with no disadvantage.

2109–28. Cf. the *Teseide,* xii. 3–5.

2133–2135. *that faire cheyne of love.* This sentiment is taken from Boethius, lib. ii. met. 8: 'þat þe world with stable feith / varieth acordable chaungynges // þat the contraryos qualite of elementz holden amonge hem self aliaunce perdurable / þat phebus the sonne with his goldene chariet / bryngeth forth the rosene day / þat the mone hath commaundement ouer the nyhtes // whiche nyhtes hesperus the eue-sterre hat[h] browt // þat þe se gredy to flowen constreyneth with a certeyn ende hise floodes / so þat it is nat l[e]ueful to strechche hise brode termes or bowndes vpon the erthes // þat is to seyn to couere alle the erthe // Al this a-cordaunce of thinges is bownden with looue / þat gouerneth erthe and see and [he] hath also commaundementz to the heuenes and yif this looue slakede the brydelis / alle thinges þat now louen hem togederes / wolden maken a batayle contynuely and stryuen to fordoon the fasoun of this worlde / the which they now leden in acordable feith by fayre moeuynges // this looue halt to-gideres peoples ioygned with an hooly bond / and knytteth sacrement of maryages of chaste looues // And love enditeth lawes to trewe felawes // O weleful weere mankynde / yif thilke loue þat gouerneth heuene gouerned[e] yowre corages.'—Chaucer's Boethius, ed. Morris, p. 62. And cf. the *Teseide*, ix. 51 ; and Homer, *Il.* viii. 19. Also Rom. de la Rose, 16988 :

> 'La bele chaéne dorée
>   Qui les quatre elemens enlace.'

2136. What follows is taken from Boethius, lib. iv. pr. 6 : 'þe engendrynge of alle þinges, quod she, and alle þe progressiouns of muuable nature, and alle þat moeueþ in any manere, takiþ hys causes, hys ordre, and hys formes, of þe stablenesse of þe deuyne þouȝt ; [and thilke deuyne thowht] þat is yset and put in þe toure, þat is to seyne in þe heyȝt of þe simplicite of god, stablisiþ many manere gyses to þinges þat ben to don.' —Chaucer's Boethius, ed. Morris, p. 134.

2147. Chaucer again is indebted to Boethius, lib. iii. pr. 10, for what follows : 'For al þing þat is cleped inperfit, is proued inperfit by þe amenusynge of perfeccioun, or of þing þat is perfit ; and her-of comeþ it, þat in euery þing general, yif þat þat men seen any þing þat is inperfit, certys in þilke general þer mot ben somme þing þat is perfit. For yif so be þat perfeccioun is don awey, men may nat þinke nor seye fro whennes þilke þing is þat is cleped inperfit. For þe nature of þinges ne token nat her bygynnyng of þinges amenused and imperfit ; but it procediþ of þingus þat ben al hool and absolut, and descendeþ so doune into outerest þinges and into þingus empty and wiþoute frvyt ; but, as I haue shewed a litel her-byforne, þat yif þer be a blisfulnesse þat be frele and vein and inperfit, þer may no man doute þat þer nys som blisfulnesse þat is sad, stedfast, and perfit.'—Chaucer (as above), p. 89.

2158. *seen at eye*, see at a glance.

2161–2210. Cf. the *Teseide*, xii. 7–10, 6, 11, 13, 9, 12–17, 19.

2184. So in Troilus, iv. 1586 : 'Thus maketh vertu of necessite ;' and in Squire's Tale, pt. ii. l. 247 (Group F, l. 593) : 'That I made vertu of necessite.' It is from Le Roman de la Rose, 14217 :—

> 'S'il ne fait de necessité
>   Vertu.'

Cf. Horace, Carm. i. 24 :—

> 'Durum ! sed leuius fit patientia
>   Quidquid corrigere est nefas.

2210. Cf. 'The time renneth toward right fast,
    Joy cometh after whan the sorrow is past.'

    Hawes' Pastime of Pleasure, ed. Wright, p. 148.

2231. *oghte to passen right*, should surpass mere equity or justice.

2236–44. Cf. the *Teseide*, xii. 69, 72, 83.

THE NONNE PRESTES TALE.

1. *stope.* Lansd. MS. reads *stoupe,* as if it signified bent, *stooped ;* but the verb *stoop* is a *weak* verb. *Stope* is the past participle of the (formerly) strong verb *steppen,* to step, advance. *Stope in age* = advanced in years. Roger Ascham has almost the same phrase : ' And [Varro] beyng depe *stept in age,* by negligence some wordes do scape and fall from him in those bookes as be not worth the taking up,' &c.—The Schoolmaster, ed. Mayor, p. 189 ; ed. Arber, p. 152.

8. *by housbondrye,* by economy.

12. *Ful sooty was hir bour, and eek hir halle.* The widow's house consisted of only two apartments, designated by the terms bower and hall. Whilst the widow and her 'daughters two' slept in the bower, Chanticleer and his seven wives roosted on a perch in the hall, and the swine ensconced themselves on the floor. The smoke of the fire had to find its way through the crevices of the roof. See Our English Home, pp. 139, 140. Cf.

> ' At his beds feete feeden his stalled teme,
>   His swine beneath, his *pullen ore the beame.*'
>
>   Hall's Satires, bk. v. sat. 1 ; v. 1. p. 56, ed. 1599.

15. *No deyntee* (Elles. &c.) ; *Noon deynteth* (Harl.).

19. *hertes suffisaunce,* a satisfied or contented mind, literally heart's satisfaction. Cf. our phrase 'to your heart's content.'

22. *wyn . . . whyt nor reed.* The white wine was sometimes called 'the wine of Osey' (Alsace) ; the red wine of Gascony, sometimes called 'Mountrose,' was deemed a liquor for a lord. See Our English Home, p. 83 ; Piers Pl. prol. l. 228.

25. *Seynd bacoun,* singed or broiled bacon.

an ey or tweye, an egg or two.

26. *deye.* The *daia* (from the Icel. *deigja*) is mentioned in Domesday among assistants in husbandry ; and the term is again found in 2nd Stat. 25 Edward III (A.D. 1351). In Stat. 37 Edward III (A.D. 1363), the *deye* is mentioned among others of a certain rank, not having goods or chattels of 40s. value. The *deye* was mostly a female, whose duty was to make butter and cheese, attend to the calves and poultry, and other odds and ends of the farm. The *dairy* (in some parts of England, as in Shropshire, called a *dey*-house) was the department assigned to her. See Prompt. Parv., p. 116.

29. In Caxton's translation of Reynard the Fox, the cock's name is *Chantecleer.* In the original, it is *Canticleer ;* from his clear voice in singing. In the same, Reynard's second son is *Rosseel ;* see l. 514.

O

31. *orgon.* This is put for *orgons* or *organs.* It is plain, from *gon* in the next line, that Chaucer meant to use this word as a plural from the Lat. *organa.* *Organ* was used until lately only in the plural, like *bellows, gallows,* &c. 'Which is either sung or said or on the *organs* played.'—Becon's Acts of Christ, p. 534. It was sometimes called *a pair of organs.* See note to P. Plowman, C. xxi. 7.

34. Cf. Parl. of Foules, 350:—

> 'The cok, that orloge is of thorpes lyte.'

35, 36. 'The cock knew *each* ascension of the equinoctial, and crew at each; that is, he crew every hour, as 15° of the equinoctial make an hour. Chaucer adds [l. 34] that he knew the hour better than the abbey-clock. This tells us, clearly, that we are to reckon clock-hours, and not the unequal hours of the artificial day. Hence the prime, mentioned in l. 377, was at a clock-hour, at 6, 7, 8, or 9, suppose. The day meant is certainly May 3, because the sun had passed the 21st degree of Taurus (see fig. 1 of Astrolabe) ... The date May 3 is playfully denoted by saying that March was complete, and also (since March began) thirty-two days more had passed. The words "since March began" are parenthetical; and we are, in fact, told that the whole of March, the whole of April, and two days of May were done with. March was then considered the first month in the year, though the year began with the 25th, not with the 1st; and Chaucer alludes to the idea that the Creation itself took place in March. The day, then, was May 3, with the sun past 21 degrees of Taurus. The hour must be had from the sun's altitude, rightly said (l. 379) to be *Fourty degrees and oon.* I use a globe, and find that the sun would attain the altitude 41° nearly at 9 o'clock. It follows that prime in this passage signifies the end of the first quarter of the day, reckoning from 6 a.m. to 6 p.m.'—Skeat's Astrolabe, p. lxi. This rough test, by means of a globe, is perhaps sufficient; but Mr. Brae proved it to be right by calculation. Taking the sun's altitude at 41½°, he 'had the satisfaction to find a resulting hour for prime of 9 o'clock A.M. *almost to the minute.*' It is interesting to find that Thynne explains this passage very well in his Animadversions on Speght's Chaucer; ed. Furnivall, p. 62, note 1.

The notion that the Creation took place on the 18th of March is alluded to in the Hexameron of St. Basil (see the A.S. version, ed. Norman, p. 8, note *j*), and in Ælfric's Homilies, ed. Thorpe, i. 100.

37. Fifteen degrees of the equinoctial = an exact hour. See note to l. 35 above.

40. *and bataild.* Lansd. MS. reads *enbateled,* indented like a battlement.

41. *as the Ieet,* like the jet. Beads used for the repetition of prayers were frequently formed of *jet.* See note to Prol. 159, p. 140.

50. *damoysele Pertelote.* Cf. our 'Dame Partlet.'

> 'I'll be as faithful to thee
> As Chauntcleer to Madame Partelot.'
>
> The Ancient Drama, iii. p. 158.

54. *in hold*, in possession. Cf. 'He hath my heart *in holde;*' Greene's George a Greene, ed. Dyce, p. 256.

55. *loken in every lith*, locked in every limb.

59. *my lief is faren in londe*, my beloved is gone away. Probably the refrain of a popular song of the time.

69. *herte deere.* This expression corresponds to 'dear heart,' or 'deary heart,' which still survives in some parts of the country.

73. *take it agrief = take it in grief*, i. e. to take it amiss, to be offended.

74. *me mette*, I dreamed; literally *it dreamed to me*.

76. *my swevene rede aright*, bring my dream to a good issue; literally 'interpret my dream favourably.'

80. *Was lyk.* The relative *that* is often omitted by Chaucer before a relative clause.

88. *Avoy* (Elles.); *Away* (Harl.).

103. See the Chapter on Dreams in Brand's Pop. Antiquities.

104. *fume*, the effects arising from gluttony and drunkenness. 'Anxious black melancholy *fumes*.'—Burton's Anat. of Mel. p. 438, ed. 1845. 'All vapours arising out of the stomach,' especially those caused by gluttony and drunkenness. 'For when the head is heated it scorcheth the blood, and from thence proceed melancholy *fumes* that trouble the mind.'— Ibid. p. 269.

108. *rede colera*. . . red cholera caused by too much bile and *blood* (sometimes called *red humour*). Burton speaks of a kind of melancholy of which the signs are these—'the veins of their eyes red, as well as their faces.'

113. *the humour of melancolye.* 'The name (melancholy) is imposed from the matter, and disease denominated from the material cause, as Bruel observes, μελανχολία *quasi* μελαιναχόλη, from black choler.' Fracastorius, in his second book of Intellect, calls those melancholy 'whom abundance of that same depraved humour of black choler hath so misaffected, that they become mad thence, and dote in most things or in all, belonging to election, will, or other manifest operations of the understanding.'—Burton's Anat. of Melancholy, p. 108, ed. 1805.

118. 'That cause many a man in sleep to be very distressed.'

120. *Catoun.* Cato de Moribus, l. ii. dist. 32; *somnia ne cures.* 'I observe by the way, that this distich is quoted by John of Salisbury, Polycrat. l. ii. c. 16, as a precept *viri sapientis.* In another place, l. vii. c. 9, he introduces his quotation of the first verse of dist. 20 (l. iii.) in this manner:—"*Ait vel Cato vel alius*, nam autor incertus est."'— Tyrwhitt.

121. *do no fors of* = take no notice of, pay no heed to.

143. 'Wormwood, *centaury*, pennyroyal, are likewise magnified and much prescribed, especially in hypochondrian melancholy, daily to be used, sod in whey. And because the spleen and blood are often mis-affected in melancholy, I may not omit endive, succory, dandelion, *fumitory*, &c., which cleanse the blood.'—Burton's Anat. of Mel. pp. 432, 433. See also p. 438, ed. 1845.

144. *ellebor.* Two kinds of hellebore are mentioned by old writers; 'white hellebore, called sneezing powder, a strong purger upward' (Burton's Anat. of Mel. p. 439), and '*black hellebore,* that most renowned plant, a famous purger of melancholy.'—Ibid. p. 442, ed. 1845.

150. *graunt mercy,* great thanks; this in later authors is corrupted into *grammercy* or *gramercy*.

156. *so mot I thee,* so may I thrive, (or prosper).

164. *Oon of the gretteste auctours.* 'Cicero, De Divin. l. i. c. 27, relates this and the following story, but in a different order, and with so many other differences, that one might be led to suspect that he was here quoted at second-hand, if it were not usual with Chaucer, in these stories of familiar life, to throw in a number of natural circumstances, not to be found in his original authors.'—Tyrwhitt. But Warton thinks that Chaucer took it rather from Valerius Maximus, who has the same story; i. 7.

184. *Oxes;* written *oxe* in Hl. Cp. Ln; where *oxe* corresponds to the older English gen. *oxan,* of an ox—*oxe* standing for *oxen* (as in Oxen-ford, see note on l. 285 of Prologue). Thus *oxes* and *oxe* are equivalent.

190. *took of this no keep,* took no heed of this, paid no attention to it.

201. *sooth to sayn,* to say (tell) the truth.

222. *gapinge.* The phrase *gaping upright* occurs elsewhere (see Knightes Tale, l. 1150), and signifies lying flat on the back with the mouth open. Cf. 'Dede he sate uprighte,' i. e. he lay on his back dead. —The Sowdone of Babyloyne, l. 530.

225. *Harrow,* a cry of distress; a cry for help. 'Harrow! alas! I swelt here as I go.'—The Ordinary; see vol. iii. p. 150, of the Ancient Drama.

227. *outsterte* (Elles.); *upsterte* (Harl.).

264. *And preyde him his viage for to lette,* And prayed him to abandon his journey.

265. *to abyde,* to stay where he was.

269. *my thinges,* my business-matters.

290. 'Kenelm succeeded his father Kenulph on the throne of the Mercians in 821 [Haydn, Book of Dates, says 819] at the age of seven years, and was murdered by order of his aunt, Quenedreda. He was subsequently made a saint, and his legend will be found in Capgrave, or in the Golden Legend.'—Wright.

St. Kenelm's day is Dec. 13. Alban Butler, in his Lives of the Saints, says:—[Kenulph] 'dying in 819, left his son Kenelm, a child only seven years old [see l. 297] heir to his crown, under the tutelage of his sister Quindride. This ambitious woman committed his person to the care of one Ascobert, whom she had hired to make away with him. The wicked minister decoyed the innocent child into an unfrequented wood, cut off his head, and buried him under a thorn-tree. His corpse is said to have been discovered by a heavenly ray of light which shone over the place, and by the following inscription:—

> 'In Clent cow-pasture, under a thorn,
> Of head bereft, lies Kenelm, king born.'

Milton tells the story in his History of Britain, bk. iv. ed. 1695, p. 218, and refers us to Matthew of Westminster. He adds that the 'inscription' was inside a note, which was miraculously dropped by a dove on the altar at Rome. Our great poet's version of it is:—

> 'Low in a Mead of Kine, under a thorn,
> Of Head bereft, li'th poor *Kenelm* King-born.'

Clent is near the boundary between Staffordshire and Worcestershire.

Neither of these accounts mention Kenelm's dream, but it is given in his Life, as printed in Early Eng. Poems, ed. Furnivall (Phil. Soc. 1862), p. 51. St. Kenelm dreamt that he saw a noble tree with wax-lights upon it, and that he climbed to the top of it; whereupon one of his best friends cut it down, and he was turned into a little bird, and flew up to heaven. The little bird denoted his soul, and the flight to heaven his death.

297. *For traisoun*, i.e. for fear of treason.

304. *Cipioun.* The Somnium Scipionis of Cicero, as annotated by Macrobius, was a favourite work during the middle ages.

318. See the Monkes Tale, B. 3917, and the note; in Ch. II., p. 193.

321. *Lo heer Andromacha.* Andromache's dream is not to be found in Homer. It is related in chapter xxiv. of Dares Phrygius, the authority for the history of the Trojan war most popular in the middle ages. See the Troy-book, ed. Panton and Donaldson (E. E. T. S.), l. 8425.

331. *as for conclusioun*, in conclusion.

334. *telle ... no store*, set no store by them; reckon them of no value; count them as useless.

336. *nevere a del*, never a whit, not in the slightest degree.

340. This line is repeated from the Compleynt of Mars, l. 61.

343–346. 'By way of quiet retaliation for Partlet's sarcasm, he cites a Latin proverbial saying, in l. 344, 'Mulier est hominis confusio,' which he turns into a pretended compliment by the false translation in ll. 345, 346.'—Marsh. Tyrwhitt quotes it from Vincent of Beauvais, Spec. Hist. x. 71.

355. *lay,* for *that lay.* Chaucer omits the relative, as is frequently done in Middle English poetry; see l. 80.

374. See note on ll. 35, 36.

385. Cf. Man of Lawes Tale, B. 421, and the note. See Prov. xiv. 13.

388. In the margin of MSS. E. and Hn. is written 'Petrus Comestor,' who is probably here referred to.

392. See the Squieres Tale, 287, and the note.

395. *col-fox,* a treacherous fox. Tyrwhitt quotes Heywood for *cole-prophet* and *colepoysoun.* See Glossary for the explanation of the prefix *col.*

407. *Genilon;* the traitor who caused the defeat of Charlemagne, and the death of Roland; see Book of the Duchesse, 1121, and the note in Skeat's edition of the Minor Poems.

408. See Vergil, Æn. ii. 259.

420. *bulte it to the bren,* sift the matter; cf. the phrase *to boult the bran.* See the argument in Troilus, iv. 967; cf. Milton, P. L. ii. 560.

422. *Boece,* i. e. Boethius. See note to Kn. Tale, 305.

Bradwardyn. Thomas Bradwardine was Proctor in the University of Oxford in the year 1325, and afterwards became Divinity Professor and Chancellor of the University. His chief work is 'On the Cause of God' (*De Causâ Dei*). See Morley's English Writers, ii. p. 62.

424. *for* was probably inserted by the scribes, who did not know that *nedely* was a word of three syllables. See l. 425, which is perhaps to be scanned with *Nedely* as a trisyllable, and *simple* as a monosyllable.

436. *Colde,* baneful, fatal. The proverb is Icelandic; 'köld eru opt kvenna-ráð,' cold (fatal) are oft women's counsels; Icel. Dict. s. v. *kaldr.*

451. *Phisiologus.* 'He alludes to a book in Latin metre, entitled Physiologus de Naturis xii. Animalium, by one Theobaldus, whose age is not known. The chapter *De Sirenis* begins thus:—

> Sirenae sunt monstra maris resonantia magnis
> Vocibus et modulis cantus formantia multis,
> Ad quas incaute veniunt saepissime nautae,
> Quae faciunt sompnum nimia dulcedine vocum.'—Tyrwhitt.

See The Bestiary, in Dr. Morris's Old English Miscellany, pp. 18, 207; and cf. Rom. Rose, 680.

457. In Douglas's Virgil, prol. to Book xi. st. 15, we have—

> 'Becum thow cowart, craudoun recryand,
> And by consent *cry cok,* thi deid is dycht;'

i. e. if thou turn coward, (and) a recreant craven, and consent to cry *cok,* thy death is imminent. In a note on this passage, Ruddiman says— '*Cok* is the sound which cocks utter when they are beaten.' But it is probable that this is only a guess, and that Douglas is merely quoting

Chaucer. To cry *cok! cok!* refers rather to the utterance of rapid cries of alarm, as fowls cry when scared. Brand (Pop. Antiq. ed. Ellis, ii. 58) copies Ruddiman's explanation of the above passage.

480. 'As I hope to retain the use of my two eyes.' So Havelok, l. 2545 :—

> 'So mote ich brouke mi Rith eie !'
>
> And l. 1743 :—'So mote ich brouke finger or to.'
>
> And l. 311 :— 'So brouke i euere mi blake swire !'

swire=neck. See also *Brouke* in the Glossary to Gamelyn, ed. Skeat.

492. *daun Burnel the Asse.* 'The story alluded to is in a poem of Nigellus Wireker, entitled Burnellus seu Speculum Stultorum, written in the time of Richard I. In the Chester Whitsun Playes, *Burnell* is used as a nickname for an ass. The original word was probably *brunell*, from its *brown* colour; as the *fox* below is called *Russel*, from his *red* colour.'—Tyrwhitt. The Latin story is printed in The Anglo-Latin Satirists of the Twelfth Century, ed. T. Wright, i. 55. There is an amusing translation of it in Lowland Scotch, printed as 'The Unicornis Tale' in Small's edition of Laing's Select Remains of Scotch Poetry, ed. 1885, p. 285. It tells how a certain young Gundulfus broke a cock's leg by throwing a stone at him. On the morning of the day when Gundulfus was to be ordained and to receive a benefice, the cock took his revenge by not crowing till much later than usual; and so Gundulfus was too late for the ceremony, and lost his benefice. Cf. Warton, Hist. E. P., ed. 1871, ii. 352. As to the name *Russel*, see note to l. 29.

509. *Ecclesiaste;* not Ecclesiastes, but Ecclesiasticus, xii. 10, 11, 16. Cf. Tale of Melibeus, B. 2368.

515. Tyrwhitt cites the O. F. form *gargate* from the Roman de Rou. Several examples of it are given by Godefroy.

527. *O Gaufred.* 'He alludes to a passage in the Nova Poetria of Geoffrey de Vinsauf, published not long after the death of Richard I. In this work the author has not only given instructions for composing in the different styles of poetry, but also examples. His specimen of the plaintive style begins thus :—

> Neustria, sub clypeo regis defensa Ricardi,
> Indefensa modo, gestu testare dolorem ;
> Exundent oculi lacrymas ; exterminet ora
> Pallor ; connodet digitos tortura ; cruentet
> Interiora dolor, et verberet aethera clamor ;
> Tota peris ex morte sua. Mors non fuit ejus,
> Sed tua, non una, sed publica mortis origo.
> *O Veneris lacrymosa* dies ! O sydus amarum !
> Illa dies tua nox fuit, et Venus illa venenum.
> Illa dedit vulnus, &c.

These lines are sufficient to show the object and the propriety of

Chaucer's ridicule. The whole poem is printed in Leyser's Hist. Poet. Med. Ævi, pp. 862–978.'—Tyrwhitt.

528. Richard I. died on April 6, 1199, on Tuesday; but he received his wound on Friday, March 26.

530. *Why ne hadde I* = O that I had.

537. *streite swerd* = drawn (naked) sword. Cf. Aeneid, ii. 333, 334 :—

> 'Stat *ferri acies* mucrone corusco
> *Stricta*, parata neci.'

538. See Aeneid, ii. 550–553.

543. *Hasdrubal;* not Hannibal's brother, but the King of Carthage when the Romans burnt it, B. C. 146. Hasdrubal slew himself; and his wife and her two sons burnt themselves in despair; see Orosius, iv. 13. 3, or Ælfred's translation, ed. Sweet, p. 212. Lydgate has the story in his Fall of Princes, bk. v. capp. 12 and 27.

574. Walsingham relates how, in 1381, Jakke Straw and his men killed many Flemings 'cum clamore consueto.' He also speaks of the noise made by the rebels as 'clamor horrendissimus.' See *Jakke* in Tyrwhitt's Glossary.

580. *houped.* See Piers Plowman, ed. Wright, p. 127, '*houped* after Hunger, that herde hym,' &c.; or ed. Skeat (Clarendon Press), B. vi. 174.

625. *My Lord.* A side-note in MS. E. explains this to refer to the Archbishop of Canterbury; probably William Courtenay, archbishop from 1381 to 1396.

Additional Note to the Knightes Tale; l. 319.

The note on p. 175 may be amended. The fable is practically the same as that of 'The Lion, the Tiger, and the Fox' in Croxall's edition of Æsop's Fables. In the modern edition by James (London, 1852), it is Fable No. 141, and is entitled 'The Lion, the Bear, and the Fox.' See N. and Q. 7 S. vi. 53, 90, 236.

GLOSSARY.

A = Prologue.   B = Knightes Tale.   c = Nonne Prestes Tale.

The following are the chief contractions used :—

A.S.	= Anglo-Saxon.	Lat.	= Latin.
Dan.	= Danish.	M. E.	= Middle English.
Du.	= Dutch.	O. F.	= Old French.
F.	= French.	O. H. Ger.	= Old High German.
Ger.	= German.	Prompt. Parv.	= Promptorium Par-
Goth.	= Gothic.		vulorum.
Gr.	= Greek.	Prov. Engl.	= Provincial English.
Icel.	= Icelandic.	Sp.	= Spanish.
It.	= Italian.	Sw.	= Swedish.

An asterisk prefixed to a form signifies that such a form is theoretical.

A.

A, one, single. A.S. *án*, Ger. *ein*, one ; Eng. indef. article *an* or *a*. Cf. M. E. *o*, *oo*, one ; *ta*, *to*, the one, the first.

A, in, on ; cf. *a-night*, B 184 ; *a-morwe*, A 822 ; *a-day*, in the day, B 1765 ; *a Goddes name*, in God's name, A 854 ; *a-three*, in three, B 2076. Cf. Mod. Eng. *a-foot*, *a-sleep*, *a-hunting*, *a-building*, &c. A.S. and O.S. *an*, in, on. It is still used in the South of England.

Abbey, abbey : C 34.

Able, fit, capable, adapted : A 167. Lat. *habilis* (Lat. *habeo*, to have), convenient, fit : O.F. *habile*, able, expert, fit.

Aboghte (the pret. of *abegge* or *abye*), atoned for, suffered for : B 1445 ; pp. *aboght*, 2242. A.S. *ábycgan*, to redeem, pay the purchase-money, to pay the penalty (from *bycgan*, to buy).

Cf. the modern expression ' to buy it dear.' 'So shalt thou honge in helle and *bye* it dere :' Occleve, De Reg. Princip. 162. Shakespeare and Milton have, from similarity of sound, given the sense of *abye* to the verb *abide*, as in the following examples :—

'If it be found so, some will dear *abide* it.'—Julius Cæsar, iii. 2. 119.

'Disparage not the faith thou dost not know,

Lest to thy peril thou *abide* it dear.'—Mids. Night's Dream, iii. 2. 175.

'How dearly I *abide* that boast so vain.'—Paradise Lost, iv. 87.

Abood, delay : B 107. See **Abyde**.

Aboven, above : A 53. A.S. *ábufan*, *be-ufan*, *ufan* ; Du. *boven*, above. Cf. the M. E. forms *buve*, *buven*, *aboon*, above.

Abrayde, started (suddenly), a-woke: C 188. A.S. *bregdan,* to move, turn, weave; Icel. *bregða,* to draw out a sword, to pull down, to awake, to leap. The M. E. *braide* has all these meanings, and signifies also to cry out suddenly, to scold; whence Eng. *braid, upbraid.* The A.S. *brægd, bregd,* Icel. *bragð,* signifies a sudden start, blow, deceit; hence the M. E. phrase 'at a braid,' = in a trice. The Icel. *bragð* is also applied to the features or to the gestures, by which an individual is characterized; hence Prov. Eng. *braid,* to resemble, pretend; Eng. *braid,* appearance (Bailey). Shakespeare uses *braid* = *braided,* of deceitful manner.

Abregge, to shorten, *abridge:* B 2141. F. *a-breger;* Lat. *abbreviare.* Cf. M. E. *agregge, a-gredge,* to aggravate, from F. *aggréger* (from Lat. *gravis*).

Abyde, Abyden (pret. *abod, a-bood;* pp. *abiden*), abide, delay, wait for, await: B 69, 2124; C 260. A.S. *abídan, bídan,* to wait, remain; Goth. *beidan,* to expect.

Accomplice, to accomplish: B 2006.

Accord, Acord, agreement: A 838, C 59.

Achat, purchase: A 571. O. F. *achepter,* to buy; F. *acheter,* It. *accattare,* to acquire, get; Low Lat. *accaptare.* Cf. M. E. *acates, cates,* victuals, provision, delicacies; *catery,* store-room; Eng. *cater.* F. *achat,* purchase.

Achatour, purchaser, caterer: A 568. See **Achat.**

Acordaunt, according to, agreeing, suitable: A 37.

Acorde, to agree, suit: A 244, 830; *pp.* **Acorded,** B 356. F. *accorder,* to agree (from Lat. *cor,* the heart).

Adamant, adamant: B 1132. Gr. ἀ-δάμας (*a* privative, δαμάω, to tame, subdue), the hardest metal, probably steel (also the diamond); whence Eng. *adamantine.*

'In *adamantine* chains and penal fire.'—Milton, Par. Lost, i. 48. Adamant is sometimes (but incorrectly) applied to the *magnet* or *loadstone.* Cf. 'Well she's a most attractive *adamant.*'—T. Heywood, ed. Collier, p. 8.

Adoun, down, downwards, below: A 393; cf. *doun,* B 245. A.S. *of-dúne* (cf. O. F. *à val,* to the valley, downwards), from the hill, downwards; from *dún,* a hill, down.

Adrad, *pp.* in great dread, afraid: A 605. Cf. M. E. *of-drad,* much afraid; where the prefix *of* is intensive, like *for-,* Lat. *per-.*

Aferd, Afered, in great fear, afraid: A 628, B 660. Cf. M. E. *ferd, ferdnesse,* fear; *offered,* much afraid. See **Adrad.**

Affeccioun, affection, hope: B 300.

Affermed, confirmed: B 1491.

Affrayed, terrified, scared: C 458. F. *effrayer,* to scare, appal; *effroi,* terror: whence *affray.*

Affyle, to file, polish: A 712. F. *affiler,* It. *affilare,* to sharpen: F. *fil,* edge; Lat. *filum,* a thread.

Afright, in fright, afraid: C 75. From A.S. *fyrhtu,* fright. Cf. Goth. *faurhts,* timid.

Agast, terrified, *aghast:* B 1483; **Agaste him,** was terrified: B 1566. Cf. M. E. *gastlic,* ghastly, *gastnes,* fear; A. S. *gǽstan,* Goth. *us-gaisjan,* to terrify; *us-geisnan,* to be amazed; Dan. *gys,* terror.

Agayn, Ageyn, again, against, towards: A 66, 801. A.S. *on-géan, on-gén, a-gén,* opposite, towards, against; *géan,* opposite, against; O. Sw. *gen,* opposite; Ger. *gegen,* against.

Agon, Agoon, gone, past, B 418, 924; the past participle of M. E. verb *agon*, to go, pass away. A. S. *ágán, ágangan*. We also meet with *ygo* in the same sense, and some etymologists have erroneously supposed that the prefix *a-* is a corruption of *y-*.

Agrief, in grief: C 73. 'To take it *agrief*' = to take it amiss, feel aggrieved, be displeased.

Al, all, whole (cf. *al a* = a whole, A 584); quite, wholly (cf. *al redy, al armed*, &c.); although (cf. *al speke he, al have I, al be it*): A 71, 76, 297, 734, B 1406. See **Alle**.

Alaunts, a species of dog: B 1290. They were used for hunting the boar. Sp. and Ital. *alano*. Tyrwhitt says they were much esteemed in Italy in the fourteenth century. *Gualv. de la Flamma* (ap. Murator. Antiq. Med. Æ. t. ii. p. 394) commends the governors of Milan '*quod equos emissarios equabus magnis commiscuerunt, et procreati sunt in nostro territorio* DESTRARII *nobiles, qui in magno pretio habentur. Item* CANES ALANOS *altae staturae et mirabilis fortitudinis nutrire studuerunt.*'

Al be, although: A 297.

Alderbest. See **Aller**.

Ale-stake, a horizontal stake projecting from an ale-house to support a sign, A 667; '*le moy d'une taverne*' (Palsgrave). It appears that a *bush* was often placed at the end of the ale-stake.

Algate, always: A 571. M. E. *algates;* cf. *swagate,* thus; North Prov. Eng. *gate,* way; Eng. *gait;* Icel. *gata,* a path; Sw. *gata,* way, street.

Alighte, (pp. *alight*), alighted: A 722, B 125. Cf. the phrase 'to *light* upon.' A. S. *álihtan,* to descend, alight.

Alle, pl. of *al* (all): A 26, 53.

Aller, of all (gen. pl. of *al*). The older forms are *alra, alre, aller*, later *alder, alther;* our *aller*, of us all, A 823; *hir aller*, of them all, A 586; *alderbest*, best of all, A 710, &c. The insertion of *d* or *th* serves merely to strengthen the word, as in *lend, spend* (older forms *lene, spene*).

Alliaunce, alliance: B 2115. F. *allier,* to ally; Lat. *ligare,* to tie; *alligare,* to bind.

Also, as: A 730. A. S. *ealswá;* M. E. *al-se, ase*. These forms shew that *as* is a contraction from *al-so*. Cf. Ger. *also, als;* O. Fris. *alsa, alse, æsa, ase*.

Amblere, a nag: A 469.

Amiddes, amidst, in the middle: B 1151.

Amonges, amongst: A 759.

Amorwe, on the morrow: A 822.

Amounte, to amount to, signify, denote: B 1504.

And = *an,* if: B 356.

Anhanged, hung up, C 242. The prefix *an* = on, up.

Anlas (or **Anelace**), a kind of knife or dagger, usually worn at the girdle: A 357.

Anoint, anointed: A 199.

Anon, Anoon, *in one* (instant), anon: A 32. M. E. *an an,* or *on an*.

Apalled, become weak, feeble, B 2195; originally 'made *pale*.' Chaucer speaks of 'an old *appalled* wight,' i. e. a man enfeebled through old age. It is connected with O. F. *appalir,* to grow pale; see Murray's Dict.

Apayd, pleased, satisfied: B 1010. F. *payer,* to satisfy, pay (Lat. *pacare*); whence M. E. *pay,* satisfaction, gratification, pleasure; Eng. *pay*.

Ape, metaphorically, a fool: A 706.

Apothecarie, apothecary: A 425.

Apparailling, preparation: B 2055.

F. *appareiller*, to fit, suit ; *pareil*, like ; Lat. *par*, equal, like. The original meaning of *appareiller* is to join like to like.

Appetyt, desire, appetite : B 822.

Apyked, trimmed : A 365. See **Piked.**

Aqueyntaunce, acquaintance : A 245.

Arest, a support for the spear when couched for the attack : B 1744. It is sometimes written *rest*. 'And there was a squyer called Albert of Colayne, he turned and couched the spere in the *rest*, and came rennyng agaynst the lorde of Poytrell.'— Berner's Froissart, i. 68.

Areste, seizure, custody : B 452, C 80.

Areste, to stop (a horse) : A 827.

Aretted, ascribed, imputed, deemed : B 1871. According to Cowell a person is *aretted* 'that is convented before a judge, and charged with a crime.' O. F. *areter, aretter*, to impute ; from Lat. *ad* and *reputare* ; see *Aret* in Murray's Dict.

Arm-greet, as thick as a man's arm : B 1287.

Armipotente, mighty in arms : B 1124.

Array, state, situation, dress, equipage : A 41, B 76.

Arrayed, set in order, dressed, adorned, equipped : B 1188. It. *arredare*, to prepare, get ready ; O. F. *arroyer, arréer*, dispose, fit out. The root is to be found in the Teutonic dialects. Cf. Sw. *reda*, to prepare ; *reda*, order ; A.S. *ráed* ; Ger. *bereit*, ready ; Dan. *rede*, plain, straight, clear.

Arrerage, arrears : A 602.

Arresten, to stop, seize, C 200. F. *arrester* (from Lat. *restare*, to stand still), to bring one to stand, to seize his person.

Ars-metrik, arithmetic : B 1040.

Arwe, arrow : A 104. A.S. *arewe* ; Icel. *ör* (gen. *örvar*).

Aryve, arrival, or perhaps disembarkation (of troops) : A 60. F. *arriver*, to arrive, from Lat. *ad-ripare*, to come to shore (*ripa*, shore).

As, as if : A 636, C 570.

Aslake, to moderate, appease : B 902. Icel. *slakr*, loose ; Norw. *slekkja*, to make slack, to *slake*, quench ; *slokna*, to go out, faint ; M. E. *sloke*. With this root we must connect A. S. *slacian*, relax, *slack* ; *sleac*, slack ; also *slack*-lime, *slag* of a furnace.

As nouthe, As now, at present : A 462, B 1406. Cf. M.E. *as-swiðe*, immediately ; *as-now, als-tite*, at once. *nouðe* = A.S. *nú* (now) and *ðá* (then). See **Nouthe.**

A-sonder, asunder : A 491.

Assaut, assault : B 131. F. *assaillir*, to assail ; *saillir*, to leap, *sally* ; Lat. *salire*, to leap, spring.

Assayed, tried : B 953. F. *essayer*, to try, *essay*.

Asseged, besieged : B 23. F. *siège* ; It. *sedia, seggia*, a seat or sitting ; It. *assedio*, with same sense as Lat. *obsidium*, the sitting down before a town in a hostile way.

Asshen, ashes : B 444.

Assoilling, absolution, acquittal : A 661. O. F. *assoiller*, Lat. *absolvere*, to loose from.

Assuren, to make sure, confirm : B 1066.

Assyse, assize : A 314. F. *asseoir*, to set (Lat. *assidere*) ; *assis*, set, seated ; *assise*, a settled tax ; *cour d'assise*, a court held on a set day. Cf. It. *assisa*, a settled pattern of dress ; Eng. *size*.

Astat, estate, rank. See **Estat.**

Asterte, to escape, B 737 : pp. *astert*, B 734. See **Sterte.**

Astoned, astonished : B 1503.

O.F. *estonnir*, to astonish, amaze (Lat. **extonare*, to thunder at).

Astored, stored: A 609.

Asur, azure: C 42.

Athamaunte, adamant: B 447.

Atrede, to surpass in council, outwit: B 1591. *at-* = A.S. *æt-*, prefix; cf. G. *ent-*, prefix.

At-renne, out-run: B 1591. See **Renne**.

Atte, at the: M.E. *at-tham*, *at-than*. Cf. *atte beste*, in the best manner, A 29, 749; *atte laste*, at the last, A 707; *atte fulle* = fully, A 651.

Attempree, *adj.* temperate, moderate: C 18.

Atteyne, to attain: B 385. F. *atteindre* (Lat. *tangere*, to touch, *attingere*, to reach to).

Auctoritee, authority; a text of Scripture, or some respectable writer: B 2142, C 155.

Auctours, authors, writers of credit: C 164.

Auter, altar: B 1047.

Avaunce, to be of advantage, be profitable: A 246. F. *avancer*, to push forward; *avant*, It. *avante*, before, forwards; Lat. *ab ante*.

Avaunt, boast, *vaunt :* A 227.

Avauntage, advantage: B 435. See **Avaunce**.

Avauntour, boaster: C 97.

Aventure, chance, luck, misfortune, adventure : A 25, 795. O.F. *avenir* (Lat. *advenire*), to happen. Hence Eng. *peradventure*.

Avisioun, vision : C 294.

Avow, vow, promise : B 1379.

Avoy, fie ! C 88. O.F. *avoi !* fie ! (interjection), of which numerous examples are given in Godefroy. (Of unknown origin).

Avys, advice, consideration, opinion : A 786, B 1010. O.F. *avis*, It. *avviso*, view, opinion, settlement ; Lat. *uisum*, from *uideri*.

Awayt, watch, wait : C 405. O.F. *waiter*, *gaiter*. This is connected with *wake*. A.S. *wæcan*, Goth. *wakan*, Icel. *vaka*, to be vigilant ; Eng. *watch*, *waits*, to *await*.

Awe, fear, dread : A 654. Icel. *agi*, Goth. *agis*, fear ; Goth. *ogan*, to fear.

Axe, to ask : B 489. A.S. *ácsian*.

Axing, asking, demand : B 968.

Ay, ever, aye : A 63.

Ayeins, against : B 929.

Ayel, a grandfather : B 1619. F. *aïeul*, O.F. *ael*, dimin. from Lat. *avus*.

B.

Bacheler, Bachiller, an unmarried man, *bachelor*, a knight : A 80. O.F. *bacelle*, *bacelote*, *bachellette*, a servant, apprentice ; *bacelerie*, youth ; *bachelage*, apprenticeship, art and study of chivalry ; *bachelier*, a young man, an aspirant to knighthood.

Bacoun, bacon : C 25. O.F. *bacon*, M.Du. *backe*, a pig.

Baillif, bailiff : A 603. M.E. *baili*. 'He is my ryve [=reeve] and *bayly*, Inquilinus prediorum urbicorum et rusticorum.'—Horman. F. *bailli*, It. *balivo*, *bailo*, from Low Lat. *baiulus*, a bearer, with the later meanings of (1) a nurse, (2) a tutor. From F. *bailler* (Lat. *baiulare*), to hand over, comes Eng. *bail*. In the Wicliffite versions, *baili* seems to imply the charge or office : 'ȝelde rekenyng of thi *baili*, for thou mighte not now be *baili*.'— Luc. xvi. 2.

Bak, back : C 516.

Bake = *baken*, baked : A 343. This verb now belongs to the *weak* conjugation.

Balled, bald : A 198, B 1660. The original meaning seems to have

been (1) shining, (2) white (as in *bald*-faced stag). Cf. Welsh *ceffyl bàl*, a horse having a white streak on the forehead.

Bane, destruction, death: B 239, 823. A.S. *bana, bona,* O.H. Ger. *bana,* Fris. *bona,* Icel. *bani,* destruction, a violent death, *bane ;* Goth. *banja,* a wound; Icel. *bana,* to slay. The M. E. *bane* sometimes signifies poison, whence hen-*bane,* fly-*bane.*

Baner, a banner: B 120, 1552. Mid. Lat. *banera, bannerium ;* F. *bannière ;* It. *bandiera.* Mr. Wedgwood suggests the Goth. *bandwo,* a sign or token, as the root, which is connected with Eng. *bind.*

Bar, bore, carried: A 105, 158, 558, 618 ; *baren us,* conducted ourselves, A 721. See **Bere.**

Barbour, a barber, B 1167. F. *barbier,* from Lat. *barba,* the beard.

Bare, bare, open: A 683, B 2019.

Bareyn, Bareyne, barren, devoid of : B 386, 1119. O.F. *baraigne, brehaigne,* sterile ; of uncertain origin.

Baronage, an assembly of barons: B 2238. It. *barone,* Sp. *varon,* F. *baron,* O.F. *baron,* accus. case of O. F. *ber, bar,* a man. Originally man, husband. 'Lo *bar* non es creat per la femna mas la femna per lo *baro*'— 'The man was not created for the woman, but the woman for the man ;' Raynouard. In our own law it was used for married men ; *baron* and *femme,* man and wife.

Barre, bar or bolt of a door: B 217. O.F. *barre,* Mid. Lat. *barra ;* of unknown origin. *Barricade* and *barrier* are formed directly from the F. *barre.* Cf. Sp. *barras,* bars ; F. *embarras,* Eng. *embarrassed.*

Barres, ornaments of a girdle : A 329. See note on l. 329 of Prologue.

Batailed, embattled : C 40. O.F. *batillé, bastillé,* built as a bastille or fortress, furnished with turrets.

Bataille, battle: A 61, B 130. F. *bataille,* a battle ; it also signifies, like M.E. *bataille,* a squadron, an armed host, a *battalion.* It. *battere;* F. *battre,* to beat. With the root *bat* are connected *battery, batter.*

Bawdrik, *baudrick,* or *baldrick,* belt, or girdle, worn transversely: A 116. It sometimes signified the *cingulum* or military belt. It was used in the sixteenth century for the jewelled ornament worn round the neck both by ladies and noblemen. O.F. *baudré,* O. H. Ger. *balderich ;* perhaps from Lat. *balteus,* a belt.

Be, (1) to be, B 1377 ; (2) been, A 60.

Bede, a bead (pl. *bedes*) : A 159. A.S. *gebed,* O.Sax. *beda,* O. Fris. *bede,* a prayer ; O. Sax. *bedon,* to pray. 'Beads were strung on a string, and originally used for the purpose of helping the memory in reciting a certain tale of prayers or doxologies. To bid one's *bedes* or *beads* was to say one's prayers.'—Wedgwood. 'Praying in gibberish, and mumbling of *beads*.'—Burton's Anat. of Mel. p. 26, ed. 1845.

Been, (1) to be ; (2) are, A 178 ; (3) been, A 199.

Beer, did bear: C 516.

Beggere, a beggar : A 252.

Beggestere, a beggar, properly a female beggar : A 242.

Bem, Beem, beam, rafter (pl. *bemes*) : C 122. A.S. *béam,* a tree, stick, beam ; Ger. *Baum,*

Du. *boom*, a tree. Cf. *boom* of a vessel, *beam* in horn-*beam*.

Bemes, trumpets, horns: C 578. A. S. *béme*, *býme*, a trumpet.

Ben, (1) to be. See **Been**.

Benigne, kind: A 518.

Bent, declivity of a hill, a plain, open field: dat. *bente*, B 1123. A. S. *beonet* (in place-names); cognate with G. *binse*, rush, reed, stout grass.

Berd, beard: A 270, B 1272.

Bere, to bear, to carry, to conduct oneself, behave: A 796; to pierce, strike, B 1398; as 'to *bere* through' = to pierce through. Imper. *ber*, B 1902. A. S. *beran*; Goth. *bairan*.

Bere, a bier: B 2013.

Bere, a bear: B 782.

Berking, barking: C 566. A. S. *beorcan*, to bark; Icel. *braka*, to crash; Dan. *brag*, crack, crash; O. H. Ger. *gebreh*, A. S. *gebræc*, a crash.

Berye, a berry: A 207.

Beste, a beast: B 451, 1118.

Bet, better: A 242. A. S. *bet*; O. H. Ger. *baz*. See **Bete**. The M. E. *go bet* = hasten, go along quickly.

Bete, (1) to beat, (2) beaten, ornamented. See **Ybete**.

Bete, to kindle, light: B 1395. The literal meaning is to mend, repair. A. S. *bétan*, O. Fris. *beta*, Goth. *bótjan*, to amend, repair, expiate. From A. S. *bót*, whence Eng. *boot*, *bootless*; cf. *better*.

Beth (3rd pers. sing. of *Been*), is; (imp. pl.), be: C 510.

Bi-bled, covered over with blood: B 1144.

Bifalle, to befall, B 947; *pp.* befallen, A 795.

Bifel, befell: A 19, B 151.

Bifore, **Biforen**, before: A 377, 450; B 518.

Bigan, began: A 44, B 690.

Biginne, to begin: A 42.

Bigonne, *pp.* begun: A 52.

Biholde, to behold (pret. *biheld*, pp. *biholde*, *biholden*): B 443, 1435.

Bihote, promise: B 996. A. S. *behátan*, to promise, vow.

Bihynde, behind: B 192.

Biknewe, *pt. pl.* acknowledged, confessed: C 241.

Biknowe, to acknowledge: B 698.

Bile, bill (of a bird): C 41. A. S. *bile*.

Biloved, beloved: A 215, B 571.

Binethe, beneath: C 133.

Binne, bin, chest: A 593. It is sometimes confused with *bing*, which seems to have signified originally a heap; cf. Sw. *binge*, heap; Icel. *bunga*, a convexity.

'You might have seen them throng out of the town,
Like ants when they do spoil the *bing* of corn.'—Surrey's Poems, p. 191, ed. Bell.

Biquethe, to bequeath: B 1910. A. S. *cweðan*, to say; whence Eng. *quoth*.

Biraft, bereft: B 503. A. S. *beréafian*, to deprive of, strip; *réafian*, to spoil, reave.

Biseken, to beseech: B 60. A. S. *sécan*, to seek, enquire, ask for, (we have the same root in *forsake*). Cf. Goth. *sakan*, to object, reprove; Ger. *Sache*, a complaint; M. E. *sake*, strife, contention; Eng. *sake*.

Bisette, to employ, use, arrange (pret. *bisette*, pp. *biset*): A 279, B 2154.

Bismotered, spotted, smutted: A 76. A. S. *besmitan*, to defile, besmut; Du. *smodderen*, to dirty, daub. Cf. Dan. *smuds*, Sw. *smuts*, spot, splash, dirt; Eng. *smut*, *smutch*, *smudgy*, &c.

Bisy, busy, industrious, anxious: A 321.

Bisyde, beside, near: A 445.

Bisydes, beside, near: A 402.

Bisynesse, labour, care, anxiety: A 520, B 149.

Bit (3rd pers. sing. of *bidden*), bids: A 187.

Bithoght, 'am bethoght,' have thought of, have called to mind: A 767.

Bitwene, between: B 2247. See **Bitwixe**.

Bitwixe, betwixt: A 277. A.S. *betwuh*, *betweox*. The second element *-tweox* is connected with *two*, and with *be-tween*.

Bitwixen, betwixt, between: B 22.

Biwreye, to make known, bewray, betray: B 1371, C 231. A.S. *wrégan*, G. *rügen*, to discover, accuse.

Blak, black (def. form. and pl. *blake*): A 557, B 41, 1659. A.S. *blæc*, black.

Blankmanger, some compound of capon minced, with cream, sugar, and flour: A 387.

Blede, to bleed, B 943 (pret. *bledde*, A 145, pp. *bled*).

Bleynte, blenched, started back: B 220. M.E. *blenchen*, to *blench*, glance.

Blis, dat. **Blisse**, bliss: B 372. A.S. *blis*, joy, gladness, is formed from the adj. *blíðe*, joyful. Cf. A.S. *blíðsian*, to rejoice.

Blisful, blessed, blissful: A 17, 770.

Blyve, quickly, forthwith: B 1839. M.E. *bilife*. Cf. Dan. *oplive*, to quicken, enliven, and the two senses of our Eng. *quick*.

Bocher, a butcher: B 1167. F. *boucher*, from *bouc*, a goat. Cf. It. *becco*, a goat; *beccaro*, a butcher; *boccino*, young beef, veal; *bocciero*, a butcher.

Bok (pl. *bokes*), a book: A 294.

Bokeler, buckler: A 112, 471. F. *bouclier*, a shield with a central boss, from *boucle*, protuberance; Mid. Lat. *buccula scuti*. It is of course connected with

Eng. *buckle*, F. *boucle*; Ger. *Buckel*, a stud; all from Lat. *bucca*, the cheek.

Bokelinge, buckling: B 1645.

Boket, a bucket: B 675. Cf. O. F. *buquet*, a milk-pail (Godefroy); cf. A.S. *búc*, a jug.

Bole, bull; pl. *boles*: B 1281.

Bond, bound, = M. E. *band* (pret. of *binden*): B 2133.

Bone, prayer, petition, *boon*: B 1411. Icel. *bón*, prayer; A.S. *bén*.

Boon, bone (pl. *bones*): A 546, B 319. The *oo* arises out of an earlier *á*, as A.S. *bán* = M. E. *bōn*.

Boor, boar (pl. *bores*): B 800. A.S. *bár*, Du. *beer*.

Boras, borax: A 630.

Bord, table: A 52, C 23. A.S. *bord*, table, margin; Du. *boord*, edge, border. See note on l. 52 of Prol.

Bore, *pp.* born: B 684.

Bores. See **Boor**.

Born, *pp.* conducted: A 87.

Borwe, pledge, security: B 764. A.S. *borh*, security, pledge; *borgian*, to lend (on security). Cf. Ger. *Bürge*, a surety, from *bergan*, to protect; *bürgen*, to become a surety, to give bail for another.

Bote, remedy: A 424. See **Bete**.

Boteler, butler: C 314. M.E. *botelere*, F. *bouteillier*. It is derived from O. F. *botel*, F. *bouteille*, a bottle.

Botes, boots: A 203, 273. Cf. F. *botte*, boot; Low Lat. *bota*. 'The boot appears to have originally been, like the Irish brogue and Indian mocassin, a sort of bag of skin or leather, enveloping the foot and laced on the instep.' (Wedgwood.)

Bothe, both: B 973. Cf. A.S. *begen*, *bá*; Goth. *bai*, *baioths*; Icel. *báðir*. Probably the *bá*

(M. E. *bo*), is seen also in Latin *am-bo*, Gr. ἄμ-φω. The E. *both*, M. E. *bo-the*, is composed of M. E. *bo*, and the def. art. *the* (see Murray).

Botme, bottom: C 281. A.S. *botme*, M. E. *bothem*, M. Du. *bodem*. Cf. *bottom*, a small valley, Lat. *fundus*, and Gr. πυθμήν.

Bouk, body: B 1888. A.S. *búc*, belly; Icel. *búkr*, the body; Sc. *bouk*, trunk, body. Early confused with *bulk*.

Bour, inner room: C 12. A.S. *búr*, bower, inner chamber; Prov. Eng. *boor*, a parlour.

Bowes, boughs: B 2059.

Bracer, guard for the arm: A 111.

Brak (the pret. of *breke*), broke: B 610. See **Breke**.

Bras, brass: C 578.

Brast (the pret. of *bersten* or *bresten*), burst: C 398. It is sometimes written *barst*; the pp. was *brusten*, *bursten*, or *borsten*. A.S. *berstan*; Du. *bersten*; Icel. *bresta*, to burst. See **Bresten**.

Braun, muscle (pl. *braunes*): A 546, B 1277. M.E. *brahun*. Cf. Eng. *brawny*; Sc. *brand*, calf of the leg; O. F. *braion*, *braoun*, a lump of flesh; from O.H.G. *bráto*, a piece of flesh for roasting; cf. Fris. *braeye*, Low Ger. *bráe*, a lump of flesh, calf of the leg, flesh of a leg of pork. In M.E. writers *brawne* often signifies the flesh of a boar.

Braunche, a branch: B 209. F. *branche*.

Brayde, started. See **Abrayde**.

Brede, breadth: B 1112. A.S. *brédu*, O. Fris. *bréde*, breadth; from A.S. *brád*, broad.

Breed, bread: A 147.

Breem, a fresh-water fish, bream: A 350. O. F. *bresme*, O. H. Ger. *brahsema*.

Breeth, breath: A 5. The A.S. *bráð* signifies vapour, smell.

Breke, to break (pret. *brak*, *brok*; pp. *broke*, *ibroken*): A 551. See **Brak**.

Breme, fiercely, furiously: B 841. A.S. *bréme*, loud, keen; M.E. *bream*, fierce. 'The Saxons fled, before that were full *brime.*' (Hardyng, p. 115.) Cf. Lat. *fremo*, to roar. Professor Max Müller has the following capital note on certain analogues connected with this root:—'What is the English *brim*? We say a glass is *brim full*, or we fill our glasses to the *brim*, which means simply " to the edge." We also speak of the brim of a hat, the Ger. *Bräme*. Now originally *brim* [in M. E. *brim* = sea, ocean] did not mean every kind of edge or verge, but only the line which separates the land from the sea. It is derived from the root *bhram*, which, as it ought, exhibits *bh* in Sanskrit, and means to *whirl about*, applied to fire, such as *bhrama*, the leaping flame, or to water, such as *bhrama*, a whirlpool, or to air, such as *bhŕimi*, a whirlwind. Now what was called *æstus* by the Romans, namely the swell or surge of the sea, where the waves seemed to foam, to flame and to smoke (hence æstuary), the same point was called by the Teutonic nations the *whirl* or the *brim*. After meaning the border-line between land and sea, it came to mean any border, though in the expression "fill your glasses to the brim" we still imagine to see the original conception of the sea rushing or pouring in toward the dry land. In Greek we have a derivative verb *phrimássein*, to toss about; in Lat. *fremo*, chiefly in the sense of raging or roaring, and perhaps *frendo*, to gnash, are akin to this root. In the Teutonic languages other words of a totally different character must be traced back to the same original conception of *bhram*, to whirl, to be confused, to be rolled up together, namely, *bramble, broom*, &c.'—Lectures on the Science of Language, Second Series, pp. 217, 218.

Bren, bran: c 420. Welsh *bren*, bran; O.F. *bren*. Cf. Gael. *brein*, stink; F. *bren*, ordure.

Brend, burnished, bright: B 1304.

Brende (pp. *brend, brent*), burnt: B 1567. See **Brenne**.

Brenne, to burn: B 1473. A.S. *brennan, bernan*, M. E. *bernen*, Goth. *brannjan*, to burn. We have the same root in *brim*-stone, M. E. *brenstone*.

Brenningly, fiercely, ardently: B 706.

Brenning, sb. burning: B 138; *pres. part.* 1142.

Brent, burnt: B 1159. See **Brenne**.

Breres, briers: B 674. A.S. *brêr*, a brier.

Brest, bursteth: B 1752.

Brest, breast: A 115, 131.

Brest-plat, breast-plate: B 1262.

Bresten, to burst (pret. *brast*, pp. *borsten, bursten*), B 1122: hence *to-breste*, break in two, B 1753. See **Brast**.

Bretful, brimfull: A 687, B 1306. Tyrwhitt says that the sense of this word is much clearer than the etymology. 'But cf. Sw. *brädfull*, brimfull, with Sw. *brädd*, a brim.'—Skeat. *Bretful* = M. E. *brurdful* = full to the brim, which is connected with A.S. *brerd*, brink, brim.

Bretherhed, brotherhood, brothers of a religious order: A 511.

Briddes, birds: c 61. A.S. *brid*, a (young) bird. So Shakespeare speaks of 'the cuckoo's *bird;*'

1 Hen. IV. v. 1. 60. Low Ger. *bridde*, a chicken.

Brimstoon, brimstone: A 629. M. E. *brenstone* = burning stone, from *brennen*, to burn.

Bristles, bristles: A 556. A.S. *byrst*, bristle; Du. *borstel*; Ger. *Borste*.

Broche, a brooch: A 160. O.F. *broche*, Sp. *broche*, a clasp. Cf. Lat. *brocchus*, a projecting tooth; It. *brocco*, a stump, peg; F. *broche*, a spit.

Brode, broad: B 2166. See **Brood**.

Brode, broadly, plainly: A 739.

Broke, broken. See **Breke**.

Brood, (def. form *brode*), broad: A 155, 471, 549. See **Brede**.

Brond, firebrand, burning log: B 1481.

Brouke, to have the use of, enjoy. *brook:* c 480. A.S. *brúcan*, O.H. Ger. *brúchan*, Ger. *brauchen*, brook, use, enjoy; and eat. Cf. Goth. *brukjan*, to enjoy; and *bruks*, useful. Lat. *frui, fructus*.

Broun, brown: A 109. A.S. *brún;* Ger. *braun*, whence F. *brun*. It is perhaps connected with *brennan*, to burn.

Broyded, braided, woven: B 191.

Browding, embroidery; B 1640.

Bulte, built: B 690.

Bulte, to bolt (corn), sift meal: c 420. Of F. origin.

Burdoun, burden (of a song), a musical accompaniment: A 673. See note, p. 166. O. F. *bourdon*, a drone of a bagpipe; Sp. *bordon*, the bass of a stringed instrument, or of an organ.

Burgeys, citizen, burgess: A. 369. O.F. *burgeois*, from Lat. *burgensis*, a citizen; F. *bourg*, It. *borgo*, a city. Cf. Goth. *baurgs*, A.S. *burh, burg*, Eng. *borough*.

Burned, burnished: B 1125. Fr. *brunir*.

But, unless: A 582.

By and by, separately: B 153.

By-cause, because: A 174.

Byde, abide, remain: B 718.

By-iaped, deceived, befooled: B 727. M. E. *jape*, joke, lie; F. *japper*, to yelp. The root *jap* is connected with *gab*, *jab*, as in *gabble*, *jabber*.

Bying, buying: A 569.

C.

Caas, case, condition, hap, A 585 (Elles. MS.); pl. cases (of law), A 323. See **Cas**.

Cacche, to catch (pret. *caughte*): A 498. It. *cacciare*, O. F. *cachier*, to catch; F. *chasser*, to drive out, chase.

Caitif, wretched, a wretch: B 66, 694, 859. It. *cattivo* (Lat. *captiuus*), a captive, a wretch: F. *chétif*, poor, wretched.

Cam, came: A 547.

Can, (1) know, knows, A 210, B 922; (2) acknowledge, as in the phrase 'can thank,' B 950 (F. *savoir gré*), where *thank* is a noun, and not a verb. A.S. *cunnan*, to know; *cunnian*, to enquire, search into; Goth. *kunnan*, to know; Sw. *kunna*, to be able. The root is preserved in *cunning*, *ken*, ale-*conner* (an inspector of ales).

Cantel, corner, cantle: B 2150. O. F. *chantel*, *chanteau*, a corner, a lump. Cf. Icel. *kantr*, side; Dan. *kant*, edge.

Cappe, a cap, hood: A 586.

Care, sorrow, grief, B 463. A.S. *caru*, Goth. *kara*.

Careyne, carcase: B 1155. F. *charogne*, It. *carogna*; from Lat. *caro*.

Carf, carved (the pret. of *kerve*, to cut, *carve*): A 100. A.S. *ceorfan*, O. Fris. *kerva*, to cut.

Carl, a churl: A 545. A.S. *ceorl*, Icel. *karl*, a man. Cf. Sc. *carlin*, an old woman; Eng. *churl*, *churlish*.

Carol, a round dance: B 1073. F. *carole* (perhaps from Lat. *corolla*, the diminutive of *corona*). Robert of Brunne calls the circuit of Druidical stones a *karole*.

Carpe, to talk, discourse: A 474. Cf. Portug. *carpir*, to cry, weep.

Carte, chariot, cart: B 1164, C 198. Icel. *kartr*.

Carter, charioteer: B 1164.

Cas, case, condition, hap, chance: A 844, B 216. See **Caas**.

Cas, case, quiver: B 1500. O. F. *casse*, It. *cassa*, Lat. *capsa*.

Cast, device, plot: B 1610. It is connected with the vb. to *cast*. Cf. M. E. *turn*, a trick; Eng. 'an *ill turn*.'

Caste, **Casten**, to plan, devise, consider, suppose: B 1314, 1996, C 255.

Catapus, **Catapuce**, a species of spurge: C 145. Cotgrave has— '*Catapuce petite*, garden spurge.' Florio's Ital. Dict. has '*Cataputia*, *Catapuzza*, the herb spurge.'

Catel, wealth, goods, valuable property of any kind, *chattels*: A 373, 540. O. F. *chatel*, *catel*, a piece of moveable property, from Lat. *capitale*, whence *captale*, *catallum*, the principal sum in a loan (cf. Eng. *capital*). The Lat. *captale* was also applied to beasts of the farm, *cattle*.

Caughte, took: A 498. Cf. Eng. 'caught cold.' See **Cacche**.

Caytyves, pl. of **Caitif**.

Ceint, cincture, girdle: A 329.

Celle, a religious house: A 172; cell (see note); B 518.

Centaure, centaury, the name of a herb: C 143.

Cercles, circles: B 1273.

Cerial, belonging to the species of oak called *Cerrus* (Lat.): B 1432. It. *Cerro*, F. *Cerre*. Cotgrave has—'*Cerre*, the holme oke.' See note.

Certein, **Certeyn**, **Certes**, certain, certainly, indeed: A 375, 451, B 17.

Certeinly, Certeynly, certainly: A 204.

Ceruce, white lead: A 630.

Champartye, a share of land; a partnership in power: B 1091.

Champioun, a champion: A 239. A.S. *camp*, O.H. Ger. *champh*, combat, contest; A.S. *cempan*, to fight; O. Fris. *kampa*, to contend; Prov. Eng. *camp*, a scuffle; *cample*, to talk, contend, argue; Ger. *kampeln*, to debate, dispute.

Chapeleyne, a chaplain: A 164.

Chapman, a merchant: A 397. A.S. *céapman*. Cf. M. E. *chafare*, *chap-fare*; A.S. *céap*, O.S. *côp*, Icel. *kaup*, O. H. Ger. *chauf*, bargain, price (cf. Eng. *dog-cheap*, *dirt-cheap*); A.S. *céapian*, O.S. *côpon*, Icel. *kaupa*, to buy; O.H. Ger. *chaufan*, to buy, sell.

Char, car, chariot: B 1280. F. *char*, Lat. *carrus*; whence F. *charrier*, to carry; *charger*, to load, charge.

Charge, harm, B 426, 1429; as in the phrase 'it were no *charge*.' It signifies literally (1) load, burden; (2) business of weight, matter for consideration.

Chasteyn, a chestnut-tree: B 2064. O. F. *chastaigne*, Lat. *castanea*.

Chaunce, chance, hap: B 894. F. *chance*, O.F. *cheance*, from *cheoir*, to fall; Lat. *cadere*.

Chaungen, to change: A 348.

Chaunterie, 'an endowment for the payment of a priest to sing mass agreeably to the appointment of the founder': A 510. There were thirty-five of these Chantries established at St. Paul's, which were served by fifty-four priests.—Dugd. Hist. pref. p. 41.' (Tyrwhitt.) See Becon's 'Acts of Christ,' p. 530.—Parker Soc.

Chees: see **Chesen**.

Chere, countenance, appearance, entertainment, cheer: A 139, 728; B 55. O. F. *chere*, *chiere*, countenance; F. *chère*, face, look.

Cherl, churl: B 1601. See **Carl**.

Chese, to choose; **Chees**, imp. sing. choose: B 737, 756. A.S. *céosan*, Du. *kieren*, *kiezen*, O. H. Ger. *chiusan*, to choose.

Cheventein, a chieftain, captain: B 1697. See **Chieftayn**.

Chevisaunce, gain, profit; also an agreement for borrowing money: A 282. F. *chevir*, to compass, make an end, come to an agreement with; *achever*, to bring to an end, achieve (from *chef*, head).

Cheyne, a chain: B 2130.

Chiden, to chide (pret. *chidde*, pp. *chid*): C 531. A.S. *cídan*, to scold.

Chief, chief: B 199. F. *chef*, head; Lat. *caput*.

Chieftayn, a leader, chief: B 1697.

Chikne, a chicken: A 380. A.S. *cicen*, M. Du. *kieken*. The word *cock*, of which *chicken* is a diminutive, is evidently formed in imitation of the sound made by young birds. Cf. *chuck*, *chuckle*, &c.

Chirking, *sb.* shrieking: B 1146. The M. E. *chirke* signifies 'to make a noise like a bird,' being a parallel form with *chirp*, and imitative of the sound made by birds. Cf. A. S. *cearcian*, to creak, crash, gnash; Prov. Eng. *chirre*, to chirp.

Chivachye, a military expedition: A 85. See next word.

Chivalrye, knighthood, the manners, exercises, and valiant exploits of a knight: A 45, B 7, 20. F. *chevalerie*, from *chevalier*, a knight, a horseman; *cheval*; It. *cavallo*, Lat. *caballus*, a horse; M. E. *capel*, *cable*, a horse.

Choys, choice: C 426. F. *choisir*,

to choose, borrowed from a Teutonic dialect; cf. A.S. *cyre*, choice. See **Chese**.

Chronique, a chronicle: C 388.

Cite, Citee, a city, B 81. F. *cité*, Lat. acc. *ciuitatem*.

Citole, a kind of musical instrument with chords: B 1101.

Clarioun, clarion: B 1653.

Clarree, wine mixed with honey and spices, and afterwards strained till it was *clear*: B 613. It was also called *Piment*.

Clasped, Clapsed, clasped: A 273. M. E. *claps*, a clasp. It is connected with M. E. *clippe*, to embrace. Cf. *gripe*, *grip*, *grasp*.

Clatere, to clatter: B 1501. M. Du. *klateren*, to clatter, rattle.

Cleer, *adj.* clear, **Clere**, *adv.* clearly: A 170, B 204. O. F. *cler*, clear; Lat. *clarus*.

Clene, *adj.* clean, pure; *adv.* cleanly: A 133.

Clennesse, cleanness, purity (of life): A 506.

Clense, to cleanse: A 631.

Clepen, to call, cry, say: A 121, 620, 643. A. S. *cleopian*, *clypian*, to call; Ger. *kläffen*, to chatter, babble; Du. *klappen*, to sound, strike. Cf. Sc. *clep*, prattle, tattle; Eng. *clap-trap*.

Cleped, called: B 930.

Clerk, a man of learning, a student at the University: A 285. O. F. *clerc*.

Cloistre, a cloister: A 181.

Cloke, a cloak: A 157.

Clomben, climbed, ascended: C 378.

Cloos, close, shut: C 512.

Clos, enclosure, yard; C 540.

Clothered = *clottred*, clotted: B 1887. M. Du. *klotteren*, to clotter, coagulate. We have the root-syllable in *clot* and *clod*; A. S. *clot*, clod; Ger. *Kloss*, a clod, a ball. Golding has 'a *clottred clod* of seeds,' and he

uses *clodded* for *clottred*. Eng. *cloud* is perhaps allied to *clod*. Cf. M. E. *clowdys*, clods (Coventry Mysteries).

Cofre, coffer, chest: A 298. O. F. *cofre*, F. *coffre*, Lat. *cophinus*, Gr. κόφινος, a basket.

Col-blak, coal-black, black as a coal: B 1284.

Cole, coal: B 1834. A. S. *col*; Icel. *kol*, Ger. *Kohle*.

Colere, choler: C 126.

Colers of, (having) collars of: B 1294.

Col-fox, a crafty fox: C 395. The prefix *col-*, deceitful, treacherous, occurs in M. E. *col-prophet*, a false prophet; *col-knyfe*, a treacherous knife; *col-warde*, deceitful, false.

Colpons: see **Culpons**.

Com, *pret.* came; *imp.* come: A 672, B 321.

Comaunde, to command: C 260.

Comaundement, commandment, command: B 2011.

Comen, *pp.* come: A 671, B 497; **Come**, C 591.

Communes, commoners, common people: B 1651.

Compas, circle: B 1031.

Compaignye, Compainye, company: A 24, C 173.

Compaignable, companionable, sociable: C 52.

Compassing, craft, contrivance: B 1138.

Compeer, gossip, a near friend: A 670.

Complet, complete: C 369.

Compleyne, to complain: B 50.

Compleynt, complaint: B 2004.

Composicioun, agreement: A 848.

Commune, common. *As in co-mune* = as in common, commonly: B 393.

Condicionel, conditional: C 430.

Condicioun, condition: A 38.

Confort, comfort: A 773, 776.

Confus, confused, confounded : B 1372.

Conne, know, be able. See **Can.**

Conscience, feeling, pity : A 150.

Conseil, counsel : B 283, 289.

Conserve, to preserve : B 1471.

Contek, contest : B 1145. O. F. *contek,* strife.

'And therwithal I termed have all strife,
All quarrels, *contecks*, and all cruell *iarres*,
Oppressions, *bryberes*, and all greedy life,
To be (*in genere*) no bet than warres.' — Gascoigne, The Fruites of Warre, st. 33.

Contenaunce, countenance : B 1058.

Contrarie, an opponent, adversary, foe : B 1001.

Contree, country : A 216, B 355. '*Gegend* in German means region or country. It is a recognised term, and it signified originally that which is before or against what forms the object of our view. Now in Latin *gegen*, or against, would be expressed by *contra;* and the Germans, not recollecting at once the Latin word *regio*, took to translating their idea of *gegend*, that which was before them, by *contratum* or *terra contra*. This became the Italian *contrada*, the French *contrée*, the English *country*.' Max Müller, Science of Language, Second Series, p. 275. (Rather, *Gegend* is a translation of *contrata*.)

Cop, top of anything : A 554. A. S. *copp*, M. Du. *kopp*, Ger. *Kopf*, top, summit.

Cope, a cloak, cape : A 260. A. S. *cop;* cf. It. *cappa*, F. *chappe*.

Coppe, cup : A 134. A. S. *cuppe* (from Latin).

Corage, heart, spirit, courage : A 11, 22. O. F. *corage*, F. *courage*, from Lat. *cor*, the heart.

Coroune, a crown : B 2017.

Corrumpable, corruptible : B 2152.

Corrumpe, to corrupt : B 888 (Harl. MS.).

Corven (pp. of *kerve*), cut : B 1838.

Cosin, a cousin, kinsman : B 273.

Cotage, cottage, C 2. A. S. *cot*, M. Du. *kote*, a cot. Cf. *sheep-cote, dove-cote.*

Cote, coat : A 103, 612. O. F. *cote.*

Cote-armure, a coat worn over armour, upon which the armorial ensigns of the wearer were usually embroidered : B 158, 1282. 'The usage of wearing an upper garment, or surcoat, charged with armorial bearings, as a personal distinction in conflict, when the features were concealed by the aventaile, commenced possibly in the reign of John, but was not generally adopted before the time of Henry III. Sir Thomas de la More relates that the Earl of Gloucester was slain at Bannockburn, 1314, in consequence of his neglecting to put on his insignia, termed in the Latin translation *togam propriae armaturae*. During the reign of Edward III the surcoat gave place to the jupon, and this was succeeded by the tabard, the latest fashion of a garment armorially decorated, and the prototype of that which is still worn by the heralds and pursuivants.' — Way, in Prompt. Parv.

Couched, (1) laid, (2) inlaid, trimmed : B 1303, 2075. F. *coucher*, O. F. *culcher*, to lay down (Lat. *collocare*).

Coude, (1) could, A 236, 326;

(2) knew, A 467 ; knew how, A 95, 106. See Can.

Counseil, counsel, advice : A 784, B 283.

Countour : A 359. See note.

Countrefete, counterfeit, imitate : A 139, C 501.

Cours, course : A 8, B 836.

Courtepy, a sort of upper coat of a coarse material : A 290. Du. *kort,* short ; *pije,* a coarse cloth ; Goth. *paida,* a coat. The syllable *pije* is still preserved in *pea*-jacket.

Couthe, well known : A 14.

Coverchief, kerchief : A 453.

Covyne, *covin,* deceit : A 604. Literally a deceitful agreement between two parties to prejudice a third. From F. *convenir,* Lat. *convenire,* to come together.

Cowardye, cowardice : B 1872. F. *couard,* from Lat. *cauda,* a tail ; O. F. *couarder,* to retire, draw backwards. The real origin of the word is a metaphor from the proverbial timidity of a hare, which was called *couard* from its short tail. (Wedgwood.)

Coy, quiet : A 119. F. *coi,* Sp. *quedo,* Lat. *quietus.*

Cracching, scratching : B 1976. Besides *cracche,* to scratch, we have *s-cratte,* and *s-cracche.* Cp. M. E. *fette* and *fecche,* to fetch ; Du. *kratsen,* Icel. *krassa,* Ger. *kratzen,* to scratch, tear.

Crafty, skilful (cf. *craftsman*) ; B 1039. A. S. *cræft,* power ; Ger. *Kraft,* strength.

Crispe, crisp, curled : B 1307. It is also written *cripse.* (Lydgate has *kirspe.*) A. S. *crisp,* crisp ; *cirpsian,* to curl ; from Lat. *crispus,* curled.

Croppe, top, shoot, A 7, B 674 (pl. *croppes*). A. S. *crop,* M. Du. *krop, kroppe,* top, summit, crop,

craw ; whence Eng. *crop, crop-full,* '*croppings* out' (of mineral strata). Cf. F. *crope, croupe,* top of a hill ; *croupe,* the rounded haunches of an animal, the *croup ; croupière,* the strap passing over the *croup ;* Eng. *crupper.* The root *crup* seems to signify a swelling out, as in Welsh *crub,* a swelling out.

Croys, cross : A 699. O. F. *crois,* from Lat. acc. *crucem.*

Crulle, curly, curled : A 81. Du. *krol, krolle,* a curl ; M. Du. *kroken,* to crook, bend ; *kroke,* a bending, *crook ;* Icel. *krokr,* a hook ; Low. Ger. *krükel,* a curl ; *krüllen,* to curl. *Crouch* (*crutch*), crook, cross, is merely a weakened form of *crook.* Cf. M. E. *cloke* and *clouch,* a claw, *clutch ;* and cf. Swed. *kyrka* with Eng. *church.*

Cryen, to cry (pret. *cride, cryde*), B 91 ; *Crydestow* = criedst thou : B 225.

Cryke, creek : A 409. Du. *kreek.* Cp. Icel. *kriki,* angle, nook. *Cryke* in M. E. signifies also a stream, a brook (as it still does in America) ; A. S. *crecca,* a bank, brink.

Culpons, Colpons, shreds, bunches, bundles, logs : A 679, B 2009. F. *coupon,* Lat. *colpo,* a shred, a portion cut off.

Curat, a curate : A 219.

Cure, care, anxiety : A 303, B 1995. Lat. *cura.*

Curious, careful : A 577.

Curs, curse : A 655. A.S. *curs.*

Curteisye, courtesy : A 46, 132. O.F. *courtoisie,* civility, courtesy.

Curteys, courteous : A 99, 250, C 51. O.F. *cortois ;* from *cort,* a court (Lat. *cohors*).

Cut, lot : A 835. '*Cut* or lote, sors.' Promptorium Parvulorum. See note.

D.

Daliaunce, gossip : A 211. '*Daly-
aunce*, confabulacio, collocacio.
Dalyyn or talkyn, *fabulor*, col-
loquor.'— Prompt. Parv. Cf.
Swiss *dalen*, *talen*, to speak im-
perfectly, to drawl. (Wedgwood.)

Damoysele, damsel : C 50.

Dampned, condemned, doomed :
B 317.

Dan, Daun, Lord, was a title
commonly given to monks ; B
521, C 492. It is also prefixed
to the names of persons of all
sorts, e g. *Dan Arcyte*, *Dan
Burnel*, &c. Lat. *Dominus*.

Dar, dare (1st pers. sing. present
tense) : B 293. **Darst** (2nd
sing.) : B 282. **Dorste, Durste**
pret.) : A 454.

Darreyne, to contest, fight out,
decide by battle, *darraign* : B
751, 773. O. F. *desrenir*, from
Lat. Mid. *disrationare*, to answer
an accusation, to settle or *arrange* a controversy. Shakespeare uses the word in the sense
of ' to make ready to fight.'
' Royal   commanders,   be   in
        readiness ;
For, with a band of thirty thou-
        sand men,
Comes Warwick, backing of
        the Duke of York ;
And in the towns, as they do
        march along,
Proclaims him king, and many
        fly to him ;
Darraign your battle, for they
        are at hand.'—3 Hen. VI,
ii. 2. 67.
' He chose a place mete and con-
veniente for twoo armies to
darrayne battail.' — Hall's
Chronicle, xlvii.

Daun : see Dan.

Daunce, Daunse, vb. to dance,

sb. a dance : B 1343, 1344.
' The olde daunce '=the old
game : A 476.

Daunger, a dangerous situation :
A 402 ; liability, B 991. *In
daunger*=in his jurisdiction,
under his control : A 663. *With
daunger*=with difficulty. O. F.
dangier, dominion, subjection,
difficulty ; from Mid. Lat. *dam-
num* (1) a legal fine, (2) terri-
torial jurisdiction. *Estre en son
danger*=to be in the danger of
any one, to be in his power. Cf.
' in *danger* of the judgment.'
Danger in the sense of *debt* or
power to harm is not uncommon
in English :
' The wandering guest doth stand
    in *danger* of his hoste.'—Gold-
    ing's Ovid.
You stand within his *danger*, do
    you not ?—Merch. of Ven. iv.
    1. 180.

Daungerous, difficult, sparing : A
517.

Daunsinge, dancing : B 1343.

Dawen, to dawn (3rd sing.
daweth) : B 818.

Daweninge, dawn, dawning : C
62. M. E. *dawe*, a day ; A. S.
dæg, Goth. *dags*, O. H. Ger.
tag ; A.S. *dagian*, to dawn ;
dagung, dawning.

Dayerye, dairy : A 597. From
M. E. *deye*, a dairy-maid. See
Deye.

Dayesye, a daisy : A 332. Chaucer
defines *daisy* as *the eye of the day*,
i. e. day's eye ; A. S. *dæges éage*.

Debonaire, kind, gracious : B
1424.

Dede, a deed : A 742. A.S. *dǽd*,
O. Fris. *dêde*, O. H. Ger. *tát*.

Deduyt, pleasure, delight : B 1319.
O. F. *dedut*, *deduit*.

Deed (pl. *dede*), dead : A 145, B
84, 147. A. S. *déad*, O. Fris.
dád, *dáth*, O. H. Ger. *tóter*, *tóder*,
dead.

Deedly, deadly, death-like: B 55, 224.

Deef, deaf: A 446. A.S. *déaf*, Goth. *daubs, daufs,* O. H. Ger. *touber,* Ger. *taub.* It is probably connected with Goth. *gadaubjan,* to harden, make insensible. Cf. Scotch *dowf,* dull, flat; M. E. and Prov. Eng. *daf, daffe,* fool, dastard; Prov. Eng. *daver,* to stun; *dover,* to slumber.

Deel, a part, bit: C 14. See **Del.**

Deeth, death: A 605, B 276. A.S. *déað,* O. Fris. *dáth,* O. H. Ger. *tód.*

Degree, (1) a step, B 1032; (2) rank or station in life, A 40, B 572, 576. F. *degré,* O.F. *degrat;* from Lat. *gradus,* a step.

Del, part, portion, whit: B 967, 1233. *Never a del* = never a whit; *somdel,* somewhat. A. S. *dél,* a part; A.S. *délan,* Icel. *deila,* to divide; Eng. *dole.*

Delen, to have dealings with: A 247.

Delivere, quick, active, nimble: A 84. F. *delivre* (Lat. *liber,* free), active, nimble.

Deliverly, quickly: C 596. Cf. M. E. *delivernesse,* agility.

Delve, to dig (pret. *delf, dalf,* pp. *dolven*): A 536. A.S. *delfan,* Du. *delven,* to dig, bury. It is probably connected with Du. *del,* valley, hollow; Eng. *dell,* dale.

Delyt, delight, pleasure: A 335, B 821. O. F. *delit,* Lat. *delectus;* Lat. *delectare,* to please.

Deme, to judge, decide, doom, suppose, deem: B 1023. A.S. *déman,* O. H. Ger. *tuomen,* to judge; A. S. *dóm,* O. H. Ger. *tuom,* doom, judgment, sentence, decree. Cf. M. E. *demere, demstere,* a judge. See **Dome.**

Departe, to part, separate: B 276.

Departing, separation: B 1916.

Depe, deeply: B 1782.

Depeynted, painted, depicted: B 1169, 1173.

Dere, dear, dearly: B 376, 2242. A. S. *déore,* dear, precious; whence *darling* (M. E. *derling*), *dearth.*

Dere, to hurt, injure: B 964. A.S. *derian,* O. H. Ger. *terran,* to harm, hurt, injure; A.S. *daru,* O. H. Ger. *tara,* harm, injury. It occurs in the works of Henry the Minstrel and Douglas.

Derk, Derke, dark: B 1137. A.S. *deorc,* dark.

Derknesse, darkness: B 593.

Derre, dearer: B 590. Cf. M. E. *herre,* higher; *ferre,* further.

Desdeyn, disdain: A 789.

Desiring, sb. desire: B 1064.

Despitous, angry to excess, cruel, merciless: A 516, B 738.

Despyt, malicious anger, vexation: B 83. O. F. *despire* (Lat. *despicere*), to despise; F. *despit,* contempt; It. *dispetto:* Sp. *despecho,* displeasure, malice.

Destreyne, to vex, constrain: B 597. F. *distraindre,* Mid. Lat. *distringere* (from Lat. *stringere,* to strain), to be severe with, *distrain. District* and *distress* are from the same source.

Destroye, to destroy: B 472. O.F. *destruir,* F. *détruire.*

Desyr, desire: B 385.

Deth. See **Deeth.**

Dette, a debt: A 280. F. *dette,* a debt; Lat. *debitum,* from *debere,* to owe.

Dettelees, free from debt: A 582.

Devoir, duty: B 1740. F. *devoir,* duty, trust; *devoir,* to owe; Lat. *debere.*

Devys, opinion, decision, direction: A 816.

Devyse, (1) to direct, order; (2) to relate, describe: A 34, B 136, 190. It. *divisare,* to think, imagine, to discourse; O. F. *deviser,* to plan, order, dispose

of, discourse; from Lat. *uisum*,
It. *viso*, view, opinion.

Devysing, a putting in order, preparation : B 1638.

Deye, a female servant, dairy-
woman : C 26. Icel. *deigja,* lit.
'kneader of bread.'

Deyen : see **Dyen.**

Deyne, to deign : C 361.

Deyntee, *sb.* a dainty, rarity ; *adj.*
rare, dainty, A 168, C 15.

Deys, dais, platform, the high
table : A 370, B 1342. ' *Dais* or
daiz, a cloth of estate, canopy or
heaven, that stands over the
heads of princes' thrones ; also
the whole state or seat of estate.'
(Cotgrave.) O. F. *dais, deis*
(Lat. *discus*). See note, p. 153.

Diapred, variegated, diversified
with flourishes or sundry figures :
B 1300. O. F. *diaspré, diapré,*
variegated ; It. *diaspro,* a jasper
(Gr. ἴασπις), which was much
used in ornamental jewellery.
Chaucer speaks of a meadow
diapered with flowers. It is now
applied to linen cloth woven
with a pattern of diamond-shaped
figures, and to church-walls when
the plain stone is carved in a
pattern.

Dich, a ditch : C 28. See **Dyke.**

Diched, diked : B 1030. See
Dich, Dyke.

Dide (pret. of *don*), did : B 891.

Diete, diet, daily food : A 435.
From Gr. δίαιτα, mode of life,
especially with reference to *food.*

Digestible, easy to be digested :
A 437.

Digestyves, things to help diges-
tion : C 141.

Dight, prepared, dressed : B 183.
A.S. *dihtan,* dress, dispose ; from
Lat. *dictare.*

Digne, (1) worthy, A 141 ; (2)
proud, disdainful, A 517. F.
digne.

Dim, dull, indistinct : B 1575.

Dischevele, with hair hanging
loose : A 683. F. *descheveler,* to
put the hair out of order ; F.
cheveux, pl., from Lat. *capillus,*
the hair.

Disconfiture, Disconfitinge, defeat : B 150, 1861. O.F. *des-
confiture,* F. *déconfiture* ; from *dé-
confire,* to non-plus.

Disconfort, discomfort, misery :
B 1152.

Disconforten, to dishearten : B
1846.

Discrecioun, discretion : B 921.

Discreet, discreet : C 51.

Disherited, disinherited : B 2068.

Disioynt, a difficult situation,
failure : B 2104.

Dispence, expense, expenditure :
A 441, B 1024.

Dispitously, angrily, cruelly : B
266.

Disport, sport, diversion : A 137,
775. O.F. *desport,* F. *déport,*
It. *disporte,* diversion, solace.

Disposicioun, control, guidance :
B 229.

Disputisoun, disputation : C 418.

Divisioun, distinction : B 922.

Divyninge, guessing, conjecture :
B 1663.

Divynistre, a divine : B 1953.

Doghtren, daughters : C 9.

Doke, a duck : C 570. M. Du.
duiken, O. H. Ger. *túhban,* Ger.
tauchen, to dive, plunge.

Dokked, cut short : A 590. M. E.
dok, O. Icel. *dockr,* a tail. Cf.
' *docked* of one's wages.'

Dome, doom, decision, judgment,
opinion : A 323. See **Deme.**

Dominacioun, power, control : B
1900.

Don, Doon, Do, to do, cause,
make, take (pret. *dide, dede,* pp.
do, don, doon) : A 78, 268, 768,
B 84, 1047.

Dong, dung : A 530.

Donge, to dung, to manure : C
216.

Dore, a door: A 550. A.S. *duru*, Ger. *Thor, Thüre.*

Dorste: A 227, C 98. See **Dar.**

Doseyn, a dozen: A 578.

Doumb, dumb: A 774.

Doun, down: B 245.

Doute, doubt, fear: A 487, B 283. *Out of doute* = without doubt, doubtless.

Douteles, adj. doubtless, without doubt: B 973.

Dowves, doves: B 1104.

Dragges, drugs: A 426 (Harl. MS.). O. F. *dragée*, It. *treggea*, Sp. *dragea*, Gr. τράγημα (Mod. Gr. τράγαλα), sweetmeats; cf. τρωγάλια, raw fruits at dessert, or sweetmeats, from τρώγειν, to gnaw. See **Drogges.**

Drawe, to draw, or to carry: B 1689.

Drecched, troubled (by dreams): C 67. A.S. *dreccan*, M. H. Ger. *trecken*, to trouble, plague. 'Dremyn or drecchyn yn slepe, sompnio.'—Prompt. Parv.

Drede, to fear, dread: A 660. *To drede*, to be feared.

Dredful, cautious, timid: B 621.

Dreem, Dreme, a dream: C 67, 109. A.S. *dréam*, O. Fris. *drám*, Ger. *Traum.* Cf. Sc. *dram, drum*, dull; *drumble* (Shakespeare), to be sluggish.

Dremen, to dream: C 109.

Dreminges, dreams: C 270.

Drenching, drowning: B 1598.

Dresse, to set in order: A 106, B 1736. O. F. *dresser*, to straighten, direct, fashion; It. *drizzare*, to address, to turn toward a place; from Lat. *directus*, pp. of *dirigere*, to direct.

Dreye, dry: B 2166.

Dreynt (pp. of *drenche*), drowned: C 262. Cf. M. E. *queynt*, quenched; *cleynt*, clenched, &c.

Drogges, drugs: A 426. See **Dragges.**

Dronken, pp. drunk: A 135, 637.

Dronken, pl. pret., drunk: A 820.

Drope, a drop: A 131. A.S. *dropa.*

Drouped, drooped: A 107. Icel. *drúpa*, to droop.

Drugge, to *drudge*, to do laborious work: B 558. Ir. *drugaire*, a slave. '[To see] a country colone toil and moil, till and *drudge* for a prodigal idle drone.' —Burton's Anat. of Mel. p. 35.

Duk, a leader, duke: B 2. F. *duc*, Lat. *dux*, from *ducere*, to lead. See Trench, English Past and Present, p. 196.

Dure, to endure, last: B 1912.

Dusked, *pt. pl.*, grew dark or dim: B 1948. Sw. *dusk*, dark, dull.

Dwelle, to tarry: B 803.

Dwelled, *pp.* dwelt: B 370.

Dyamaunts, diamonds: B 1289.

Dyen, to die: B 251. Icel. *deyja.*

Dyere, a dyer: A 362. A.S. *déagian*, to dye.

Dyete. See **Diete.**

Dyke, to make *dikes* or *ditches*: A 536. A.S. *díc*, O. Fris. *dik*, M. H. Ger. *tich*, a ditch.

Dys, dice: B 380.

E.

Ecclesiaste, an ecclesiastical person: A 708.

Ech, Eche, each: A 39, 369. A.S. *álc*; from *á*, ever, *ge*, and *líc*, like. Cf. M. E. *iwhere*, everywhere.

Echon, Echoon, each one: A 820.

Eek, also, moreover, *eke*: A 5, 41. A.S. *éc, éac*; Goth. *auk*, also; A.S. *écan*, to increase, *eke.*

Eet, ate, did eat: *ete*, imp. eat: B 1190, C 147. See **Ete.**

Eft, again: B 811. Cf. M. E. *eftsone, eftsones*, afterwards, presently; A.S. *eft.*

Eir, air, B 388.

Elde, age, old age: B 1589, 1590. A. S. *eald*, old; *yldo*, age.

Elles, else: A 375. A.S. *elles,* O.H. Ger. *elles, alles.* (A.S. *el-* in composition signifies another, foreign. Cf. Gr. ἄλλος, Lat. *alius,* other.)

Embrouded, embroidered: A 89.

Emforth, to the extent of, even with: B 1377. A.S. *em-* in composition signifies *even,* equal; being short for *efn = efen.*

Empoysoning, poisoning: B 1602.

Empryse, an undertaking, enterprise: B 1682. O.F. *emprendre;* cf. F. *entreprendre,* to undertake; F. *entreprise,* an enterprise.

Encens, incense: B 1571.

Encombred, (1) wearied, tired, B 860; (2) troubled, in danger, A 508. It is sometimes written *acombred.* O.F. *encombrer,* to hinder, trouble, grieve, annoy. Cf. Du. *kommer,* trouble; Ger. *kummer,* trouble, grief.

Encres, sb. increase: B 1326.

Encresen, to increase: B 457.

Endelong, lengthways, along: B 1133, 1820. A.S. *andlang,* Ger. *entlang.*

Endere, one who causes the death of another: B 1918.

Enduren, to endure: C 161.

Endyte, to dictate, relate: A 95, B 522.

Engendred, produced: A 4.

Engyned, tortured, racked: C 240. O.F. *engin,* contrivance, craft, an instrument of war, torture, &c.

Enhauncen, to raise: B 576. Formed from Lat. *ante.*

Enhorte, to encourage: B 1993. We have *discourage* and *dishearten,* but *enhorte* has given way to *encourage:* B 1993.

Enoynt, anointed: B 2103.

Ensample, example: A 496.

Entente, intention, purpose: B 142.

Entuned, intoned: A 123.

Envyned, stored with wine: A 342.

Er, ere, before: B 182, 297.

Erchedeknes, archdeacon's: A 658.

Ere, to plough, *ear:* B 28. *Earing* is used in our Eng. Bible. A.S. *erian,* Du. *eren.*

Eres, ears: A 556, B 664. A.S. *eáre,* Goth. *auso,* an ear.

Erly, early: A 33, 809. A.S. *aér,* before, *ere; aérlice,* early.

Ernest, earnest: B 267, 268. A.S. *eornest,* earnest; M. Du. *ernsten,* to endeavour.

Erst than, for *er than,* before that: B 708. *Er* = before; *erst* = first, A 776.

Erthe, earth: B 388. A.S. *eorðe,* Ger. *Erde.*

Eschaunge, exchange: A 278.

Eschue, to avoid, shun: B 2185. O.F. *eschever,* It. *schivare,* to avoid; Dan. *skiev,* oblique, *a-skew.*

Ese, pleasure, amusement, ease: A 768. F. *aise,* opportunity, ease.

Esed, entertained, accommodated: A 29. See below.

Esen, to entertain: B 1336.

Esily, easily: A 469.

Espye, to see, discover: B 254, 562. F. *espier, épier;* It. *spiare;* Ger. *spähen.*

Est, east, B 1743; *estward,* B 1035.

Estat, estate, state, condition: A 203, 522.

Estatlich, Estatly, stately, dignified: A 140, 281.

Estres, the inward parts of a building: B 1113. O.F. *estre,* state, plan.

Esy, easy, A 223; moderate, 441.

Ete, to eat: C 593. See **Eet.**

Eterne, eternal: B 251, 1132.

Evel, evil. **Evele,** badly: B 269.

Everich, every, A 241; every one, A 371, B 1269.

Everich a, every, each: A 733.

Everichon, every one: A 31, 747.

Ew, a yew-tree : B 2065.

Expounede, expounded : C 295.

Ey, an egg : C 25. A.S. *æg,* pl. *ægru* (M. E. *eyren*) ; hence Eng. *eyry.*

Eyen, eyes ; A 152, 267. O. Merc. *ége,* pl. *égen ;* A.S. *éage,* pl. *éagan.*

Eyle, to ail : B 223.

F.

Fader, father : A 100 ; gen. sing. *fader :* A 781. (The gen. sing. in A.S. was *fæder,* not *fædres.*)

Fadme, fathoms : B 2058.

Fair, adj. beautiful, fair, good ; **Faire,** adv. gracefully, well, neatly : A 94, 124, 273.

Fairnesse, (1) beauty, B 240 ; (2) honesty of life, A 519.

Falding, a sort of coarse cloth : A 391. See note, p. 155.

Falle, befall : A 585.

Fals, false : B 295. Lat. *falsus.*

Falwe, pale : B 506. A.S. *falwe,* Ger. *falb,* pale, faded, yellow.

Famulier, familiar, homely : A 215.

Fare, proceeding, affair : B 951. A.S. *faru,* Icel. *för,* course, proceeding, movement, bustle, ado.

Fare, Faren, to go, proceed ; pp. **Faren, Fare,** pl. pres. **Faren :** B 403, 407, 537, 1578, C 59. A.S. *faran,* to go, pret. *fór,* pp. *gefaren.* The English *to fare,* in 'fare thee well,' is allied to the Greek *póros,* a passage. *Welfare, wohlfahrt,* would be Greek *euporia,* opposed to *aporia,* helplessness.

Farsed, stuffed : A 233. M.E. *farce,* to stuff ; F. *farcir,* Lat. *farcire (farsum),* to stuff.

Faste, near : B 618, 830.

Faught (also *faght*), fought : A 399.

Fayn, glad, gladly : A 766.

A.S. *fægen,* M. E. *fayn,* also *fawen,* glad, fain.

Fedde, pret. fed : A 146.

Fee, money, reward : B 945. A.S. *feoh,* Icel. *fé,* Lat. *pecus,* cattle, property, money.

Feeld, a field : B 28. A.S. *feld,* O. Fris. *feld,* Ger. *Feld,* the open country. (Horne Tooke is wrong in connecting it with the verb to *fell.*)

Feend, Fend, a fiend, devil : C 466. A.S. *féond,* Ger. *Feind,* an enemy, fiend : orig. pres. pt. of A.S. *féon,* to hate.

Feith, faith, C 593. Anglo-French *feid, fei,* F. *foi,* Lat. *fides.* See **Fey.**

Fel, voc. **Felle,** cruel, fierce : B 701, 1772. A.S. *fel,* M.Du. *fel,* O.F. *fel,* cruel, fierce ; O. F. *felon,* cruel ; O. F. *felonie,* anger, cruelty, treason ; any such heinous offence committed by a vassal against his lord, whereby he is worthy to lose his estate. (Cotgrave.)

Felawe, a fellow : A 650. Also *felaghe.* The syllable *fe*=fee, goods, and *law*=order, law. Cf. Icel. *félagi,* a fellow, a sharer in goods ; Icel. *fé,* money, goods ; and *lag,* order, society.

Felawschipe, fellowship : A 32.

Feld, felled, cut down : B 2066.

Felle ; see **Fel.**

Felonye, crime, disgraceful conduct : B 1138. See **Fel.**

Fend, fiend. See **Feend.**

Fer, far : A 388, 491, B 992. (Comp. *ferre :* B 1202, superl. *ferrest :* A 494). A.S. *feor,* far ; O. Fris. *fer.*

Ferde, (1) went, proceeded ; (2) acted, B 154 ; pl. *ferden,* B 789. A.S. *féran,* to go.

Fere, fear, terror : B 475, 1486. A.S. *fǽr.*

Fered, frightened, terrified : C 566. See **Aferd.**

Ferforthly, far forth : B 102.

Fermacie, a medicine, pharmacy : B 1855.

Ferme, rent. See note to l. 252, p. 146. F. *ferme*.

Ferne, distant : A 14. See note, p. 129.

Ferre, Ferrer, farther : A 48, 835.

Ferther, further, A 36.

Ferthing, farthing, fourth part ; hence a very small portion of anything : A 134, 255.

Feste, a feast : B 25. Lat. *festum*.

Feste, to feast : B 1335.

Festne, to fasten : A 195.

Fet, fetched, brought : A 819, B 1669. A. S. *fetian*, M. Du. *vatten*, to fetch.

Fether, a feather : A 107. 'The English *feather* would correspond to a Sanskrit *pattra*, and this means the *wing* of a bird, i.e. the instrument of flying, from *pat*, to fly, and *tra*. As to *penna*, it comes from the same root, but is formed with another suffix. It would be a Sanskrit *patana*, *pesna* and *penna* in Latin.' Max Müller, Science of Language, Second Series, p. 221.

Fetis, neat, well-made : A 157. O. F. *faictis* (Lat. *facticius*), well-made, neat, *feat*, from O. F. *faire*; Lat. *facere*.

Fetisly, neatly, properly : A 124.

Fettres, fetters (for the *feet* and legs) : B 421.

Fey, faith : B 268.

Feyne, to feign : A 705, 736. O. F. *feigner*, F. *feindre*, to feign ; Lat. *fingere*, to form.

Fiers, fierce : B 740, 1087. O. F. *fiers*; Lat. *ferus*.

Fil (pret. of *fallen*), fell : A 845. *Fillen*, pl. ; B 91. *Fille*, might fall, A 131.

Fithele, fiddle : A 296. A. S *fiðele*; Mid. Lat. *fidula*, *vitula*.

Flatour, flatterer : C 505.

Flee, to flee, flee from : B 312.

Flesh, flesh, meat : A 147.

Flete, to float, swim : B 1539. A. S. *fléotan*, O. H. Ger. *fliozan*, to flow, float, swim ; whence Eng. *fleet*, *float*.

Fleting, floating : B 1098.

Flex, flax : A 676. A. S. *fleax*. Cf. *flix*, fur of a hare (Dryden) ; Prov. Eng. *fleck*, down of rabbits. The A. S. had *flax-fote* = web-footed, so that there must have been a verb corresponding to Icel. *flétta*, to weave.

Fley (pret. of *fle*), flew : C 352.

Flikeringe, fluttering : B 1104. A. S. *flicerian*, to flicker ; Ger. *flackern*, to flare.

Flotery, wavy, flowing : B 2025. (Tyrwhitt renders it *floating*.) *Flotery berd* = a long, flowing beard. In Early Eng. Alliterative Poems we find the phrase *floty valez* (vales), where *floty* has the sense of streaming. A. S. *floterian*, to flutter, to be borne on waves. Ger. *flotern*, *flutern*, to flutter.

Flough, 2nd p. pret. flew : C 411.

Flour, flower : A 4, B 124.

Flowen, pret. pl. flew : C 571.

Floytinge, playing on a flute : A 91. O. F. *flahute*, *flaute*, F. *flûte*, a flute ; cf. O. F. *flagoler*, to pipe, whence *flageolet*.

Folk, people : A 25.

Folwe, to follow : B 1509.

Fomy, foamy, foaming : B 1648.

Fond, found, provided for : C 9.

Foo, Fo, foe, enemy : A 63. A. S. *fá*, enemy. See **Fend**.

Foom, foam : B 801. A. S. *fám*.

For, (1) because, A 443 ; (2) 'for al,' notwithstanding, B 1162.

For, for fear of, against : A 276, C 297.

Forbere, to forbear : B 27.

For-blak, very black : B 1286.

Fordo, pp. ruined, destroyed : B 702.

Forgete, to forget (pp. *forgeten*, *foryeten*) : B 1163, 2196.

Forheed, forehead : A 154.

Forn-cast, pre-ordained : C 397.

Forneys, furnace : A 202. F. *fournaise*, It. *fornace*; from Lat. *furnus*, an oven.

For-old, very old : B 1284.

For-pyned, wasted away (through *pine* or torment), tormented : A 205. See **Pyne**.

Fors, force : B 1865. ' *Do no fors of* '=make no account of, C 121.

Forsleuthen, to lose through sloth : C 276.

Forster, a forester : A 117.

Forthermoor, furthermore : B 1211.

Forthren, to further, aid : B 279. A.S. *fyrðrian*, to promote, support.

Forthy, therefore, B 983. A.S. *-thý* = the instrumental case of the def. article.

Fortunen, to make fortunate, to give good or bad fortune : A 417, B 1519.

Forward, covenant, agreement : A 33, 829. A.S. *foreweard*, Icel. *forvörðr*, a compact, covenant.

Forwityng, foreknowledge : C 423. See **Wite**.

Forwot, foreknows : C 414.

Foryete, forget : B 1024. See **Forgete**.

Foryeve, to forgive : A 743, B 960.

Fother, a load, properly a carriage-load : A 530, B 1050. It is now used for a certain weight of lead. A.S. *fóther*, Du. *voeder*, Ger. *Fuder*.

Foughte, pl. pret. fought, B 320.

Foughten, pp. fought : A 62.

Founden, pp. found : B 754.

Foundre, to founder, fall down : B 1829. O. F. *fondrer*, to sink, fall down (Godefroy).

Fowl, Fowel, a bird, *fowl* : A 9, 190; B 1579. A.S. *fugol*, a bird.

Foyne, Foynen, to make a pass in fencing, to push, thrust : B 796, 1692. Perhaps from O. F. *foine*, an eel-spear ; Lat. *fuscina* (because used for thrusting).

Fraknes, freckles : B 1311. Prov. Eng. *frackens*, Icel. *freknur*, freckles ; cf. Ger. *Fleck, Flecken*, a spot, stain.

Fredom, freedom, liberality : A 46.

Free, free, generous, liberal : C 94.

Freend, Frend, a friend : A 299, B 610. ' The English *friend* is a participle present. The verb *frijon*, in Gothic, means to love, hence *frijonds*, a lover. It is the Sanskrit *pri*, to love.' (Max Müller.)

Frendly, Frendlich, friendly : B 794, 1822.

Frendschipe, friendship : A 428.

Frere, a friar : A 208.

Fresh, fresh : A 365, B 1318. A.S. *fersc*, Icel. *friskr*. The Eng. *frisk, frisky*, are from a Scandinavian source.

Freten, to eat (pp. *freten*) : B 1161. A.S. *fretan*, Ger. *fressen*, devour, eat ; Eng. *fret*.

Fro, from : A 324. Icel. *frá*, from. It still exists in the phrase ' to and *fro*,' and in *fro-ward*.

Frothen, to froth, foam : B 801.

Fulfild, filled full : B 82.

Fume, effects of gluttony or drunkenness : C 104. Hence the use of *fume* in the sense of ' the vapours, dumps.' Cf. ' Some (bees are) angry, *fumish*, or too teastie.'—Topsell's Serpents, p. 66.

Fumetere, name of a plant, fumitory : C 143.

Fyled, cut, filed smooth : B 1294.

Fyn, fine : B 614.

Fynde, to invent, provide : A 736.

Fyr, fire : B 2084, 2093. **Fyry**, fiery : B 706.

Fyr-reed, red as fire : A 624.

G.

Gabbe, to lie : C 246. A.S. *gabban*, Icel. *gabba*, to lie, jest ; Icel. *gabb*, a jest. We have the same root in *gabble, gibberish*.

Gadre, to gather : A 824.

Galingale, sweet cyperus : A 381.

Game, pleasure, sport : B 948. A.S. *gamen*, O. Fris. *game*, sport, play ; A.S. *gamenian*, to sport.

Gamed, verb. impers. pleased : A 534.

Gan (pt. t. of *ginnen*) is used as a mood-auxiliary, e. g. *gan espye* = did see, B 254 ; began, B 682.

Gaping, having the mouth wide open, gaping : B 1150. A.S. *geapian*, Icel. *gapa*, Ger. *gaffen*, to stare (i. e. with open mouth). *Gasp* (for *gap-s*) is from the same root. Cf. M. E. *galping*, gaping.

Gappe, gap : B 781. Icel. *gap*, a gap.

Gargat, the throat : C 515. F. *gorge*, a throat ; It. *gorgo*, a gurgle ; Ger. *Gurgel*, the gullet, throat. See note.

Garleek, garlick, A 634 ; the spearplant, from A.S. *gár*, a spear, *léac*, an herb, plant, *leek*. We have the second element in other names of plants, as *hemlock* (M. E. *hemlick*), *charlock*.

Gaste, to terrify. See **Agast**.

Gastly, horrible : B 1126. See **Agast**.

Gat, got, obtained : A 703, 704.

Gattothed, having teeth far apart, hence, perhaps, lascivious : A 468. Du. *gat*, a hole. It is sometimes written *gaptothed*, and *gagtoothed* = having projecting teeth, which also signifies lascivious. 'If shee be *gaggetoothed*, tell hir some merry jest, to make her laughe.'—Lyly's Euphues, ed. Arber, p. 116. See note.

Gaude grene, a light green colour : B 1221. 'Colour hit *gaude grene*.'—Ord. and Reg. p. 452.

Gayler, a gaoler : B 206. From Anglo-F. *gaole*, It. *gaiola*, Sp. *gayola*, a cage.

Gayne, to avail : B 318. Icel. *gegna*, to meet, to aid ; Icel. *gegn*, A.S. *gegn*, against ; whence *ungainly*.

Gaytres beryis, berries of the dogwood-tree, *Cornus sanguinea* : C 145. A.S. *gáte-tréow*, cornel-tree, A.S. Leechdoms, ii. 86.

Gees, geese : C 571.

Gentil, noble : A 72.

Gentilesse, gentleness, nobleness : C 476.

Gere, manner, habit : B 514, 673.

Gere, gear, all sorts of instruments, tools, utensils, armour, apparel, fashion : A 352, B 158, 1322. A.S. *gearwe*, clothing ; *gearwian*, to prepare ; cf. Eng. *yare*.

Gerful, changeable : B 680. See **Gery**.

Gerland, a garland : B 196.

Gerner, a garner : A 593. F. *grenier*, garner, corn-loft ; *grene*, grain. (Cotgrave.)

Gery, changeable : B 678.

Gesse, to deem, suppose, think, guess : A 82, 118. Du. *gissen*, Sw. *gissa*, Dan. *gisse*, to believe, suppose.

Gete, to get, obtain, pp. *geten* : A 291.

Gigginge, fitting or providing with straps : B 1646. Godefroy gives O. F. *guige, guigue,* a strap for hanging a buckler over the shoulder, a handle of a shield. Cotgrave gives the fem. pl. *guiges,* 'the handles of a targuet or shield.'

Gilt, guilt : B 907, C 553.

Giltelees, free from guilt, guilt-less : B 454.

Ginglen, to jingle : A 170.

Gipoun, a short cassock : A 75, B 1262.

Gipser, a pouch or purse : A 357. F. *gibecière,* a pouch ; from O. F. *gibbe,* a bunch. See Scheler.

Girdel, girdle : A 358.

Girles, young people, whether male or female : A 664. Low G. *gör,* a child.

Girt, pp. girded, girt : A 329.

Girt, pierced : B 152. *Thurgh-girt,* pierced through, is used also by Grimoald :—

'With throat ycut he roars, he lieth along,
His entrails with a lance *through-gyrded* quite.' — Poems by Surrey, &c., p. 215, ed. Bell.

The M. E. *girde,* or *gride,* signifies also to strike, and may be connected with E. *yard* (as in *yard*-measure), A. S. *gyrd,* Du. *garde,* Ger. *Gerte,* a rod.

Gladdere, adj. more glad, B 2193.

Gladen, to console, gladden: B1979.

Gladere, sb. one who makes glad, B 1365.

Glaring, staring (like the eyes of the hare) : A 684. Norse *glora,* to stare.

Glede, a live coal, *gleed* : B 1139. A.S. *gléd,* Du. *gloed.* Cf. Icel. *glóa.* to burn, *glow* ; *glóð,* a live coal ; Ger. *glühen,* to glow ; *gluth,* hot coals.

Gliteren, to glitter, shine : B 2032. Icel. *glitra,* to glitter.

Glowen, to glow, shine ; Glowe-

den (pl. pret.), shone, B 1274. See Gleed.

Go, Gon, Goo, Goon (pp. *go, gon, goon*), to go, walk : A 450, 771. **Goth,** goes : B 213, 598. **Goon** (pl.), go : A 771, C 32.

Gobet, piece, morsel, fragment : A 696. O. F. *gobet,* a morsel of food, *gober,* to devour ; cf. Prov. Eng. *gob,* Gael. *gob,* the mouth ; whence *gobble, gabble,* &c.

Godhede, godhead, divinity : B 1523.

Golde, or **Gulde,** a flower commonly called a *turnsol* : B 1071. O. F. *goude,* a *marigold,* so called from its golden colour. See note.

Goliardeys, a buffoon : A 560. See note.

Gonne (pl. of *gan*), began, did : B 800.

Good, property, goods : A 581.

Goon, to go : A 12, 377 ; see Go.

Goost, ghost, spirit : A 205.

Goot, a goat : A 688.

Goune, a gown : A 93. It. *gonna,* Mid. Lat. *guna, gouna.*

Governaunce, management, control, management of affairs, business matters : A 281, B 455, C 45. Also = self-control, virtuous conduct :

'Grace groweth after [according to] *governance*
Is an old said saw in each place.' (Becon.)

Governing, control : A 599.

Graunte, grant, permission : B 448.

Graunte, to grant, consent to : A 786.

Graunting, consent, grant : B1581.

Grece, grease : A 135.

Gree, the prize, superiority, B 1875. See note.

Greet, Gret (def. form and pl. *greete, grete*), great (comp. *gretter,* superl. *gretteste*) : A 84, 120, 137, 197 ; B 5, 218, 1271.

Grene, green : A 103. A.S. *gréne.*

Greve, to grieve. **Agreved**, angry, B 1199.

Greve, a grove : B 637. This form is used by some of the Elizabethan poets.

Greyn, grain : A 596.

Griffoun, a griffin : B 1275.

Grim, fierce : B 1661. A.S. *grimm*, fierce, furious ; Du. *grimmen*, to snarl ; It. *grima*, wrinkled ; F. *grimace*, a wry mouth, *grimace*.

Grisly, horrible, dreadful, B 505 ; from M. E. *grise*, *agrise*, to terrify. A.S. *agrísan*, to dread, fear ; M. Du. *grijsen*, Prov. Eng. *gryze*, to snarl, grind the teeth.

Gronen, to groan : C 66 ; **Groning**, groaning : C 87. A.S. *gránian*, to groan, murmur.

Grope, to try, test : A 644. It signifies originally to feel with the hands, to grope (A. S. *grápian*, Icel. *greipa* ; cf. *grabble*, *grip*, *grasp*, &c.) ; hence to probe a wound, to test, put to the proof.

Grote, a groat : C 138.

Groyning, grumbling, murmuring, discontent : B 1602. O. F. *grognir* (Godefroy), F. *grogner*, to grunt, murmur, grumble.

Grucchen, to murmur, grumble, *grudge* : B 2187. F. *groucher*, to murmur. Gr. γρύζειν, to murmur, mutter.

Gruf, with face flat to the ground : B 91 ; whence Eng. *grovelling*, *grovel*. M. E. *grovelinges*, *gruflinges*, Icel. *grúfa*, to stoop down. *Liggja á grúfu*, to lie with the nose to the ground.

Grys, fur of the gray squirrel or rabbit : A 194.

Gulty, guilty : A 660.

Gye, to guide : B 1092. O.F. *guier*, F. *guider*.

Gyle, deceit : B 1738. O.F. *guile*, deceit, from the O. H. G. form cognate with E. *wile*.

Gyse, guise, fashion, mode, *wise*,

A 663, B 135, 350. F. *guise*, Ger. *Weise*, Eng. *wise*, mode, fashion.

H.

Haberdassher, a seller of hats : A 361. 'The *Haberdasher* heapeth wealth by *hattes*;' Gascoigne, The Fruites of Warre ; st. 64. See note.

Habergeoun, a diminutive *hauberk*, a small coat of mail : A 76, B 1261. O. F. *hauberc*, O. H. Ger. *halsberc*, A. S. *healsbeorg*, a coat of mail ; from *heals*, the neck, and *beorgan*, to cover or protect.

Hade = M. E. *havede* (sing.), had : A 554.

Hakke, to hack : B 2007. Du. *hakken*, Ger. *hacken*, to cut up, chop ; Dan. *hakke*, to peck ; F. *hacher*, to mince ; whence Eng. *hash*, *hatchet*.

Halwes, saints : A 14. A.S. *hálga*, a saint (as in 'All Hallows' E'en') : from *hál*, whole.

Hamer, a hammer : B 1650.

Han = *haven*, to have : A 224.

Happe, to happen, befall : A 585. Whence *happy*, mis-*hap*, per-*haps*, may-*hap*. M. E. *happen*, happy ; Icel. *happ*, fortune, luck.

Hardily, certainly : A 156.

Hardinesse, boldness : B 1090.

Haried, harried, taken as a prisoner : B 1868. F. *harier*, to hurry, harass, molest (Cotgrave).

Harlot : A 647. This term was not confined to females, nor even to persons of bad character. It signifies (1) a young person ; (2) a person of low birth ; (3) a person given to low conduct ; (4) a ribald.

Harlotryes, ribaldries : A 561.

Harneised, equipped : A 114.

Harneys, armour, gear, furniture, *harness* : B 148, 755. O. F. *harneis*, F. *harnois*, all manner of

harness, equipage, furniture;
Ger. *Harnisch*, armour.

Harre, a hinge: A 550. A.S. *heor, heorr*, M.E. *herre*, a hinge.

Harrow, a cry of distress: C 225. O. F. *harau, hare! Crier haro sur*, to make hue and cry after. O. H. Ger. *haren*, to cry out; Scottish *harro*, a cry for help.

Hauberk, a coat of mail: B 1573. See Habergeon.

Haunt, (1) an abode, (2) custom, practice, skill: A 447. F. *hanter*, to frequent.

Heed, Hede, head: A 198, 455. A. S. *héafod*, M. Du. *hoofd*, head; Scottish *haffet*, side of the head.

Heeld, held: A 337. A.S. *héold*.

Heep, heap, assembly, host: A 575. A.S. *héap*, Ger. *Haufe*, heap, band, crowd. Cf. M. E. '*a heep* of houndes;' *heep*, a band of armed men.

Heer, here: B 933.

Heer, hair: A 589, B 1285. **A.S.** *hǽr, hér*.

Heeth, a heath: A 6, 606. A. S. *hǽð*, heath; Goth. *haithi*, the open country; Icel. *heiðr*, a waste; Ger. *Heide*, a heath; whence *heathen, hoyden* (M. Du. *heyden*, a clown, rustic).

Hegge, a hedge: C 398. A. S. *hegge*, a bush, shrub, hedge. We have other forms of the word in *haw-thorn* (A.S. *haga*, a hedge), and in the local name *Hays* (A.S. *hege*, a hedge); '*Broken hayes*' (Oxford).

Heigh, high, B 207; great, B 940.

Hele, health: B 413. A. S. *hǽl*, whole; *hǽlu*, health.

Heled, hidden, kept secret, C 235. A. S. *helan*, to cover, conceal; prov. Eng. *hele, hill*, to cover, *hull*, cod of pease; cf. G. *Hülle*, a cover.

Helpen of, to help off, get rid of (pret. *halp*, pp. *holpen*): A 632.

Hem, them : A 18.

Hemself, themselves: B 396.

Hemselve, Hemselven, themselves.

Heng (pret. of *honge*), hanged: A 160, 358; pl. *henge*, A 677.

Henne, hence: B 1498. M. E. *hennes, hens*. A more modern form is our *hence*.

Hente, Henten, seize, take hold of, get : A 299, 698; B 46. (Pret. *hente*, B 442; pp. *hent*, B 723.) A. S. *hentan*.

Heraud, a herald: B 159, 1675. F. *hérauld, héraut*, from O. H. Ger. *haren*, to shout.

Herbergage, Herberwe, lodging, inn, harbour: A 403, 765, C 169. A. S. *here*, an army, and *beorgan*, to protect, defend. 'A good *harborough* for the ship.'— Hakluyt's Voyages, iii. p. 35.

Herd, haired: B 1660.

Herde, a herd, keeper of cattle, a shep*herd*: A 603. A. S. *hyrde*, a keeper, guardian; Ger. *Hirte*, a herdsman; Icel. *hirða*, to keep guard.

Here, to hear: A 169, C 432.

Heres, hairs: A 555. See Heer.

Herknen, to hark, hearken, listen: B 668, 985, 1674.

Hert, a hart: B 831.

Herte, heart : A 150.

Herteles, without heart, cowardly: C 88.

Hertely, heartily: A 762.

Herte-spoon: B 1748. The provincial *heart-spoon* signifies the navel. Tyrwhitt explains it as 'the concave part of the breast, where the lower ribs unite with the *cartilago ensiformis.*'

'.... He that undoes him (the deer),
Doth cleave the *brisket-bone*, upon the *spoon*
Of which a little gristle grows.'
Sad Shepherd, act i. sc. 6.

Hest, command, *behest:* B 1674.

A. S. *hǽs*, a hest, from *hátan*, to command.

Hete, to promise : B 1540. A. S. *hátan*, O. Sax. *hétan*, Icel. *heita*, to call, promise.

Hethen, a heathen : A 66.

Hethenesse, the country inhabited by the heathens, A 49 ; in contradistinction to *Christendom.*

Heve, to heave, raise : A 550. *Heve of* = to lift off (pret. *haf, hof:* Eng. *hove*). A.S. *hebban*, O. Fris. *heva*, to heave, lift.

Hevenly, heavenly : B 197.

Hewe, colour, complexion, *hue :* B 506. **Hewes,** colours for painting : B 1230. A.S. *hiw.*

Hewed, coloured : C 49. See Hew.

Hewen, to cut : B 564. A. S. *héawan*, Ger. *hauen.*

Hey, Heye, Heygh, Heyh, high, highly. A.S. *héh.*

Hider, hither : A 672.

Hidous, hideous : B 1120. **Hidously,** hideously, dreadfully : B 843. O. F. *hide, hisde, hidour, hisdour*, dread ; *hidus*, dreadful.

Hight, promised ; **Highte,** was called : A 616, 719, B 333, 1614. **Highte,** to be called, B 699. A.S. *héht, hét* ; pret. of *hátan*, to command, promise. The preterite of *hátan* (Ger. *heissen*), to call, be called, was *hátte* ; so two distinct usages have been confounded.

Highte. ' *On highte* ' = aloud : B 926.

Himselve, Himselven, dat. and acc. of *himself :* A 184, 528.

Hindreste, hindmost : A 622.

Hipes, hips : A 472. A.S. *hype*, Du. *heup*, Ger. *Hüfte*, the flank, hip.

Hir, her : A 120.

Hir, their, of them : A 11, B 320. *Hir aller* = of them all, A 586.

Hit, it.

Ho, an interjection commanding a cessation of anything : B 848,

1675. Cf. the carter's *whoa !* to his horse to stop.

Hold, ' in hold,' in possession, custody : c 54. A.S. *ge-heald*, Icel. *hald*, custody, *hold* ; A.S. *heald-an, haldan*, to hold, retain.

Holde, Holden, beholden, B 449 ; esteemed, held, A 141, B 832, 1861.

Holpen, helped : A 18. See **Helpen.**

Holt, a wood, grove : A 6. A.S. *holt*, O. H. Ger. *holz*, a wood. *Holt* is still used in some parts of England for an orchard or any place of trees, as a *cherry-holt*, an *apple-holt.* In Norfolk a plantation is called a *holt*, as *nut-holt, osier-holt, gooseberry-holt.* It occurs frequently as an element in local names, as *Holt*, a wood near Havant (Hants); *Knock-holt*, a wood near Tenterden (Kent).

Holwe, hollow : A 289. A.S. *hol*, a hole ; *holh*, a ditch ; Low Ger. *holig*, hollow. The termination *-we* or *-ow* had originally a diminutival force.

Homicydes, murderers : C 404.

Homward, homeward : B 2098.

Hond, hand : A 193.

Honest, creditable, honourable, becoming : A 246.

Honge, to hang (pret. *heng*) : B 1552.

Hool, Hole, whole : A 533, B 2148. A.S. *hál*, whole, sound ; whence, *wholesome, holy*, &c.

Hoolly, wholly : A 599.

Hoom, home : A 400, B 1881. **Hoomly,** homely : A 328. A.S. *hám*, Ger. *Heim.*

Hoppesteres (applied to ships), dancing : B 1159. *-ster* is a termination marking the feminine gender, as in modern Eng. *spinster.* See note.

Hors, horse : A 168. Pl. *hors*, horses, A 74, 598, B 1634. A.S. *hors* ; pl. *hors.*

Hoste, host: A 751.

Hostelrye, an hotel, inn: A 23, 722. O. F. *hostel*, Mid. Lat. *hospitale*, a hostel, inn (whence Eng. *hospital*), from Lat. *hospes*, a guest.

Hostiler, innkeeper: A 241. O. F. *hostelier*, F. *hôtelier*.

Hote, hot, hotly; A 97, 394. A. S. *hát*, hot.

Houped, = *houped*, whooped: C 580. F. *houper*, to call out. [*Whooping-cough* is properly *hooping-cough*.]

Hous, house: A 343

Housholdrye, economy: C 8.

Housholdere, householder: A 339.

Humblesse, humility: B 923.

Hunte, a hunter: B 820, 1160. A. S. *hunta*, a hunter.

Hunten, to hunt: B 782. *On hunting* = *a-hunting*: B 829.

Hunteresse, a female hunter: B 1489.

Hurtle, to push: B 1758. F. *heurter*, Du. *horten*, to dash against. *Hurt*, *hurl*, are connected with the base *hort*, to butt.

Hust, hushed: B 2123.

Hye, Hyghe, high, highly: B 39, 1217, 1605.

Hye, haste, B 2121; to hasten, B 1416. *In hye* = in haste, hastily.

Hyer, upper: A 398.

Hyne, hind, servant: A 603. A. S. *hína*, *híne*, a servant, domestic; from *híwa*, family.

I (vowel).

Ilke, same: A 64, 175. A. S. *ylc*. Cp. 'of that *ilk*.'

Imagining, plotting, B 1137

In, Inne, house, lodging, inn: B 1579, C 206.

Inequal, unequal: B 1413.

Infect, invalid: A 320.

Inne, adv. in: A 41, B 760.

Inned, lodged, entertained: B 1334.

Inspired, quickened: A 6.

I (consonant).

(*J* was formerly denoted by *i*, especially by a capital *I*.)

Ialous, jealous: B 471.

Iangle, to prate, babble: C 615.

Ianglere, a prater, babbler: A 560. O. F. *jangler*, to prattle, jest, lie.

Iape, a trick, jest: A 705, C 271.

Iape, to befool, deceive: B 871. F. *japper*, to yelp. It is probably connected with Eng. *gabble*, *gabbe*, &c.

Ieet, jet: C 41. F. *jaiet*, Lat. *gagates*. Used for beads, and held in high estimation. Bp. Bale makes allusion to this in Kynge Johan, p. 39:

'Holy water and bredde shall dryve
   awaye the devyll ;
Blessynges with *blacke bedes* wyll
   helpe in every evyll.'

Iet, fashion, mode: A. 682.

Iolitee, joyfulness, amusement: A 680, B 949.

Iolyf, joyful, pleasant: C 254. F. *joli*, It. *giulivo*, gay, fine, merry. Diez connects it with Icel. *jól*, Eng. *yule*, Christmas.

Iournee, a day's journey: B 1880.

Iuge, a judge: A 814, B 854. F. *juge*, Lat. acc. *iudicem*.

Iugement, judgment: A 778.

Iuste, Iusten, to joust, tilt, engage in a tournament: A 99, B 1628. O. F. *jouster*, to tilt; hence Eng. *jostle*.

Iustes = *jouste*, a tournament: B 1862.

Iuwyse, judgment: B 881. O.F. *juise*, judgment, from Lat. *iudicium*.

K.

Keep, care, attention, heed. *Take keep* = take care: A 398, 503: B 531.

Kembd (pp. of *kembe*), combed, neatly trimmed : B 1285.

Kempe, shaggy : B 1276. From Icel. *kamp*, a beard, the stiff whiskers of a seal, cat, or lion. Cf. *Camp* in Murray's Dict. See note.

Kene, sharp : A 104.

Kepe (pret. *kepte*, pp. *kept*), to guard, preserve, take care (as in *I kepe nat* = I care not) : A 276, B 1380. A. S. *cépan*.

Kervere, a carver : B 1041.

Kerving, cutting, carving : B 1057. See **Carf**.

Kindled, lighted : B 1437. Icel. *kynda*, to set fire to ; *kyndill*, a torch ; cf. Eng. *cannel* coal. From Lat. *candela*.

Kinrede, kindred : B 428. With A. S. suffix *-réden*. The affix *-rede* is equivalent to *-ship*, and occurs in *hat-red*, *kin-d-red*. The M. E. has *frend-reden*, friendship ; *fo-reden*, enmity.

Knarre, a knotted, thick-set fellow : A 549. Cf. M. E. *gnarr*, a knot ; *gnarled*, knotted ; Swed. *knorla*, to twist, curl.

Knarry, full of *gnarrs* or knots : B 1119.

Knave, a boy, a servant : B 1870. A. S. *cnapa*, Ger. *Knabe*, a boy, youth, servant ; M. E. *knave-child*, a male-child.

Knighthede, knighthood : B 1931.

Knobbe, a large pimple : A 633.

Knowe, pp. known : B 345, 1442.

Knyf, a knife : B 1141.

Kyn, kine : C 11.

Kynd, Kynde, nature : B 1593. *By kynde* = by nature, naturally : C 376. Cf. 'the *kindly* (natural) fruits of the earth.' A. S. *cynd*, nature.

L.

Lacerte, a fleshy muscle : B 1895 (Lat. *lacertus*).

Lacing, lacing, fastening : B 1646. See **Las**.

Lad (pp.), B 1762 ; **Ladde** (pret.), B 588 ; led, carried.

Lafte (pret. sing.), left, ceased : A 492. Cf. the phrase '*left off*.'

Lak, want, lack : C 24. Du. *lak*, fault, want.

Lakke, to lack, be wanting : B 1422.

Langage, language : A 211.

Large, adj. free ; adv. largely. Chaucer says, 'at his *large*,' B 425, where we should say 'at large.'

Las, a lace, belt : B 1093 ; net, snare : B 959. F. *lacs*, Prov. F. *laz* (Lat. *laqueus*), a lace, snare.

Lasse, less : B 898.

Lat, imp. let : A 188 ; *lat be*, cease.

Late, lately, recently. '*Late* y-come ;' '*late* y-shave :' A 77, 690.

Latoun, a kind of brass, or tinned iron, *latten* : A 699. F. *laiton*, brass ; It. *latta*, tin-plate.

Laughe, to laugh : C 267.

Launde, a plain surrounded by trees, hunting-grounds : B 833. Cotgrave has '*lande*, a land or *launde*, a wild untilled shrubbie or bushy plaine.' It seems to be, with a difference of meaning, our modern word *lawn*. Welsh *llan*, a clear space. Shakespeare used the word in 3 Henry VI. iii. 1. 2 :

'Under this thick-grown brake we'll shroud ourselves ;
For through this *laund* anon the deer will come.'

Laurer, a laurel : B 169. 'In a fayre fresh and grene *laurere*.' (Lives of Saints, Roxb. Club, p. 51.)

Laxatif, Laxatyf, a purging medicine : C 123.

Laynere, a lanner or whiplash :

B 1646. F. *lanière*, a thong, *laniard*, lash of a whip.

Lazar, a leper: A 242, 245.

Lechecraft, the skill of a physician, B 1887; from *leche*, a physician. A. S. *læce*, a leech, physician.

Leed, a cauldron, copper: A 202. It also signifies a kettle.

    ' Mowe hawme to burne,
    To serve thy turne,
    To bake thy bread,
    To burne under *lead*.'—
    Tusser, Husbandry, 56. 14.

Leef (pl. *leves*), leaf: B 980.

Leef (def. form voc. case *leve*), dear, beloved, pleasing : B 278, 979. ' Be him looth or *leef* '= be it displeasing or pleasing to him. A. S. *léof*, dear; Eng. *lief*, *liefer*.

Leen, *imp. s.* give (lit. lend): B 2224. See **Lene**.

Leep, leaped: B 1829.

Leet (pret.), let: A 128, 508; B 348. A. S. *lǽtan* (pret. *lét*, pp. *lǽten*). *Leet brynge* = caused to be brought. See **Lete**.

Leme, gleam: C 110. A. S. *léoma*. (Allied to E. *light*, but not to E. *gleam*.)

Lene, to lend, give: A 611. A. S. *lǽnan*, to give, lend; *lǽn*, a loan; Ger. *leihen*, to lend. See **Leen**.

Lene, lean, poor: A 287, 591. A. S. *hlǽne*, lean; from *hlinian*, to lean, bend.

Lenger, longer: A 330, 821.

Lepart, a leopard: B 1328.

Lere, to learn: C 286. A. S. *lǽran*, to teach; from *lár*, doctrine, *lore*.

Lerne, to learn: A 308.

Lese, to lose: B 357, 432 : C 322. A. S. *léosan*, pret. *léas*, pp. *loren*; the old pp. occurs in *for-lorn*.

Lesing, loss: B 849.

Lesinges, leasing, lies: B 1069. A. S. *léas*, false, loose; *léasung*,

falseness; Goth. *laus*, empty, vain; whence the affix *-less*.

Lest, Leste, least: B 263.

Lest, pleasure, delight, joy: A 132. A. S. *lust*, desire, love; *lystan*, to wish, will, desire; Eng. *list*, *listless*, *lust*, *lusty*.

Leste, pret. of vb. impers. pleased: A. 750. ' Me *list* '= it pleases me; ' him *liste* '= it pleased him; ' hem *liste* '= it pleased them; ' us *leste* '= it pleased us. See **List**, **Lest**.

Lete, to leave: B 477. See **Leet**.

Lette, to hinder, delay, tarry, put off (pret. *lette*): B 31, 1034; C 264. ' *Letten of* '= refrain from : B 459. A. S. *lettan*, to hinder; Goth. *latjan*, to delay; Icel. *latr*, lazy, slow. Cf. Eng. *late*.

Lette, delay, hindrance. See previous word.

Letuaries, electuaries: A 426.

Leve, to believe: B 2230.

Leve, *imp.* leave: B 756.

Levere, rather (comp. of *leef*): A 293, C 300. ' Him was *levere* ', = it was more agreeable to him, he would rather.

Lewed, Lewd, ignorant, unlearned. *Lewed man*, a layman : A 502. A. S. *lǽwed*, pertaining to the laity. ' It is not meet for the *lewd* people to know the mysteries of God's word.' — Becon, Acts of Christ, p. 527.

Leye, to lay (imp. *ley*, pret. *leyde*, pp. *leyd*) : A 81, 841.

Leyser, leisure: B 330. Ang. F. *leisir*, F. *loisir*, from Lat. *licere*.

Licenciat, one licensed by the Pope to hear confessions in all places, and to administer penance independently of the local ordinaries: A 220.

Liche-wake, the vigil, *watch*, or *wake* held over the body of the dead: B 2100. A. S. *líc*, Ger. *Leiche*, Goth. *leik*, a corpse; whence *lich-gate*, the gate where

the corpse is set down on enter-
ing a churchyard, to await the
arrival of the minister.

Licour, liquor, sap: A 3.

Lief, beloved: C 59. See **Leef.**

Ligge, to lie: B 1347, C 404.
A. S. *liecgan,* to lie, whence
lecgan, to lay.

Lightly, (1) easily, (2) joyfully,
B 1012.

Like, vb. impers. to please: A
777.

Limes, limbs: B 1277.

Limitour, a friar licensed to ask
alms within a certain limit: A
209.

Linage, Ligne, lineage: B 252,
693.

Linde, lime-tree: B 2064.

Lipsed, lisped: A 264. Cf. Du.
lispen.

List, it pleases: A 583; pret.
liste: A 102, B 194. See **Leste.**

Listes, lists, a place enclosed for
combats or tournaments: B
1687. ' *Barres* (=barriers) or
lists.' — Cowel's Interpreter,
1701.

Litarge, white lead: A 629.

Litel, little: A 438. A. S. *lyt,
lytel,* Goth. *leitils,* Du. *luttel.*

Lith, a limb, any member of the
body: C 55. A. S. *lið,* Ger.
Glied, a joint, limb ; Norse *lida,*
to bend the limbs; cf. Eng. *lithe,
lissome.*

Liveree, livery: A 363. See
note.

Lode, a load: B 2060.

Lodemenage, pilotage: A 403.
Used in this sense in 3 George I,
c. 13. Courts of *Lodemanage*
are held at Dover for the appointment of the Cinque Port pilots.
See **Lodesterre.**

Lodesterre, a loadstar, the polestar: B 1201. The first element
is the A. S. *lád,* a way, whence
lǽdan, to lead, conduct. It
occurs again in *loadstone; lode,* a

vein of metal ore; M. E. *lode-
men, loders,* carriers, pilots;
lode-ship, a kind of fishing-vessel
mentioned in early statutes; Prov.
Eng. *loads,* ditches for straining
away the water from the fens;
loadstone, a leading stone for
drains.

Logge, to lodge; sb. a lodging,
dwelling-place: C 33, 176.
Logging, lodging: C 175. F.
loge, a hut or small apartment ;
loger, to sojourn.

Loken, to see, look: B 925.

Loken, locked, enclosed: C 55.

Lokkes, locks (of hair), curls: A
81.

Loking, appearance, sight: B
1313.

Lond, Londe, land: A 14.

Longe, Longen, to belong: B
1420.

Longen, to desire, long for: A 12.

Longes, lungs: B 1894.

Looth, odious, hateful, disagree-
able, *loath,* unwilling: A 486, B
979.

Lordinges, lordlings (a diminutive of *lord*), sirs, my masters:
A 761.

Lore, precept, doctrine, learning:
A 527. See **Lere.**

Lorn, lost. See **Lese.**

Los, loss: B 1685.

Losengeour, a flatterer, liar: C
506. O. F. *losengier.*

Losten (pl. pret.), lost: B 78. See
Lese.

Lovyer, a lover: A 80.

Loud, loud, loudly: C 543.

Luce, a pike: A 350.

Lust, pleaseth. See **List.**

Lust, pleasure: A 192.

Lustinesse, pleasure: B 1081.

Lusty, pleasant, joyful, gay: A 80,
B 655. **Lustily,** merrily, gaily:
B 671.

Lyf, life: A 71, B 1918.

Lyfly, in a lifelike way: B 1229.

Lyk, like: A 590, B 443.

Lyte, little: A 494; B 335, 476.

Lyth, lies: B 360.

Lyve, dat. of *lyf*, life; hence *alyve*, in life, alive, B 1840.

Lyves, alive, living: B 1537.

M.

Maad, Mad, pp. made: A 394, 668.

Maat, Mat, dejected, downcast: B 98. F. *mat*, faded, quelled; Du. *mat*, exhausted; Ger. *matt*, feeble, faint; all from Pers. *mát*, dead; from the game of chess; E. *mate* in *check-mate*.

Maist, mayest: B 385. **Maistow**, mayest thou: B 378, C 286.

Maister, a master, chief, a skilful artist: A 261, 576. *Maister-streete* = the chief street: B 2044.

Maistrye, skill, power, superiority: A 165.

Make, a companion or *mate*: B 1698. A. S. *maca*, a companion; Icel. *maki*, a spouse; cf. Eng. *match*.

Maked, pp. made: B 1666.

Male, a portmanteau, bag, *mail*: A 694. O. F. *male*, a great budget, F. *malle*.

Malencolye, sb. melancholy: C 113. Adj. **Malencolyk**: B 517.

Manace, Manasing, a threat, menace: B 1145, 1178. F. *menace*, Lat. *minae*, *minaciae*, threats.

Maner, Manere, manner, kind, sort: A 71, 858, B 1017, C 26. *Maner*, sort of (without *of*). 'A *maner* deye' = a sort of dey, or dairy-maid.

Manhod, manhood, manliness: A 756.

Mansioun, a mansion: B 1116.

Mantelet, a little mantle, a short mantle: B 1305.

Manye, mania, madness: B 516.

Many oon, many a one: A 317.

Marchant, a merchant: A 270.

Marshal, marshal of the hall: A 752. Mid. Lat. *marescalcus*, F. *maréchal*, the master of the horse; O. Ger. *mähre*, a horse, and *schalk*, a servant. 'The *marshal of the hall* was the person who, at public festivals, placed every person according to his rank. It was his duty also to preserve peace and order. The *marshal of the field* presided over any out-door game.'—Halliwell.

Martirdom, torment, martyrdom: B 602.

Martyre, a torment: B 704.

Mary, marrow: A 380. A.S. *mearh*, marrow; Dan. *marv*, G. *Mark*.

Mase, a wild fancy: C 273. Icel. *masa*, to jabber, chatter; Norse *masast*, to drop asleep, to begin to dream; Prov. Eng. *mazle*, to wander, as if stupefied. Cf. the phrase 'to be in a *maze*.'

Mat; see **Maat**.

Matere, matter: A 727, B 401.

Matrimoine, matrimony: B 2237.

Maugree, in spite of: B 311, 1760. F. *malgré*, against the will of, in spite of; *mal*, ill, and *gré*, will, pleasure.

Maunciple, an officer who has the care of purchasing victuals for an Inn of Court or College: A 544. Lat. *manceps*, a purchaser, contractor.

Maydenhode, maidenhood: B 1471.

Mayntene, to maintain: B 583.

Mayst, mayest. See **Maist**.

Mede, a reward, *meed*: A 770. A.S. *méd*, Ger. *Miethe*, hire; whence M. E. *meedful*, meritorious.

Mede, a mead or meadow, hayland: A 89. A.S. *mǽd*, *mǽdu*, a meadow.

Medlee, of a mixed colour: A 328. O.F. *medler*, *mesler*, to mix.

Meek, meek : A 69.

Meel, a meal : C 13. A.S. *mǽl*, what is marked out, a separate part, a meal, a mark, spot. Cf. M.E. *cup-mele*, cup by cup ; *stound-mele*, at intervals ; Eng. *piece-meal* ; Ger. *ein-mal*, once.

Men, one ; used like the F. *on* : A 149.

Mencioun, mention : B 35.

Mene, to mean, intend (pret. *mente*) : A 793, C 605.

Mere, a mare : A 541. A.S. *mere*, a mare ; *mearh*, a horse.

Meriely, pleasantly : A 714.

Mermayde, a mermaid : C 450. A.S. *mere*, a lake, sea ; Ger. *Meer*, the sea.

Mervaille, marvel : C 256. F. *merveille ;* from Lat. pl. *mirabilia*, wonderful things.

Mery, Merye, Myrie, pleasant, joyful, merry : A 208, 757 ; B 641, C 251. A.S. *merg*, merry ; *myrhð*, pleasure, joy, *mirth*.

Meschaunce, Mischaunce, mischance, misfortune : B 1151, C 280.

Meschief, Mescheef, misfortune, what turns out ill : A 493, B 468. F. *meschef* (*mes = minus*, less ; *chef = caput*, head).

Messager, a messenger : B 633.

Mester, need, necessity : B 482. O. F. *mester*, need ; the same as O. F. *mestier*, business ; from Lat. *ministerium*.

Mesurable, moderate : A 435.

Met, pp. dreamed : C 106.

Mete, meat, food : A 136. Cf. Goth. *mats*, food ; O. H. Ger. *maz*, food, dish.

Mete, to meet : B 666.

Mete, to dream, pret. *mette.* It is used impersonally, as *me mette*, I dreamed : C 74. A.S. *mǽtan*.

Meth, mead, a drink made of honey : B 1421.

Mewe, a *mue* or coop where fowls were fattened : A 349. *Mew* also

signified a place where *hawks* were confined while moulting. F. *muer*, to change ; It. *muta*, a change ; Lat. *mutare*, to change ; whence also Du. *muiten*, M.E. *moute*, to moult.

Meynee, household, attendants, suite, domestics : B 400, C 574. O. F. *mesnée*, *maisnée* ; Mid. Lat. *maisnada* (from Low Lat. *man-sionata*), a family, household, suite ; from Lat. *mansio*.

Middel, middle, midst : C 228.

Minister, an officer of justice : C 223. 'Minister* meant etymologically a small man ; and it was used in opposition to *magister*, a big man. *Minister* is connected with *minus*, less ; *magister* with *magis*, more. Hence *minister*, a servant, a servant of the crown, a minister. From *minister* came the Lat. *ministerium*, service ; in F. contracted into *métier*, a profession. A *minstrel* was originally a professional artist, and more particularly a singer or poet. Even in the Mystery Plays—the theatrical representation of the Old or New Testament story—*mystery* is a corruption of *ministerium ;* it means a religious ministry or service, and had nothing to do with *mystery.* It ought to be spelt with an *i*, therefore, and not with a *y*.'—Max Müller, Science of Language, Second Series, p. 254.

Minstralcye, minstrelsy, B 1339, 1666.

Mirour, a mirror : B 541.

Mirthe, pleasure, amusement : A 766, 767.

Misboden (pp. of *misbede*), insulted, injured : B 51. A.S. *béodan*, = to offer, as in our phrases 'to *bid* the banns,' '*bid* for a thing.'

Mischaunce. See **Meschaunce**.

Mishappe, to mishap, turn out badly for, B 788.

Mo, more : *namo,* no more, A 544. A. S. *má.*

Moche, Mochel, Muchel, adj. much, great ; adv. greatly : A 132, 258, 467, B 1992. *Moche and lite* = great and small. A. S. *mycel,* great, *mickle.*

Moder, mother : C 476.

Moevere, mover, first cause : B 2129.

Mone, the moon : A 403.

Mone, a moan, lamentation : B 508. A. S. *mán,* a moan ; whence *mǽnan,* to moan.

Month, Moneth, a month : A 92.

Mood, anger : B 902. A. S. *mód,* Ger. *Muth,* mind, courage, passion. Cf. Eng. *moody.*

Moorning, mourning : B 2110.

Moot, may, must, ought (pl. pres. *moten,* pret. *moste, muste*) : A 232, 735, B 27. A. S. *mót,* 1st and 3rd pers. sing. ; *móst,* 2nd pers. ; *móton,* pl. ; *moste,* pret.

Mordre, sb. murder, C 201, 231, 398 ; vb. to murder, C 221, 405.

Mordrer, a murderer : C 406.

Mordring, murdering : B 1143.

More, greater, more : B 898.

Mormal, a cancer, sore, or gangrene : A 386. See note.

Morne, adj. morning : A 358.

Mortreux, a kind of soup or pottage : A 384. See note.

Morwe, Morweninge, morning, morrow : A 334, 780, B 204.

Mosel, F. *museau,* muzzle, nose of an animal : B 1293. It. *musolare,* to muzzle.

Most, most : A 561. **Moste,** greatest, B 37.

Moste, must : A 712. See **Moot.**

Mot, may, must. **Mote,** pl. must : A 742. See **Moot.**

Mottelee, motley : A 271.

Mountaunce, amount, value : B 712.

Mous, a mouse : B 403.

Mowe, are able : B 2141.

Murmure, murmuring : B 1601.

Murye, glad, merry : B 528.

Mynde, dat. remembrance : B 544, 1048.

Mynour, a miner : B 1607.

My-selven, myself : A 803.

N.

Nacioun, nation : A 53.

Naker, a kettle-drum : B 1653. See note.

Nam = *ne* + *am,* am not : B 264.

Namely, especially : B 410, 1851.

Namo (*for* na mo), no more, A 101, 544. See **Mo.**

Narwe, close, narrow : A 625, C 2.

Nas = *ne* + *was,* was not : A 251.

Nat, not : A 428.

Nath = *ne* + *hath,* hath not : B 65.

Natheles, nevertheless : A 35.

Ne, adv. not, A 70 ; conj. nor, A 526. *Ne . . . ne* = neither . . . nor, A 603. *Ne . . . but,* only : B 254.

Nede, needful : A 304.

Nedely, of necessity : C 424.

Nedes, of necessity : B 311. *Nedescost* = *nedes-ways,* of necessity : B 619.

Nedeth, must of necessity (die) : B 2170.

Neer, Ner, near : B 581, 992 ; nigher : A 839.

Neet, neat, cattle : A 597.

Nekke, neck : A 238. *Nekke-boon,* bone of the neck.

Nercotikes, narcotics : B 614.

Nere = *ne* + *were,* were not : B 17.

Newe, newly, recently : A 428. *Al newe* = recently, lately ; *of newe* = anew.

Nexte, nearest : B 555.

Nigard, a niggard : C 95. M. E. *nig, nigon,* a niggard ; Norse *nyggja,* to gnaw, scrape ; Sw. *njugga,* to scrape up (money) ; *njugg,* sparing.

Night, pl. nights : C 53.

Nightertale, the night-time: A 97. *-tale* = reckoning, period.

Nis, Nys = *ne* + *is*, is not: B 43.

Noght, not: A 253.

Nolde = *ne* + *wolde*, would not: A 550.

Nombre, number: A 716.

Non, Noon, none: A 449, 654.

Nones, nonce: A 379, 523.

Nonne, a nun: A 118.

Noot, Not, = *ne* + *wot*, know not, knows not: A 284, B 181, 482. See **Wost**.

Norice, nurse: C 295.

Norissing, Norisshinge, nutriment, nurture: A 437, B 2159.

Nose-thirles, nostrils: A 557. See **Thirle**.

Not = *ne* + *wot*, knows not. See **Noot**.

Notabilitee, a thing worthy to be known: C 389.

Note, a note (in music): A 235.

Not-heed, a crop-head: A 109. Cf. *not-pated*, 1 Hen. IV. ii. 4. 78.

Nother, neither, nor.

Nothing, adv. not at all: B 1647.

Nouthe = *nou* + *the* = *now* + *then*, just now, at present. *As nouthe* = at present: A 462. A.S. *ðá*, then.

Ny, nigh, nearly: B 472; *as ny as*, as near (close) as: A 588.

Nyce, foolish: C 495.

O.

O, one: A 304, 738; B 354. See **Oo**.

Obeisaunce, obedience: B 2116.

Observaunce, respect: B 187, 642.

Of, off: B 1818.

Offende, to hurt, injure, attack: B 51.

Offensioun, offence, hurt, damage: B 1558.

Offertorie, a sentence of Scripture said or sung after the Nicene Creed in the Liturgy of the Western Church: A 710.

Offring, the alms collected at the Offertory: A 450.

Ofte sythes, oftentimes: A 485.

Oghte, ought: A 660.

Oo, Oon, one: A 148. See **O**. **Ones**, once: A 765.

Ook, an oak: B 1432, 2159.

Oon and oon, one by one: A 679.

Oonly, only: B 515.

Opie, opium: B 614.

Oratorie, a closet set apart for prayers or study: B 1047. 'Oratorys, .. wherein our prayers may the sooner be heard and the better accepted.'—Becon's Acts of Christ, p. 533, Parker Soc.

Ordeyne, to ordain: B 1695.

Ordinaunce, plan, orderly disposition: B 1709.

Orisoun, prayer, orison: B 1514.

Orlogge, a clock: C 34.

Oth, Ooth, an oath: A 810.

Ounce, a small portion: A 677.

Outhees, outcry, alarm: B 1154. Mid. Lat. *hutesium* (Ducange); O. F. *huteys* (Britton, i. 179).

Outher .. or = either .. or: B 627, 628.

Outrely, utterly, wholly: C 409.

Out-sterte, started out: C 227.

Over, upper: A 133. **Overest**, uppermost: A 290.

Overal, everywhere: A 216. Cf. Ger. *überall*.

Over-riden, ridden over: B 1164.

Overspradde, pret. spread over: A 678.

Over-thwart, athwart, across: B 1133. A.S. *pweor*, crooked, oblique. (Eng. *queer* = M. E. *quer*, Ger. *quer*, athwart.)

Owen, Owene, own: B 2219, C 134.

Owher, anywhere: A 653.

Oynement, ointment, unguent: A 631.

Oynouns, onions: A 634.

P.

Pace, to pass, B 2140 : pass on, A 36 ; pass away, B 744 ; to surpass, A 574.

Pacient, patient : A 484.

Paleys, palace : B 1341. ' A palace is now the abode of a royal family. But if we look at the history of the name we are soon carried back to the shepherds of the Seven Hills. There, on the Tiber, one of the seven hills was called the *Collis Palatinus*, and the hill was called *Palatinus* from *Pales*, a pastoral deity, whose festival was celebrated every year on the 21st of April, as the birthday of Rome. It was to commemorate the day on which Romulus, the wolf-child, was supposed to have drawn the first furrow on the foot of that hill, and thus to have laid the foundation of the most ancient part of Rome, the *Roma Quadrata*. On this hill, the *Collis Palatinus*, stood in later times the houses of Cicero and of his neighbour and enemy Catiline. Augustus built his mansion on the same hill, and his example was followed by Tiberius and Nero. Under Nero, all private houses had to be pulled down on the Collis Palatinus, in order to make room for the emperor's residence, the *Domus Aurea*, as it was called, the Golden House. This house of Nero's was henceforth called the *Palatium*, and it became the type of all the *palaces* of the kings and emperors of Europe.' —Max Müller, Science of Language, Second Series, p. 251.

Palfrey, a horse for the road : A 207. F. *palefroi*, Mid. Lat. *paraveredus, palafridus*, an easy-going horse for riding ; *veredus*, a post-horse, whence Ger. *Pferd*, Du. *paard*, a horse.

Pan, the skull, brain-pan : B 307. Cf. M. E. *hern-pan*, brain-pan.

Paraments, ornamental furniture or clothes : B 1643.

Paramour, by way of love : B 297.

Paramours, with great affection : B 1254. Cf. Barbour's Bruce, xiii. 485.

Parde, Pardee = *par Dieu*, a common oath : A 563.

Pardoner, a seller of indulgences : A 543.

Parfit, perfect : A 72, 422, 532.

Parisshen, a parishioner : A 482.

Parte, party, company : B 1724.

Partrich, a partridge : A 349.

Party, partly : B 195. **Partye**, a part : B 2150 ; adj. partial : B 1799.

Parvys : A 310. See note.

Pas, foot-pace : A 825 ; pl. paces, B 1032. F. *pas*, Lat. *passus*.

Passe, to surpass : A 448. **Passant, Passing**, surpassing : B 1249, 2027.

Payen, pagan : B 1512. F. *paien*, a pagan.

Peer, equal (as in *peerless*) : C 30.

Pees, peace : B 589.

Peire, pair : A 159.

Pekke, to pick : C 147. A. S. *pycan*, to pick, pull ; Du. *pikken*, to pick.

Penaunce, penance, pain, sorrow : B 457.

Penoun, a pennant or ensign (borne at the end of a lance), B 120. F. *penoun* ; Lat. *penna, pinna*, a feather, wing.

Perce, to pierce : A 2. F. *percer*.

Perrye, jewelry : B 2078. F. *perré*.

Pers, of a sky-blue colour : A 439. O. F. *pers*.

Persoun, a parson or parish-priest : A 478.

Perturben, to disturb : B 48.

Pestilens, pestilence, plague : C 590.

Peyne, sb. pain, grief : B 439 ; torture, B 275.

Peyne, Peynen, to take pains, endeavour : A 139.

Peynte, to paint : B 1076.

Peyre, a pair : B 1263.

Pighte, pitched : B 1831.

Piked, adj. trimmed. '*Pykyd*, or *purgyd*, fro fylthe or other thynge grevows, *purgatus* ;' Promptorium Parv. See **Apiked**.

Piled, stripped of hair, bald : A 627. Norse *pila*, to pluck ; Low Ger. *pulen*, to pluck, pick ; Eng. *peel*; F. *piller*, to rob. ' Pill and poll.'—Burton's Anat. of Mel. p. 31.

Piler, a pillar : B 1135.

Pilour, a plunderer : B 149. See **Piled**.

Pilwe-beer, a pillow-case : A 694. Cf. Low G. *büren*, a case ; *kussen-büren*, a pillow-case ; Dan. *vaar*, cover, case.

Pinche, to find fault (with) : A 326.

Pitaunce, a mess of victuals ; properly an additional allowance served to the inmates of religious houses at a high festival : A 224.

Pitous, compassionate, piteous : A 143.

Pitously, piteously : B 259.

Plat, plain, flat : B 987.

Plentevous, plentiful : A 344.

Plesaunce, pleasure : B 713.

Plesaunt, pleasant : A 254.

Plesen, to please : A 610.

Pley, play, pleasure : B 267.

Pleye, Pleyen, to play, take one's pleasure : A 236, 758, 772. **Pleyinge**, playing, amusement : B 203.

Pleyn, plain : A 790.

Pleyn, full, fully, openly : A 315, 327. *Pleyn bataile* = open battle : B 130.

Pleyne, to complain : B 462.

Pleynen, to complain : B 393.

Pleynly, fully : B 875.

Pocok, peacock : A 104, Harl. MS.; **Pecok**, Elles. MS. It is also written *pacok*. Lat. *pauo*.

Pollax, a halberd, pole-axe : B 1686. We have also *bole-axe*, Icel. *bol-öx*, M. E. *bul-axe*, falx arboraria.

Pomel, top of the head : B 1831.

Pomely, marked with round spots like an apple, dappled : A 616. *Pomely gray* = apple-gray ; Low Lat. *grisius pomellatus*. F. *pomme*, Lat. *pomum*.

Poplexye, apoplexy : C 21.

Poraille, the poor : A 247.

Pore. See **Povre**.

Port, carriage, behaviour : A 69.

Portreiture, a set of pictures : B 1057, 1110.

Portreying, painting : B 1080.

Portreyour, a painter : B 1041. F. *pourtraire*, to draw ; from *traire*, Lat. *trahere*, to draw.

Pose, to propose, put the question : B 304.

Post, pillar, support : A 214.

Poudre-marchaunt, a kind of spice : A 381. See note.

Poupe, to make a noise with a horn : C 579.

Poure, to pore, to look close and long : A 185.

Povre, poor : A 225, 478. **Povre-ly**, poorly : B 554. O. F. *povre*, Lat. *pauper*.

Poynaunt, pungent : A 352.

Poynt, particle, particular : B 643.

Practisour, practitioner : A 422.

Preche, to preach : A 481. F. *prêcher*, Lat. *predicare*.

Preest, Prest, a priest : A 164.

Preisen, Praysen, to praise. F. *prix*, price ; It. *precio*, price, worth ; Sp. *prez*, honour, glory.

Presse, to press : B 1672.

Prest, ready. Lat. *praesto*, in readiness ; M. E. *in prest* = in hand; *press money = prest money*, money given in hand, earnest money received by a soldier at impressment; hence 'to *press*' (= to *prest*), to engage soldiers.

Preve, sb. proof, C 163. See **Proven**.

Preye, to pray: B 625. F. *prier*, It. *pregare*, Lat. *precari*.

Preyeres, prayers: A 231.

Pricasour, a hard rider: A 189.

Prike, (1) to prick, wound; (2) to spur a horse, to ride hard; (3) to incite, spur on: A 11, B 185, 1820. Low Ger. *prikken*, to pick, stick; *an prikken*, to stimulate, set on. See **Prikke**.

Priking, riding: A 191.

Prikke, a point, piercing stroke: B 1748. Du. *prik*, a stab: Sw. *prick*, a point.

Prively, secretly: A 652.

Propre, peculiar, own: A 581.

Proven, to prove, prove true, be proved: A 547.

Prow, advantage, profit: C 130. (Cf. Eng. *prowess*, F. *prouesse*.) Prov. F. *pros*, good (for its purpose); O. F. *preux*, valiant, loyal; *prou*, much, enough.

Privetee, privity, privacy, private business: B 553.

Pryme, the first quarter of the artificial day: B 1331.

Prys, price, A 815; praise, fame, A 67, 237, B 1383. See **Preisen**.

Pulle, to pluck: A 652. *Pulle a finch* = pluck a pigeon (Lyly has *gull a chuff*), cheat a novice.

Pulled, plucked: A 177. See note.

Pultrye, poultry: A 598. F. *poule*, a hen; Lat. *pullus*, young of an animal.

Purchas, anything acquired (honestly or dishonestly); proceeds of begging: A 256. 'Tailors in France . . . grow to great abominable *purchase* and become great officers.' — The Devil's

Law Case, ii. 1. See Duchess of Malfi, iii. 28. F. *pourchasser*, It. *procacciare*, to hunt after, chase, catch.

Purchasour, conveyancer: A 318.

Purchasing, conveyancing: A 320.

Pure, mere, very: B 421.

Purfiled, embroidered, fringed: A 193. It. *porfilo*, a border in armoury, a worked edge, a *profile*; *porfilare*, to overcast with gold or silver lace. F. *pourfiler*, to tinsel or overcast with gold or silver lace (Cotgrave). Bailey has the contracted form *purl*, a kind of edging for bone-lace.

Purpos, purpose, design: B 1684. F. *proposer*, which has supplanted O. F. *pourpenser*, to bethink himself; *pourpens*, purpose.

Purs, purse: A 656. A.S. *purs*; F. *bourse*; Lat. *bursa*, hide, skin.

Purtreye, pourtray, draw: A 96.

Purveiaunce, foresight, providence, plan: B 394, 807, 2153. O. F. *pourveoir*, Lat. *prouidere*.

Pykepurs, a pickpurse: B 1140.

Pyne, sb. torment, pain, grief.

Pyne, Pynen, to torment, grieve: B 888, C 239. A.S. *pin*, pain, torment (Du. *pijn*); *pinian*, to torment: Eng. *pine*, to languish (as one does who suffers pain). All from Lat. *poena*.

Q.

Qualm, sickness, pestilence: B 1156. A.S. *cwealm*, *cwylm*, destruction, pestilence, death; Dan. *quæle*, to choke; Sw. *qual*, torment; *qualm*, hot, stifling weather; Ger. *Qualm*, vapour. See below.

Quelle, to kill: C 570. A.S. *cwellan*, to kill. See **Qualme**.

Queen, a queen : B 24. Goth. *qens, qino,* wife, woman.

Queynt, pp. quenched, pret. *queynte,* was quenched : B 1463, 1476. Cf. *dreynte* = drenched. A. S. *cwincan,* O. Fris. *kwinka,* to waste away ; A. S. *cwencan,* to quench.

Queynte, strange, quaint, uncouth : B 673, 1475. F. *coint,* Lat. *cognitus,* known, acquainted with.

Quike, alive, quick : B 157 ; vb. to revive, B 1477. A. S. *cwic,* alive. Cf. ' the *quick* and the dead ; ' ' cut to the *quick* ; ' *couch* - grass (= *quitch* - grass), called in Norfolk *quicken.*

Quitly, free, at liberty : B 934.

Quod, quoth : B 49, 376.

Quook, quaked, trembled : B 718, 904. A. S. *cwacan,* to quake, tremble ; Ger. *quackeln,* to waver. To this family of words belong *quag, quaver.*

Quyte, to free, as in our phrase ' to get *quit* of,' hence to set free, B 174 ; to requite : A 770. Lat. *quietus,* at rest, free from all claims ; It. *quieto,* a discharge from legal claims. Hence *acquite, requite.*

R.

Rad (pp. of *rede,* to read), read : B 1737.

Rage, vb. to play, toy wantonly : A 257 ; sb. a raging wind, B 1127. F. *rage,* Lat. *rabies.*

Ransake, to search (for plunder), ransack : B 147. The M. E. *ransake* also signifies to search, try, probe. Sw. *ransaka,* to search ; *ran* (= Icel. *rannr,* Goth. *razn*), house ; *saka* (= Sw. *soka*), to seek.

Rasour, a razor : B 1559. F. *ras,* shaven, cut close to the ground ; Lat. *radere, rasum,* to shave ;

whence ' to *raze* ' = to lay even with the ground.

Rather, sooner : B 295. Milton uses *rathe* in the sense of ' early.' A. S. *hræð,* swift, quick ; Icel. *hraðr,* quick.

Raughte (pret. of *reche*), reached : A 136, B 2057. A.S. *ræcan,* pret. *ræhte ;* Ger. *reichen,* reach, extend ; whence *rack* (from the Dutch), an instrument of torture.

Raunsoun, ransom : B 166, 318. F. *rançon,* O. F. *raention, raençon,* Lat. *red-emptio,* a purchase back, *redemption.*

Rebel, rebellious : A 833, B 2188. **Rebelling**, rebellion : B 1601.

Recche, Rekke (pret. *roghte, roughte*), to care, take heed to, *reck* : B 540, 1387, 1399. A.S. *reccan,* to care for, regard.

Recchelees, reckless, careless : A 179, Elles. MS.

Reconforte, to comfort : B 1994.

Recorde, to remember, remind : A 829.

Rede, to advise, explain, interpret : B 2213, C 76. A.S. *rædan,* to advise, explain ; Sw. *reda,* to disentangle ; Ger. *rathen,* to conjecture, ' to *read* a riddle.'

Rede, to read : A 709. See above.

Redoutinge, reverence : B 1192. M. E. *redoute,* to fear.

Redy, ready : A 21, 352.

Reed, plan : B 358. See **Rede.**

Reed, Rede : A 90, 153, 458.

Reed (imp. of *rede*), read : C 310.

Reed, counsel, adviser : A 665 ; also plan, line of conduct.

Refresshe, to refresh : B 1764.

Regne, a kingdom, reign : B 8, 766.

Reherce, to rehearse : A 732. F. *rehercer,* to go over again, like a harrow (F. *herce*) over a ploughed field. Cf. our phrase to ' *rake up* old grievances.'

Rehersing, rehearsal: B 792.

Rekene, Rekne, to reckon: A 401, B 1075. A.S. *reccan*, to say, tell, number; Ger. *rechnen*, to reckon.

Rekening, reckoning: A 600.

Reme (pl. *remes*), realm: C 316. O. F. *realme*, It. *reame*, a kingdom; according to Diez, from Lat. *regalis* (giving Low Lat. *regalimen*).

Remenant, Remenaunt, a remnant: A 724, C 84.

Rending, tearing (of hair): B 1976. A.S. *rendan, hrendan*, to tear.

Renges, ranks: B 1736. F. *rang*, O.F. *reng*; Sc. *raing*, a row, line, *range*; O. H. Ger. *hring*, a ring, whence also *harangue*.

Renne (pret. *ron, ran*; pret. pl. *ronne*; pp. *ironne, ironnen, ronne, ronnen*), to run: A 1777. We have this form in *rennet*, or *runnet*, that which makes milk *run* or curdle.

Renning, running: A 551.

Rente, revenue, income, profits: A 373. F. *rendre*, It. *rendere*, Lat. *reddere*, to give up, yield: F. *rente*, income, revenue.

Repentaunce, penitence: B 918.

Repentaunt, penitent: A 228.

Replicacioun, a reply: B 988.

Reportour, reporter: A 814.

Rescous, rescue: B 1785. O. F. *rescourre*, to deliver; *rescous*, recovered; It. *riscuotere* (Lat. *re-excutere*), to fetch a thing out of pawn; Lat. *excutere*, to tear from, take by force; F. *escourre*, to beat corn from the chaff (Cotgrave).

Rese, to quake, shake: B 1128. A.S. *hrysian*.

Resons, opinions, reasons: A 274.

Resoun, reason, right: A 37, 847.

Resoune, to resound: B 420.

Respyt, delay: B 90. Lat. *respectus*, It. *rispetto*, F. *respit*, regard, consideration, delay, respite.

Rethor, a rhetorician: C 387.

Rette, to ascribe, impute: A 726, Harl. MS. See **Aretted**.

Reule, sb. rule, A 173; vb. to rule, A 816, B 814, C 224. A. S. *regol*, Lat. *regula*.

Reve, steward, bailiff: A 542, 599. A. S. *geréfa*. Hence *shire-reeve* or *sheriff*; also *port-reeve*, *borough-reeve*.

Revel, feasting, merry-making: B 1859. O. F. *revel*, noise, gaiety.

Reverence, respect: A 141.

Revers, reverse, contrary: C 157.

Rewe, to be sorry for, to have compassion or pity on, to *rue*: B 1005, 1375. '*Me reweth*' = I am sorry, grieved. A.S. *hréo-wan*, to be sorry for, grieve; Ger. *Reue*, mourning.

Rewe, a row, line: B 2008. A.S. *réwe*, a line.

Rewfulleste, most sorrowful: B 2028.

Rewthe, ruth, pity: B 56.

Reyn, sb. rain, A 492, 595; **Reyne**, vb. to rain, B 677.

Reyse, to make an inroad or military expedition: A 54. A German word; from O. H. G. *reisa*, M. H. G. *reise*, a military expedition (the invariable term).

Richesse, riches: B 397. This word, as well as *alms* (M. E. *al-messe*), is a singular noun; derived immediately from the French.

Riden, pret. pt. rode, A 825. See **Ryden**.

Rightes, rightly: B 994. *At alle rightes* = rightly in all respects.

Ringen, ring, resound: B 1742.

Rit, rides: B 123. Cf. *bit* = bids, *sent* = sends.

Roghte, cared for: C 520. See **Recche**.

Roial, royal, B 160: **Roially,** royally, B 855; **Roialliche,** A 378.

Rome, to walk, roam: B 207.

Ronnen, pret. pl. *ran*: B 2067.

Rood, rode: A 169. See **Ryden.**

Roos, rose: A 823.

Roost, a roast: A 206.

Rore, to roar: B 2023. A. S. *rárian.*

Roste, to roast: A 147, 383. F. *roster* (from O. H. Ger. *rôsten*), to roast; It. *rosta,* a fryingpan; Ger. *Rost,* a grate.

Rote, a stringed instrument: A 236. Roquefort supposes it to be a fiddle with three strings. O. F. *rote,* O. H. G. *hrotá*; of Celtic origin; cf. W. *crwth,* a fiddle.

Rote, rote: A 327. *By rote* = by rote. O. F. *rote,* a route, track.

Rouke, to lie close, cower down, to *ruck*: B 450. Low Ger. *hurken,* to squat down; Dan. *ruge,* to brood.

Rouncy, a hackney: A 390. F. *roncin.*

Roundel, a kind of song: B 671.

Route, a company, assembly: A 622. O. F. *route.*

Rudeliche, rudely: A 734.

Ruggy, rugged, rough (lit. torn, broken, uneven): B 2025. M. E. *rogge,* to shake, tear; Norse *rugga,* to rock, shake. Shakespeare uses *ragged* for *rugged,* rough, harsh.

Rumbel, a deep roaring noise: B 1121.

Ryden, to ride; pret. *rood;* pret. pl. *riden;* pp. *riden*: A 780, 825.

S.

Sad, sober, staid: B 2127.

Sadly, firmly: B 1744. M. E. *sad,* firm. Cf. 'in good *sadness.*'—The Snow Storm, ed Hindley, p. 7.

Salue, to salute: B 634.

Saluing, salutation: B 791.

Sangwyn, of a blood-red colour: A 333.

Sauce, sauce: A 129, C 14. F. *sauce,* It. *salsa;* Lat. *salsa,* salted things, salted food; from Lat. *sal,* salt.

Saufly, safely: C 388.

Saugh (pret. of *se*), saw: A 850, 764.

Sautrye, a psaltery, a musical instrument something like a harp: A 296.

Save, save, except: A 683.

Save, the herb sage or *salvia*: B 1855. F. *sauge.*

Sawceflem, pimpled: A 625. See note.

Sawe, a saying, word, discourse: B 305, 668. A.S. *sagu,* a saying; whence *seegan,* to say.

Say (pret. of *se*), saw: C 294.

Scalled, having the scall, scale, or scab, scabby, scurfy, A 627. Cf. '*scald* head.'

Scape, to escape: B 249. O. F. *eschapper,* It. *scappare.*

Scarsly, parsimoniously: A 583.

Scathe, loss, misfortune, harm: A 446. As in *scath-ing, scatheless.* A.S. *sceaðan,* to injure.

Sclendre, slender, slight: A 587, C 13. M. Du. *slinder,* thin.

Scole, school, style: A 125.

Scoler, scholar: A 260.

Scoleye, to attend school, to study, A 302.

Seche, Seke, to seek (as in *beseech*): A 784.

Secree, secret: C 95.

Seen, to see: B 56, 415, 499.

Seet (pl. *seten*), sat: B 1217, 2035.

Sege, a siege: B 79. F. *siège,* It. *sedia, seggia,* a seat or sitting; Lat. *sedes,* a seat; *obsidium,* the sitting down before a town in a hostile way.

Seigh (pret. of *se*), saw: A 193.

Seint, saint: A 173.

Seistow, sayest thou: B 267.

Seith, saith, says: A 178.

Seke, to seek: A 13, 17. See Seche.

Seke, pl. sick: A 18, 245. A.S. *séoc*. It is perhaps connected with *sigh*, M. E. *sike*.

Selde, seldom: B 681.

Selle, give, sell: A 278.

Selve, same: B 1726. Cf. 'the *self-same* day,' &c. A.S. *seolf*, Ger. *selbst*.

Sely, simple, poor: C 555. A.S. *sǽlig*, whence Eng. *silly*; Ger. *selig*, blessed, happy.

Seme (vb. impers.), to seem: A 39.

Semely, seemly, comely: A 751; becomingly, A 123, 136. M. E. *seme*, seemly; Icel. *sama*, to fit, adorn; Norse *sam*, like; A.S. *sama*, the same.

Semicope, a short cope: A 262.

Sendal, a thin silk: A 440. See note.

Sene, visible: A 134. Cf. *y-sene*, A 592. A.S. *geséne*, adj. visible. (An adj., not a pp.)

Sentence, sense, meaning, judgment, matter of a story: A 306, 798, B 1244. 'Tales of *sentence* and solas' = instructive and amusing tales.'

Sergeant (or Sergeaunt) of lawe = *serviens ad legem*, a servant of the sovereign for his law business : A 309. The king had formerly a sergeant in every county. F. *sergent*, It. *sergente*.

Sermoning, preaching: B 2233. M. E. *sermounen*, to preach, discourse, from Lat. *sermo*.

Servage, bondage: B 1088.

Servant, a servant, B 1377; a lover, B 956.

Servisable, willing to be of service: A 99.

Serye, series, train of argument: B 2209.

Sesoun, season: A 19.

Seten (pret. pl.), sat, B 2035; (pp. of *sette*), sat: B 594.

Sethe, to boil, seethe: A 383. A.S. *séoðan*, to boil, cook; whence Eng. *sodden*, *suds*.

Seththen, since. See Sith.

Seurtee, security, surety: B 746.

Sewed, followed: C 517. O.F. *sewir*, Lat. *sequi*, Eng. *sue*, to follow; whence *suite*, *suit* (at law), *suit* (of clothes).

Sey, saw. See Seigh.

Seyde, pret. of *seye*, said: A 183.

Seye, Seyn, to say (pret. *seyde*): A 181, 468, 738, 787. A.S. *secgan*.

Seyh, saw. See Seigh.

Seyl, a sail: A 696.

Seyn, pp. seen: C 461.

Seyn, to say: A 284.

Seynd (pp. of *senge*), singed, toasted, broiled: C 25.

Seynt, Seynte, holy, a saint: A 697, B 863. See Seint.

Shaft, an arrow, shaft: B 504. A.S. *sceaft*, an arrow, pole (Du. *schaft*, a reed, rod, pole); from A.S. *scafan*, to shave.

Shake, pp. shaken: A 406.

Shamfast, modest: B 1197. **Shamfastnesse**, modesty: A 840.

Shap, form, shape; B 1031.

Shape, Shapen, to plan, purpose, ordain: A 772, 809. **Shapen**, ordained: B 250, 534. (Pret. *shop*, *shoop*.) A.S. *scapan*, to form, create; Icel. *skap*, form, shape.

Shaply, fit, likely: A 372.

Shave, shaven: A 588.

She, she, A 446. E. E. *scæ*, *sco*, A.S. *séo*, *sío*.

Sheef, a sheaf: A 104. A.S. *scéaf*, Du. *schoof*, Ger. *Schaub*.

Sheeldes, coins called crowns: A 278. F. *écus*, i. e. shields, coins so called.

Sheld, a shield: B 1264.

Shene, bright, fair, beautiful: A 115, B 210. A.S. *scýne*, bright, clear; Ger. *schön*, beautiful.

Shent, pp. of *schende*, hurt, destroyed: B 1896. A.S. *scendan*, to confound, shame.

Shepne, stables: B 1142. A.S. *scypen*, a stall (for sheep), a stable.

Shere, shears: B 1559. A.S. *sceran*, to cut, divide, *shear*; Icel. *skera*, to cut. To this root belong *shear*, *share*, *shore*, *plough-share*, a *sheard*, or *sherd* (as in *pot-sherd*), *short*, *skirt*, *shirt*.

Sherte, a shirt: C 300.

Shet, pp. shut: B 1739. A.S. *scyttan*, to shut. It is connected with *shoot*; for to *shut* is to close the door by means of a bolt or bar driven forwards.

Shipman, a sailor: A 388.

Shires ende = end of a *shire* or county: A 15.

Shirreve, the governor (reeve) of a shire or county: A 359. See **Reve**.

Sho, a shoe: A 253.

Shode, the temple (of the head), properly the parting of the hair of a man's head, *not*, as Tyrwhitt and others say, the hair itself: B 1149. ' *Schodynge* or departynge. Separacio, divisio.' —Prompt. Parv. ' *Schodynge* of the heede, discrimen.'—Ibid. A.S. *sceádan*, *scádan*, Ger. *scheiden*, to separate, divide. To this family of words belong *shide*, a board, lath; M.E. *shider*, a shiver; *shider*, to shiver to pieces; Eng. *sheath*, *skid*. Cf. 'the schedynge of tonges.'— Trevisa, ii. 251. ' The longages and tonges of the bulders were *i-schad* and to-schift.'—Ibid.

Sholde, **Shulde**, should: A 249.

Shoon (pret. of *shine*), shone: A 198.

Shorte, to shorten: A 791. See **Shere**.

Shortly, briefly: B 627.

Shoute, to shout: C 567.

Shrewe, to curse, beshrew: C 607; hence *shrewd*. Originally M.E. *shrewed* = wicked, and hence crafty, sharp, intelligent, clear-sighted. A horsekeeper calls a vicious horse a *screw*. The *shrewmouse* was so called because its bite was supposed to be fatal. Cf. ' they (hornets) are *shrewd*, fierce, and cruel.'— Topsell's Serpents, p. 93.

Shrighte, **Shryked**, shrieked: B 1959, C 580. Sw. *skrika*, to cry, screech, shriek.

Shul, pl. shall: B 889.

Shulder, a shoulder: A 678. **Sholdred**, shouldered, having shoulders: A 549. A.S. *sculder*, Ger. *Schulter*, a shoulder. (Root unknown.)

Shine, shin, leg: A 386. **Shines**, shins, legs: B 421. A.S. *scina*, the shin; Ger. *Schiene*, Dan. *skinne*, a splint.

Shivere, to be shattered: B 1747.

Shortely, shortly, briefly: B 627.

Sight, providence: B 814.

Sik, sick: B 742. See **Seke**.

Siker, sure, certain: B 2191. Comp. *sikerer*, C 33. Cf. Ger. *sicher*; from Lat. *securus*.

Sikerly, surely, certainly, truly: A 137.

Siknesse, sickness: B 398, 453.

Sin, since: A 601. Short for *sithen*; see **Sith**.

Sit, sits: B 741.

Sith, **Sithen**, since, afterwards: B 72, 434, 545, 663, 1244. A.S. *sið*, time; *siððan*, after, afterwards. Eng. *since* = *sins*, for *sithens*. Cf. Du. *sinds*, Ger. *seit*, since. *Sith* is used by Elizabethan writers. See Gosson's Schoole of Abuse, p. 18 (Eng. Reprints).

Slake, slow: B 2043. See **Aslake**.

Slaughtre, a slaughter: B 1173.

Slawe (pp. of *slee*), slain: C 194.

Slee, Sleen, to slay: A 661, B 364. A. S. *sléan*, to strike, slay (Ger. *schlagen*, to *strike*); whence, *slaughter, sledge* (in sledge-hammer).

Sleep (pret. of *slepe*), slept: A 98, 397.

Sleere, a slayer: B 1147.

Sleeth, slays: B 260.

Sleighte, contrivance, craft: A 604. Icel. *slægr*, crafty, *sly*; *slægð*, contrivance, cunning. The M. E. *sly* = wise; *sleight* = wisdom, prudence. See **Slyly**.

Slepen, to sleep: A 10.

Sleping, sleep: C 192.

Slepy, causing sleep: B 529.

Sleves, sleeves: A 193.

Slider, slippery: B 406. See note. With the root *slide* are connected *sledge* (M. E. *sled*), *slade*, &c.

Slogardye, sloth: B 184. M. E. *slogge*, to be sluggish; whence *slug, sluggish*. 'I *slogge*, I waxe slowe or draw behynde.'—Palsgrave.

Slough, Slow (pret. of *sle*), slew: B 122, 1608.

Slyly, prudently, wisely (used in a good sense): B 586.

Smal, Smale, small: A 9, 146, 153.

Smerte, adj. smarting, sharp, grievous, A 149; adv. sharply, smartly.

Smerte (pret. *smerte*), to pain, hurt, displease: A 230, 534, B 536. A. S. *smeortan*, to smart; Du. *smart*, Ger. *Schmerz*, pain, ache.

Smoking, perfuming, causing to be perfumed: B 1423.

Smoot, Smot (pret. of *smite*), smote: A 149, B 846.

Smothe, smooth, smoothly: A 676.

Snewede, *snowed*, swarmed, abounded: A 345. Prov. Eng. *snee, snie, snive, snew*, to swarm.

Snibbe, to reprove, snub: A 523. Fris. *snubbe*, to reprove; Icel. *snubba*, to chide; *snoppa*, a snout; Dan. *snubbed*, stumpy (cf. *snub*-nose). Cf. M. E. *snub*, a jag, knot; Prov. Eng. *snoup*, a blow on the head. To this class of words belong *snip, snap, snape, sneap*, to nip with cold.

So, so: A 102.

Soberly, sad, solemn: A 289.

Socour, succour: B 60.

Sodein, Sodeyn, sudden. **Sodeynliche, Sodeynly**, suddenly: B 260, 717. O. F. *suobdain, soudain*, Lat. *subitaneus, subitus*, sudden.

Solaas, Solas, solace, mirth: A 798.

Solempne, festive, A 209; important, A 364.

Solempnely, pompously: A 274.

Solempnitee, feast, festivity: B 12.

Som, some: A 640. *Som . . . som* = one . . . other: B 397, 399.

Som-del, somewhat: A 174.

Somer, summer: A 394.

Somnour, an officer employed to summon delinquents to appear in ecclesiastical courts, now called an apparitor: A 543.

Sond, sand: C 447.

Sondry, sundry, various: A 14.

Sone, soon: B 1412, 1812.

Sone, a son: A 79.

Song, pret. sang: B 197. **Songe**, pp. sung: A 266, 711.

Sonne, the sun: A 7, B 5, 204.

Soor, adj. sore: B 1837.

Soote, sweet: A 1.

Sooth, Sothe, sb. truth; adj. true: A 845, B 767. It still exists in *forsooth, soothsayer*. A. S. *sóð*, truth; *sóð*, true; *sóðe*, truly. Cf. Sansk. *satya*, true, Gr. *eteós*, an adjective formed from the participle present of the auxiliary *as*, to be. *Sat* is allied to the Lat. *ens*, being. (Max Müller.)

Soothfastnesse, truth ; c 507.

Soothly, truly: A 117, 468.

Sop (in wyn): A 334. See note.

Soper, supper: A 348, B 33.

Sore, adv. sorely: A 230, B 536.

Sort, destiny, chance : A 844.

Sorwe, sb. sorrow : B 361, 419. A. S. *sorh*, Ger. *Sorge*. **Sorwen**, vb. to be sorrowful, grieve.

Sorweful, sorrowful : B 212.

Sory, sorrowful : B 1146, 1152. '*Sory* comfort' = discomfort ; '*sory* grace' = misfortune. A.S. *sárig*, sore ; *sár*, a wound.

Sotil, subtle, fine-wrought : B 196 ; thin, 1172.

Soule, soul : A 781, B 1005. A.S. *sáwel*.

Soun, a sound : A 674.

Souple, supple, pliant : A 203.

Sovereyn, high, supreme, sovereign : A 67.

Sovereynly, surpassingly : c 542.

Sowne, vb. to sound, A 275, 565 ; sb. sound : B 1564.

Sowninge in, tending to : A 307. Chaucer uses *sownen into goode* = to tend to good.

Spak, spake : A 124. See **Speken**.

Spare, to refrain, abstain from : A 192, 737.

Sparre, bar, bolt (Eng. *spar*) : B 132, 218. M.E. *sparre*, to bolt ; A.S. *sparran*, Ger. *sperren*, to shut, bolt ; M. Du. *sperre, sparre*, a spar, bar ; Dan. *sparre*, Ger. *Sparren*, a rafter.

Sparth, a battle-axe, or halberd : B 1662. Icel. *sparða*, an axe.

Sparwe, a sparrow : A 626.

Special ; ' in special,' specially : A 444.

Spede, to speed, hasten, prosper (pret. *spedde*) : A 769, B 359.

Speken, to speak (pret. *spak*) : A 142. See **Spak**.

Spere, a spear : B 781, 795.

Spores, spurs : A 473. A.S. *spura, spora*, Ger. *Sporn*; cf. Eng. *spurn*.

Sprad, pp. spread: B 2045.

Springen, to spring : B 1013, 1749. A.S. *sprengan*; Sw. *springa, spricka*, to burst, spring ; Ger. *sprengen*, to scatter, burst open ; Eng. *sprig, spray, sprinkle*, belong to this family of words.

Spronge (pp. of *springe*), sprung, widely spread : B 579.

Spyced, sophisticated, or scrupulous : A 526. See note.

Spycerye, spices : B 2077. *spices* = species, kinds. F. *épices*, Lat. *species* ; cf. the phrase ' a *general* dealer'; Sp. *generos*, kinds. 'All maner of *spices*, grocery wares.'— Hakluyt, iii. p. 22.

Squyer, a squire : A 79.

Stablissed, established : B 2137.

Stalke, to step slowly and stealthily : B 621. A.S. *stælcan*, to step ; Dan. *stalke*, to go with long steps. Cf. M.E. *stalker*, a goer upon stilts.

Starf (pret. of *sterve*), died : B 75. See **Sterve**.

Steer, a yearling bullock, a *steer* or stirk : B 1291. A.S. *stéor*, a bullock ; Prov. Ger. *ster, sterch*, the male sheep ; *stier*, an ox-calf ; O.H. Ger. *stero*, a ram ; Ger. *Stier, Stierchen*, a bull.

Stele, to steal (pret. *stal*, pp. *stole, stolen*) : A 562.

Stemed, shone : A. 202. M.E. *stem, steem*, a gleam of light. '*Steem* or lowe of fyre, *flamma*'; Prompt. Parv.

Stenten (pret. *stente*, pp. *stent*), to stop, cease : B 45, 510. A.S. *stintan*, to be blunt ; *stunt*, blunt, blockish ; Icel. *stuttr*, short ; O. Sw. *stunt*, short. Cf. Eng. *stunted* and *stinted*.

Stepe, bright, glittering ; (not deep

or sunken, as it is generally explained): A 201. See note.

Sterre, a star: A 268. A.S. *steorra*, a star; Sansk. *stri*, to scatter; M. E. *stare*, to glitter, shine.

Stert, start: B 847. *At a stert* = in a moment, immediately.

Sterte, to start, leap, escape (pret. *sterte*, pp. *stert*): B 186, 222, 644. Prov. Engl. *startle*, to fall, scatter, sparkle; Du. *storten*, to tumble, fall.

Sterve (pret. *starf*, pp. *y-storve*, *storven*): B 286. A.S. *steorfan*, Du. *sterven*, Ger. *sterben*, to die.

Steven, Stevene, (1) voice, sound, B 1704; (2) a time appointed by previous agreement, B 666. A.S. *stefn* (1) voice, message ; (2) agreement.

Stewe, a fish-pond: A 350. M. E. *steeve*, Low Ger. *stau*, a dam.

Stille, quietly, secretly: B 145, C 401.

Stint, imp. sing. stop: B 1490.

Stinte, to stop (pret. *stinte*): B 1563. See **Stenten**.

Stith, an anvil: B 1168. Icel. *steði*, an anvil; whence Eng. *stithy*.

Stiward, a steward: A 579. A.S. *stiward*, a steward; Icel. *stívardr*, the person whose business it is to look to the daily work of an establishment; *stjá*, domestic occupation; Norse *stia*, to be busy about the house; Icel. *stía*, a sheep-house (Eng. *sty* = A. S. *stigo*). The syllable *-ward* = keeper.

Stoke, to stick, stab: B 1688.

Stole, pp. stolen: B 1769.

Stomble, to stumble: B 1755. M. E. *stumpe*, Icel. *stumra*, to totter, fall. It is connected with *stammer*, *stem*.

Stonde, Stonden, to stand (pret. *stood*, pp. *stonde*, *stonden*): A 88, 745.

Stongen, pp. stung: B 221.

Stoon, stone: A 774. A.S. *stán*.

Stoor, Store, stock (of a farm): A 598. O. F. *estor*, Mid. Lat. *staurum*, store. O. F. *estorer*, to erect, build, garnish (Lat. *instaurare*). *Telle no store* = set no value upon, set no store by: C 334.

Stope (pp. of *steppe*, to step), advanced: C 1. A. S. *steppan* (pret. *stóp*, pp. *ge-stapen*), to step, advance.

Stot, a stallion, a *stoat* (which also signifies a weasel): A 615. A.S. *stotte*, a horse, hack ; M. Du. *stuyte*. The Promptorium Parvulorum has ' *stot*, a horse, caballus.'

Stounde, a moment, a short space of time: B 354. A.S. *stund*, a short space, space of time; O.H. Ger. *stunt*, a moment; Ger. *Stunde*, an hour.

Stoute, strong, brave: B 1296.

Straughte (pret. of *strecche*), stretched: B 2058.

Straunge, foreign: A 13, 464. O. Fr. *estrange*, Lat. *extraneus*, from *extra*, without.

Strecche, to stretch: C 488. M.E. *streke*, to stretch ; A.S. *streccan*, to stretch; *strec*, violent; cf. Eng. *stark*.

Stree, straw: B 2060. A.S. *streow*, Icel. *strá* ; A. S. *streowian*, Ger. *streuen*, to strew.

Streem, stream, river : A 464.

Streite, drawn: C 537. See note.

Strepe, to strip: B 148. We have the other form of this root in *strip*, *stripe*.

Streyne, to constrain : C 424.

Streyt, close, narrow, stinted, *strict :* A 174, C 169.

Streyte, closely : A 457. O. F. *estroit*, It. *stretto*, strait, narrow; Lat. *stringere*, *strictum*, to strain.

Strike (of flax), a hank : A 676.

Strof (pret. of *strive*), strove, dis-
puted, vied with : B 180.

Strond, strand : A 13.

Strook, a stroke : B 843.

Stryf, strife, contest : B 1580.
O. F. *estrif*, strife ; *estriver*, Ger.
streben, to strive.

Stubbes, stumps, trunks : B 1120.
A. S. *styb*, Du. *stobbe*, stump ; cf.
stubborn, stubble.

Subtilly, craftily : A 610.

Suffisaunce, sufficiency : A 490.

Suffisaunt, sufficient : B 773.

Surcote, an upper coat : A 617.

Sustene, to sustain : B 1135.

Suster (pl. *sustren*), a sister : B 13,
161.

Swelte, fainted : B 498. A. S.
sweltan, to die, perish (through
heat) ; M. E. *swelte*, to faint
(through heat). The Prompt.
Parv. has 'Sweltrynge or swal-
terynge or swownynge (sincopa).'
'Swelteryn for hete or febylnesse,
or other cawsys (or swownyn)
exalo, sincopizo.' Cf. A. S.
swǽlan, to be hot ; Prov. Eng.
sweal, Eng. *sultry* (= *sweltry*),
'*sweltering* heat.'

Swerd, a sword : A 112, B 717.
A. S. *sweord*.

Swere (pret. *swor, swoor*; pp. *y-*
swore, y-sworen), to swear : A
454, B 963. We have the same
root in an-*swer*.

Swete, sweet : A 5, 265, B 1569.
A. S. *swéte*.

Swevene, a dream : C 76. A. S.
swefen, from *swefan*, Icel. *sofa*,
to sleep. We have the same
root in Lat. *somnus* (= *sop-nus*).

Swich, such : A 3 ; *swich a*, so
great a : B 4. A. S. *swilc*, such =
swá, so, and *líc*, like.

Swink, sb. labour, toil : A 188,
540.

Swinken, to labour, toil : A 186.
A. S. *swinc*, labour, toil ; *swincan*,
to toil.

Swinkere, a labourer : A 531.

Swor, Swore. See **Swere**.

Swough, the raging of the elements, a storm : B 1121. Cf.
Sc. *souch, swouch, sough*, the
sound of the wind. A. S. *swég*,
a sound ; *swógan*, to sound.

Swowne, to swoon : B 55, 1961.
The M. E. *swogh*, a sound, a
swoon, shews that *swoon* is connected with *sough*, &c.

Swymbul, a moaning, sighing
sort of noise, caused by the
wind (or perhaps, a shivering
movement) : B 1121, Harl. MS.
Swymbel = *swymel*, is a diminutive of M. E. *swim* or *sweem*,
mourning, sighing. Allied to
Icel. *sweima*, to move to and fro.
(Cf. 'a *swimming* in the head.')

Swyn (sing. and pl.), swine : A
598.

Syke, sb. a sigh, B. 1062 ; vb. to
sigh, B 682, 2127. A. S. *sícan*.

Sythe, Sythes, times : A 485, B
1019.

T.

Taas. See **Tas**.

Tabard, the sleeveless coat on
which arms were embroidered ;
a herald's coat of arms : A 20,
541. It was the old dress of the
labourer, and Chaucer applies
it to the loose frock of the
ploughman. It. *tabarro*, over-
coat.

Taffata, taffeta : A 440.

Taille, a tally, an account scored
in two notched pieces of wood :
A 570. F. *tailler*, to cut.

Tak, imper. take : B 226.

Take, pp. taken : B 1789.

Takel, an arrow : A 106. It seems
to have signified (like *loom*,
M. E. *lome*) any sort of implement or utensil, whether used
as a tool or weapon. See note ;
and Strutt's Sports and Pastimes,
2nd ed., p. 59. Cf. Swed. *tackel*,
Ger. *Takel*, tackle.

Tale, speech, discourse, story: A
831. *Telle tale* = take account
of, estimate ; 'litel *tale* hath he
told,' C 298, = little heed has he
paid ; 'telle no *tale*' = take no
notice of, make no account of.

Talen, to tell tales : A 722.

Tapicer, an upholsterer : A 362.
F. *tapis*, a carpet.

Tappestere, a female tapster : A
241.

Targe, a target or shield : A 471.
F. *targe*.

Tas, sb. heap : B 147, 151, 162.

Tathenes = to Athens : B 165,
Harl. MS.

Teche, **Techen**, to teach, direct :
A 308, C 129.

Tendite, to endite, tell : B 351.

Tene, vexation, annoyance : B
2248. A. S. *téon*, *téona*, injury,
wrong ; *téonan*, *týnan*, to anger,
incense.

Teres, tears : B 422.

Tespye, to espy : C 468.

Testers, head-pieces, or helmets :
B 1641. O. F. *teste*, F. *tête*, the
head.

Thabsence, the absence, B 381.

Than, **Thanne**, then : A 12.

Thank, thanks : A 612.

Thankes, **Thonkes**, the genitive
of *thank* : B. 768, 1249. Used
adverbially with the personal
pronouns (possessive) : *his
thankes*, he being willing ; *hir
thankes*, they being willing ; like
the F. *son gré*, *leur gré*, with his
or their good-will.

Tharmes, the arms : B 2058, Harl.
MS.

Tharray, the array : A 716.

Thavys, the advice : B 2218.

Thee, to thrive, prosper : C 156.
A. S. *þeon*, to flourish, grow.

Theffect, the effect : B 331.

They, they : A 475. The
Northern form is *tha* or *thai*;
the Southern *heo*, *hi*.

Thencens, the incense : B 1419.

Thenchauntements, the enchant-
ments : B 1086.

Thencrees, the increase : A 275.

Thenke, to think. *Thank* is a
related word. Distinct from
Thinke.

Thentree, the entrance : B 1125.

Ther, there : A 43 ; where, A 547.
Ther as = where that ; A 34,
172.

Therto, besides : A 153, 757.

Thestat, the state or rank : A
716.

Thider, thither : B 405.

Thikkeherd, thick-haired : B
1660.

Thilke, the like, that : A 182, B
335, 1525. A.S. *þillic*, *pylc*, the
like, that.

Thinke, **Thynke**, to seem. It is
used impersonally, as 'me
thinketh' = it seems to me, A 37 ;
me *thoughte*, it seemed to me,
A 385 ; 'him *thoughte*' = it
appeared to him, A 682 ; *us
thoughte*, A 785. A. S. *þyncan*,
Ger. *dünken*.

Thirle, to pierce : B 1852. A.S.
þirel, a hole ; *þirlian*, to pierce,
thrill, drill ; whence *nostrils*
(M.E. *nosethirles*). The A.S.
þirel seems to be a diminutive,
and a simpler form is found in
A.S. *þurh*, through ; we may
compare O. H. Ger. *durchil*,
pierced, from *durch*, through.

Thise, pl. these : A 701, B 673.

Tho, pl. the, those : A 498, B 265,
1493. A.S. *ðá*.

Tho, then : B 135. A.S. *ðá*.

Thoffice, the office : B 2005.

Thombe, thumb : A 563.

Thonder, thunder : A 492. A. S.
þunor, Ger. *Donner*.

Thorisoun, the orison or prayer :
B 1403.

Thral, slave, serf, one enslaved : B
694. Icel. *þræll*, a servant. It
is probably connected with A.S.
þrægian, Goth. *thragjan*, to run.

Thred, Threed, thread: B 1172;
Thredbare, threadbare: A 260.

Thresshe, to thrash; A 536.
A. S. *perscan,* Icel. *preskja.*
Threshold also occurs as M. E.
thresch-wold, from A.S. *perscan,*
to beat; and *wold* (= A. S.
wald), wood; as if it signified
the part beaten by the foot;
but this was merely due to a
popular etymology.

Threste, to thrust, press: B 1754.
Icel. *prýsta.*

Thridde, third: B 605.

Thryes, thrice: A 63.

Thurgh, through: B 362. A. S.
purh.

Thurgh-fare, a *thorough-*fare: B
1989. Cf. Goth. *thairh,* Ger.
durch, Eng. *through* and *thorough.*

Thurgh-girt, pierced through, B
152. See **Girt.**

Til, to: B 620. Icel. *til,* to.

To, at, gone to: A 30.

To, toe: B 1868. See **Toon.**

To-, as a verbal prefix, = Ger. *zer-,*
Goth. *dis-,* in twain, Lat. *dis-.*

To-breste, burst asunder: B 1753.
See **Breste.**

To-brosten, burst or broken in
pieces: B 1833, 1899.

To-hewen, hewed or cut in
pieces: B 1751.

Tollen, to take toll or payment:
A 562. A. S. *toll,* tax. It
seems connected with E. *tale, tell.* See
Zoll in Kluge.

To-morwe, to-morrow, A 780.
See **Morwe.** The *to* (as in *to-
yere* = this year) is the prep. *to,*
as in M. E. *togedere,* together.

Tonge, tongue: A 265, 712.

Tonne-greet, having the circum-
ference as great as a tun: B
1136.

Tool, weapon: C 96. A. S. *tól.*

Toon, toes: C 42; **Toos,** C
360.

Top, head: A 590.

Torets, small rings or swivels: B
1294. See note.

Torne, to turn: B 630. F. *tourner.*
The root *tor,* turn, twist, is seen
in the Lat. *tornus,* a lathe: *tor-
quere,* to twist; *turben,* a whirlwind.

To-shrede, cut in shreds: B
1751. See **Schere.**

Toun, town: A 478.

Tour, tower: B 172, 419.

Touret, turret: B 1051.

Trace, track, path. 'Trace, of a
wey over a felde, *trames.*'—
Prompt. Parv. F. *trace.* See
note to A 176.

Trapped, having trappings: B
2032. 'vi horses richely *trapped*
with several armes.'— Hall's
Chronicles, lxxxii.

Trappures, trappings of a horse:
B 1641.

Traunce, a trance: B 714.

Trays, the traces by which horses
draw, horse-harness: B 1281.

Trecherye, treachery: C 510. F.
tricherie, trickery; *tricher,* to
trick.

Trede, to tread: B 2164.

Tresoun, treason: B 1143.

Trespas, trespass: B 960.

Tresse, a tress, plait: B 191. F.
tresse, It. *treccia.*

Tretee, treaty: B 430.

Tretys, long and well-proportioned: A 152.

Trewe, true: A 531. **Trewely,**
truly: A 481. In M. E. we have
a form *tryg,* corresponding to
Icel. *tryggr,* Goth. *triggws,* true.

Trompe, a trumpet: A 674, B
1316.

Tronchoun, a headless spear or
broken shaft of a spear (E.
truncheon): B 1757. F. *tronçon,*
from Lat. *truncus.*

Trouthe, truth: A 46, 763; troth,
B 752.

Trowe, to believe: A 155, 524.
I trowe = I think it to be true.

Hence E. *tro-th;* like *tru-th* from *true.*

Trussed up, packed up : A 681. O. F. *trousser, torser,* to pack up. Cf. Eng. *truss,* a bundle.

Tukked, tucked up : A 621.

Turneyinge, a tournament : B 1669. See **Torne.**

Tweye, two, twain : A 704, 792 ; B 40, 270. A.S. *twegen* (m.), *twā* (f. n.) ; Goth. *twai* (m.), *twos* (f.), *twa* (n.) ; Icel. *tveir* (m.), *tvær* (f.), *tvau* (n.). With this root we may connect *twin, twine, twill, twig.* Tusser calls ewes that bear twins by the name of *twiggers.* ' An hower or *twaine.*'—The Schoole of Abuse, p. 17. It appears also in *twelve* (= 2 + 10), and *twenty* (2 × 10).

Twinne, to depart, separate : A 835. See above.

Two, two : A 639.

Tyde, time : C 196. **Tydes,** tides, A 401. A.S. *tíd,* time ; whence, *tidy, tides.*

U.

Unce, a small portion : A 677, Harl. MS. (Eng. *ounce.*)

Uncouth, unknown, rare, *un-couth :* B 1639. See **Couthe.**

Undergrowe, undergrown : A 156.

Undern, the time of the mid-day meal : C 402. A.S. *undern,* the third hour of the day, 9 A.M. It signifies literally the inter-vening period, and hence the middle of the forenoon, or a meal taken at that time. In the present passage, it probably means 11 A.M. In mod. Eng. dialects it means mid-afternoon, or 4 P.M. The labourers call their meals *elevenses* and *fourses.*

Undertake, to affirm : A 288, C 391.

Unknowe, unknown : A 126, B 548.

Unkonning, unknowing, not *cun-ning* (knowing), ignorant : B 1535. In our English Bible the word *cunning* is used in a good sense.

Unset, not at a set time, not ap-pointed : B 666.

Unwist, unknown : B 2119. See **Wite.**

Unyolden, not having yielded : B 1784 See **Yolden.**

Up-haf (pret. of *upheve*), upheaved, uplifted : B 1570. See **Heve.**

Up-right, flat on the back : B 1150.

Up-riste, dat. uprising : B 193.

Up-so-doun, upside down : B 519.

Up-sterte, upstarted, arose : B 441. See **Sterte.**

Up-yaf, gave up : B 1569.

V.

Vasselage, valour, courage (dis-played in the service rendered by a *vassal*) : B 2196.

Vavasour, A 360. O. F. *vavaseur.* This term is explained in various ways : Tyrwhitt says it means a middle-class landholder ; Blount explains it as one next in dignity to a baron. A *Vavasour* was most probably a sub-vassal holding a small fief, a sort of esquire.

Venerye, hunting : A 166, B 1450. Lat. *uenari,* to hunt, chase ; whence *venison* (= *uenationem*).

Venim, poison, venom : B 1893, 1896.

Ventusyng, cupping, a surgical term : B 1889.

Verdit, verdict, judgment, sen-tence : A 787.

Vernicle : A 685. See note.

Verray, Verrey, true, very : A 72, 422. **Verraily,** truly : A 338.

Vese, a rush of wind, draught, gush ; lit. an impulse : B 1127.

Lat. *impetus* (gloss in Elles. MS). See note. 'The oldest form is the O. H. Ger. *funs*, prompt, quick; whence, by dropping the *n*, the A. S. *fús*, quick, eager; Icel. *fúss*, eager; hence the verbal forms in Swed. *fösa*, to drive, Icel. *fýsa*, to impel, exhort, A. S. *fésian*, to drive away (whence probably the Prov. Eng. *feaze, feeze*, or *pheese*, which means both to *drive*, as in Stanyhurst's Virgil (Nares), and to *chastise*, as in Shakespeare's Troilus and Cressida, ii. 3. 215); also the Icel. sb. *fýsi*, an impulse, inclination, wish, which exactly corresponds to the word in question. For examples, observe—'ac he fýsde forð fláne genehe,' but he poured forth arrows enough (Death of Byrhtnoth, ed. Grein, l. 269); and 'fús and forðgeorn,' eager and desirous of going forward (id. l. 281). Hence probably the modern Eng. *fuss.*'—Skeat.

Vestimens, vestments : B 2090.

Veyn, vain : B 236.

Veyne-blood, blood of the veins : B 1889.

Viage, voyage : A 77, 723.

Vigilyes, vigils : A 377.

Vileinye, sb. unbecoming conduct or talk, disgrace : A 70, 726 : B 84.

Vitaille, victuals : A 569, 749.

Vouche-sauf, to vouchsafe, grant : A 807, 812.

Voyden, to expel : B 1893.

W.

Waar, aware, wary. See **War**.

Wake-pleyes, ceremonies attending the vigils for the dead : B 2102. A.S. *wæcan, wacian*, to watch, keep watch; Eng. *watch, waits*.

Walet, a wallet : A 681, 686.

Wan, won, conquered : B 131. See **Winne**.

Wanhope, despair : B 391. See **Wanie**.

Wanie, to decrease, diminish : B 1220. A.S. *wanian*, to diminish; *wan*, a deficiency. To the root *wan* belongs possibly A.S. *wann*, pale; whence *wan*.

Wantown, wanton, free, unrestrained : A 208. The prefix *wan*-implies lack; *-town = -togen*, trained, from A.S. *téon* (to lead, educate, pp. *getogen*). Cf. Ger. *ungezogen*.

Wantownesse, wantonness : A 264.

War, aware, cautious, prudent : A 309. A.S. *wær, war*, cautious. 'I was *war* ' = I perceived, A 157.

War him, to beware : A 662. (Infin. governed by *oghte*). A.S. *warian*, to be ware, be cautious. With this root are connected *ward, warder, warn, guard, guardian.*

Wastel-breed, bread-cake : A 147. O. F. *wastel*, later *gasteau*, a cake, F. *gâteau*. See note.

Waterlees, without water : A 180.

Wawes, waves : B 1100. A.S. *wǽg*, a wave; *wagian*, to wave, wag.

Wayke, pl. weak : B 29. Icel. *veikr*; cf. M. E. *wóc*, A. S. *wác*, weak, mean, worthless.

Waylaway, alas! well-a-way! well-a-day! B 80, C 560.

Waymenting, Waymentinge, a lamentation, wailing : B 137, 1063. O. F. *waimenter*, to lament; literally to cry *wai*! or *woe*. Cf. Ital. *guaiolore*, to cry *guai*!

Wayte, to be on the look out for, to look for : A 525, 571 ; B 364. See **Awayt**.

Webbe, a weaver : A 362. Cf. M. E. *hunt-e*, a hunter; *tromp-e*, a trumpeter; *prison-e*, a prisoner.

Wed (dat. *wedde*), pledge, security; *to wedde*, in pledge, as a pledge : B 360. A. S. *wed*, agreement; whence Eng. *wed*, *wedding*, *wedlock*.

Wedden, to wed : B 974.

Wede, clothing : B 148. A. S. *wǽd*, clothing, attire of men and women. It is still retained in 'widow's *weeds*.'

Weel, well : B 68, 1265.

Weep, wept : B 1487. Cf. M. E. *creep*, *leep* = crept, leapt.

Wel, adv. full, very, B 653 ; much, B 396.

Wele, weal, prosperity, wealth : B 37.

Welle, source, fountain : B 2179.

Wende, weened, thought : B 411. See **Wene**.

Wende, Wenden, to go, pass away : A 16, 21 ; B 1356. The Eng. *went* is the past tense of *wende*. Cf. the phrase 'to *wend* one's way.'

Wene, to ween, think : B 797. A. S. *wén*, hope ; *wénan*, to hope, suppose. It is preserved in E. *ween*, *over-weening*, &c.

Wepe, Wepen (pret. *weep*, *wep*; pp. *wepen*), to weep : A 144, 230.

Wepne, a weapon : B 733.

Were, to defend, guard : B 1692. A. S. *werian*, to defend.

Wered, wore : A 75, 564.

Werken, Wirche, to work : A 779, B 1901.

Werre, war : A 47, B 429. Du. *werre*, strife, war ; F. *guerre*.

Werreye, Werreyen, to make war against : B 626, 686.

Werte, a wart : A 555. A. S. *weart* (*wear*, a knot, wart), Icel. *varta*, Ger. *Warze*.

Wessh (pret. of *wasche*), washed : B 1425.

Wete, wet, moist : B 422, 1480.

Wette, wetted : A 129.

Wex, sb. wax : A 675.

Wexe, to increase, grow, become. A. S. *weaxan*, to increase. **Wex**, increased, became : B 504. Shakespeare has 'a man of *wax*' = an adult, a man of full growth.

Wexing, growing, increasing : B 1220.

Wey, Weye, a way : A 34, 467.

Weyeth, weigheth, esteems : B 923.

Weyle, to wail ; to cry *wei* ! or *woe* ! B 363.

Weymentinge : B 44. See **Waymenting**.

Whan, Whanne, when : A 15, 18, 179.

What, wherefore, why, lo ! A 184, 854.

Wheel, wheel : B 68, 1165.

Whelkes, pimples, blotches : A 632.

Wher, where : B 1952.

Wher, whether : B 1394.

Whether, whether, which of two : B 998.

Which, what. *Which a* = what a, B 1817.

Whippeltre, the cornel-tree : B 2065. Cf. Mid. Low Ger. *wipel-bom*, the cornel-tree (Pritzel).

Whyl, whilst : A 35, 397. **Whyle**, time. A. S. *hwil*, time ; Norse *hvíla*, to rest. It is retained in *awhile* ; 'to *while* away the time' = to pass the time away in rest or recreation.

Whylom, formerly, once : B 1, 1545. A. S. *hwílum*. The *-um* was an old adverbial ending, as seen in M. E. *ferrum*, afar ; Eng. *seldom*.

Whyt, white : A 238. Comp. **Whitter**.

Widwe, a widow : A 253.

Wight, any living creature ; a person, male or female : A 71, 326. A. S. *wiht*.

Wighte, weight : B 1287.

Wikke, wicked, bad, untoward :

B 229. M. E. *wikke*, poor, mean,
weak; A. S. *wican*, to be weak.

Wilfully, willingly : C 276.

Wilne, to desire : B 751. A.S.
wiln, wish; *wilnian*, to desire.

Wiltou, wilt thou : B 298.

Wilwe, willow-tree : B 2064.

Wimpel, a covering for the neck :
A 151. **Ywimpled**, decked
with a *wimple* : A 470. F.
guimple, M. Du. *wimpelen*, to
wrap; *wimpel*, a veil, flag. See
p. 140.

Winged, winged : B 527.

Winne (pret. *wan, won;* pp.
wonne, wonnen), to win, obtain,
gain : B 759.

Winnyng, gain, profit : A 275.

Wirche, to work : B 1901. See
Werken.

Wis = *ywis*, certainly : B 1928.
As wis, = as certainly, as truly :
C 588. See **Ywis**.

Wisly, truly : B 1376. See **Ywis**.

Wit, understanding, judgment,
wisdom : A 279, 746.

Wite, to know, to learn : B
402; 1st and 3rd pers. sing.
indic. *wot, woot;* 2nd pers.
wost; pl. *witen, wyten;* pret.
wiste. A. S. *witan*, to know;
whence *wit, to wit, witty,* &c.

Withholde, maintained : A 511.

Withouten, without : A 538;
besides, A 461.

Withseyn, **Withseye**, to gainsay : A 805, B 282.

Witing, knowledge : B 753. See
Wite.

Wlatsome, loathsome, hateful :
C 233. A. S. *wlátian*, to nau-
seate, loathe.

Wo, **Woo**, sb. sorrow, woe, B
1766; lament, B 42; adj. sorrowful, grieved, displeased, A
351.

Wode. See **Wood**.

Wodebynde, woodbine, B 650.

Wofullere, the more sorrowful :
B 482.

Wol, **Wole**, vb. will, A 42; pt. s.
wolde, would, A 144; pl. *wolden*,
A 27.

Woln, **Wolle** (pl. of *wol*), will : B
1263.

Wolt, wilt; **Woltow**, wilt thou :
B 686.

Wommanhede, womanly feeling : B 890.

Wonder, wonderful : B 1215;
wonderfully : A 483, B 796.

Wonderly, wonderfully : A 84.

Wone, custom, usage : A 335, B
182. A. S. *wune.*

Wone, to dwell : A 388, B 2069.
A. S. *wunian*, Ger. *wohnen*, to
dwell, inhabit, rest.

Woning, a dwelling, habitation :
A 606.

Wonne, **Wonnen** (pp. of *winne*),
conquered, obtained : A 51, B
19.

Wood, mad : A 582, B 471. A. S.
wód, mad; *wódnes*, madness.

Woodly, madly, B 443.

Woodnesse, madness : B 1153.

Wook, awoke : B 535.

Woot (1st pers.), know : A 389,
659; (3rd pers.), knows, B 28.
See **Wite**.

Worse, worse : B 366.

Worship, sb. honour; **Worschip-
ful**, honourable : B 1054.

Worshipe, to honour, to pay
proper respect to another's
worth : B 1393.

Wortes, herbs : C 401. A. S.
weort, wyrt. It still exists in
cole-wort, orchard (= *wort-yard*,
herb-garden).

Worthinesse, bravery : A 50.

Worthy, brave : A 47, 68.

Wost, knowest : **Wostow**, knowest thou, B 305. See **Wite**.

Wrastle, to wrestle : B 2103.

Wrastling, wrestling : A 548.

Wrecche, a wretch, wretched : B
73, 248.

Wreke, to revenge, avenge,
wreak : B 103.

Wrethe, a wreath (a derivative from the vb. to *writhe*): B 1287.

Wrighte, a carpenter (literally a workman): A 614. Cf. *wheel-wright, play-wright.*

Writ, writeth: C 303.

Wrooth, angry: A 451.

Wyd, wide: A 491; **Wyde**, pl. A 557.

Wyf, wife, woman: A 445; **Wyves**, wives, A 234.

Wyke, a week: B 681. A. S. *wice*, O. N. *vika.*

Wyn, wine: A 334.

Wys, wise, A 68, 309; **Wyse**, pl. 569.

Wyse, mode, manner; B 480, 882. See **Gyse**.

Wyte, Wyten, know. See **Wite**.

Wyve, dat. of *wyf.*

Y.

Y-, a prefix used especially with the pp., like the A.S. *ge-*, Ger. *ge-*. See below.

Yaf (pret. of *yeve* or *yive*), gave; hence, cared: A 177.

Yate, a gate: B 577, Harl. MS. This old pronunciation still survives in some parts of England.

Y-been, been, C 477.

Ybete, beaten: B 1304; beaten on, B 121.

Y-bore, borne, carried, A 378; *y-born*, born, B 161.

Y-bounden, bound, B 291.

Y-brent, burnt: B 88.

Y-broght, brought: B 253.

Y-buried, buried: B 88.

Y-chaped, having *chapes* or caps of metal at the end of a sheath, A 366.

Y-clenched, clinched, fastened, B 1133.

Y-cleped, Yclept, called: A 376, 410, B 9. See **Clepe**.

Y-come, come: A 77.

Y-corve, cut: B 1155.

Y-don, done: B 167, C 599; **Y-do**, B 1676.

Y-drawe, drawn: A 396, B 86, 1784.

Ydriven, driven: B 1149.

Y-dropped, bedropped, covered with drops: B 2026.

Ye, yea, the answer to a question asked in the affirmative form: B 890; *yis*, yes, being the affirmative answer to a question asked in the negative form.

Yë, eye, A 10. (Dissyllabic; pronounced *y-e*, with *y* like *i* in *machine*, and *e* like Ger. final *e*).

Yeddinges, songs; properly the gleeman's songs: A 237. Norse *gidda*, to shake; whence *giddy*. A. S. *gidd*, a song; *geddian*, to sing. The Prompt. Parv. has '*Yeddynge*, or *geest*, *idem quod geest* (a romaunce).' See note.

Yeer, Yer, year: A 347, B 523: pl. *yeer*, years, A 82. A. S. *gér*, *géar*.

Yeldhalle = *geldhall*, a guildhall: A 370.

Yeldyng, yielding, return, produce: A 596.

Yelle, to yell: **Yelleden** (pl. pret.), yelled: C 569.

Yelpe, to boast: B 1380. (Eng. *yelp*.) A.S. *gelpan*.

Yelwe, Yelow, yellow: B 191, 1071. A.S. *geoluwe*, Ger. *gelb*. It is connected with *gall, yolk*, &c.

Yeman, a yeoman, commoner, a feudal retainer: A 101. See note. Tyrwhitt refers it to *yeongman*, a young man, a vassal. The A. S. *geongra* = a vassal, and *geongorscipe* = service (Cæd-mon.) Mr. Skeat refers it to the Old Friesic and Old Saxon *ga* or *go*, O. H. Ger. *gou*, Ger. *gau*, a village, a district; O. Friesic *gaman*, a villager, rustic.

Yerd, Yerde, rod, A 149, B 529;

as in *yard*-measure. A.S. *gerd, gyrd*, twig, rod, stick.

Yerd, enclosure, yard : C 27. A.S. *geard*, hedge, enclosure, garden ; Eng. *yard, orchard* (=*wort-yard*), garden.

Yet now=just now : B 298.

Yeve, Yeve, Yiven, to give : A 223.

Y-falle, fallen : A 25.

Y-fetered, fettered : B 371.

Y-founde, found : B 353, C 362.

Y-go, gone, A 286.

Y-grounde, pp. ground, sharpened : B 1691.

Y-holde, pp. esteemed, held : B 1516, 2100.

Yifte, gift : B 1340.

Yive, Yiven, to give : A 225 ; pp. given, B 57.

Y-knowe, known : A 423.

Y-lad, carried (in a cart) : A 530. Pp. of *leden*, to lead, carry.

Y-laft, left : B 1888. Pp. of *leven*, to leave.

Y-liche, *pl.* alike, B 1668.

Y-logged, lodged : C 171.

Y-lyk, alike, A 592, B 1876 ; Ylyke, B 681.

Y-maked, pp. made : B 1207, 1997.

Y-met, pp. met : B 1766.

Y-meynd (pp. of *menge*), mingled, mixed : B 1312. A.S. *mengian*, to mix.

Y-nogh, enough : A 373.

Yolden, pp. yielded : B 2194. Pp. of *yelden*. A.S. *gildan*, to pay, give up.

Yolle, to yell : B 1814. Prov. Eng. *goul, youl.*

Yond, yonder : B 241.

Yong, Yonge, young : A 7, 79, 213.

Yore, of a long time. *Yore agoon* =a long time ago, B 955 ; *of yore*, in olden time. A.S. *geára*, of yore, from *géar*, a year.

Youling, yelling : B 420.

Yow, you : A 34, 38.

Y-payed, payed : B 944.

Y-pinched, tightly plaited : A 151.

Y-preved, proved to be : A 485.

Y-raft, bereft : B 1157. Pp. of *reven*, to snatch, bereave.

Y-ronne, run, A 8 ; clustered, B 1307. Y-ronnen, run, coagulated : B 1835. Pp. of *rennen*, to run.

Y-scalded, scalded : B 1162.

Ysene, adj. pl. visible : A 592. See Sene. (Distinct from the pp. *y-seen*.)

Y-served, pp. served : B 105.

Y-set, appointed : B 777.

Y-seyled, sailed : C 279.

Y-shave, shaven : A 690.

Y-shrive, shriven : A 226.

Y-shorn, cut : A 589. Pp. of *sheren*, to shear.

Y-slayn, slain : B 1850.

Y-spreynd (pp. of *sprenge*), sprinkled, scattered : B 1311. A.S. *springan*, to spring ; Ger. *sprengen*, to scatter, burst open ; Sw. *springa*, to split. Cf. the phrase ' to *spring* a leak.'

Y-stiked, pierced, B 707.

Y-storve, dead : B 1156. Pp. of *sterven*, to die.

Y-sworn, sworn : B 274.

Y-taught, taught : A 127.

Y-teyd, tied : A 457.

Y-turned, turned : B 380, 1204.

Y-warned, warned : C 412.

Y-wedded, wedded : B 2240.

Y-wimpled, decked with a wimple : A 470. See Wimpel.

Y-wis, certainly, truly, C 379, 622. A.S. *gewis.*

Y-wont, wont, accustomed. See Wone.

Y-wroght, worked, wrought, made : A 196. Pp. of *werken, werchen.*

Y-wrye, covered : B 2046. A.S. *gewrigen*, pp. of *wréon* or *wríhan*, to cover.

ADDITIONAL NOTES. (1911).

It would be easy to add to the preceding Notes (at pp. 127–202) to a very great extent ; especially from the Notes in vol. v of the Complete Works of Chaucer, published at Oxford in 1895. A small selection of Additional Notes is here given ; most of which have been suggested by a correspondent.

NOTES TO THE PROLOGUE. 107. The sense is—' His arrows did not present a draggled appearance owing to the feathers being crushed ' ; i. e. the feathers stood erect and regularly, as necessary to secure for them a good flight.—Skeat.

263. ' That stood out round, like a bell, when taken out of the press (in which it was kept flat).'

264. Cf. the following, from Barbour's Bruce, i. 393-4, descriptive of Sir James Douglas :—

> And in spek [speech] wlispyt he sum deill ;
> But that sat [became] him rycht wondre weill.

468. The allusion is best explained by help of folk-lore. ' A young lady the other day, in reply to an observation of mine—" What a lucky girl you are ! "—replied : " So they used to say when I was at school." " Why ? " " Because my teeth were set *so far apart ;* it was a sure sign *I should be lucky and travel.*" '—Notes and Queries, 1 Ser. vi. 601 ; cf. the same, 7 Ser. vii. 306.—Skeat.

701. This passage from Heywood will also be found in his ' playe betwene the pardoner and the frere ' ; see the extract printed in Pollard's English Miracle Plays, at pp. 116-18.

NOTES TO THE KNIGHTES TALE. 319. The fable is practically the same as that of ' The Lion, the Tiger, and the Fox ' in Croxall's edition of Æsop's Fables. In the modern edition by James (London, 1852), it is Fable No. 141, and is entitled ' The Lion, the Bear, and the Fox,' See N. and Q., 7 Ser. vi. 53, 90, 236.

365. It occurs also below, at line 684 (p. 54).

852. *What mister men*, what sort of men. *What mister men* came to be analysed as ' men of what mister ' or craft, and was subsequently interpreted as ' men of what craft, class, or sort ' ; see *Mister* in the Additions to the Glossary, at p. 261.

1071. Yellow was the colour of jealousy ; see *Yellowness* in Nares'

Glossary. In the Rom. de la Rose, 22037, Jealousy is described as wearing a 'chapel de *soussie*,' i. e. a chaplet of marigolds.—Skeat.

1186. *sterres*, stars. Not stars of the sky, but the star-like points used in constructing geomantic figures, such as are given in Cornelius Agrippa, De Occulta Philosophia, lib. ii. c. 48 : De *Figuris* Geomanticis, which explains the word *figures* in l. 1185. The 'figures of stars' called Rubeus and Puella are thus depicted by Agrippa:—

```
        * *                    *
Rubeus   *         Puella    * *
        *  *                  * *
        * *                    *
```

Rubeus stood for Mars, the red ; and Puella for Venus, with whom Mars is so often associated.—Skeat (revised).

1435. *dide hir thinges*, performed her rites, or her sacrifice ; see Pollard's note to The Sacrifice of Isaac, l. 230, in English Miracle Plays, p. 185.

1855. Wright's note is only correct so far as relates to *salvia* (sage). But *save* is altogether a different word, representing the O. F. *save*, L. *sapa*. The L. *sapa* meant 'must, or new wine boiled thick ' ; but the M. E. *save* was applied to a compound healing drink made of fifty different herbs, all duly enumerated in a MS. printed in Henslow's Medical Works of the Fourteenth Century, at p. 55 (p. 194 of the MS.). The account begins by saying that '*Saue* is a drynke that wol hele al maner wounde with-oute plaistere or ani outher selue [salve].' At p. 125 of the same work, we read that a man can be cured of any wound, if he will only 'drynke *saue* or Antioche.' There is no description of *Antioche*. See also p. 126 of the same.—Skeat.

NOTE TO THE NONNE PRESTES TALE. 14. See the note to the Prologue, l. 351 (p. 151).

ADDITIONS TO THE GLOSSARY.

Anight, by night, B 184, 1149.

As, an expletive, expressing a wish, used with an imperative, nearly equivalent to *so*. Thus *as keep*, so keep, I pray you keep, B 1444; *as sende*, so send, pray send, B 1459, 1467. *As in this cas*, with regard to this case, in the present case, B 1499.

Aspye, spy, discern, B 562.

Buskes, bushes, B 721.

Charge. In B 426, it means regard, consideration, heed. In B 1429, it means burden, trouble.

Colera (Latin), choler, choleric complexion, C 108. The old medical school recognized four complexions or temperaments among men, viz. the sanguine, the choleric, the phlegmatic, and the melancholy.

Cote, cot; hence, dungeon, wretched abode, B 1599.

Endere; in mod. E., 'ender.'

Endure; *doth me endure*, makes me suffer, B 1538.

Everydeel, every whit, A 368.

Felawe, companion, friend, B 334, 336.

For, because of, for the sake of, B 1455; *for which*, on which account, B 1857.

Herte; *of herte*, from his heart, with all his heart, C 483.

Holm, holly, B 2063 (N. E. D.).

Hond, hand; *knighthod of hir hond*, knightly deeds of their hands, B 1245.

Ianglere, babbler, A 560; perhaps here a story-teller. But we must not confuse him with the O. F. *jongleur*, who was a professional minstrel.

Kyn, kindred; *for your fader kyn*, for the sake of your father's kindred, for the credit of your family, C 148.

Laas, lace; hence, a thick string, band, A 392.

Large; *at thy large*, at thy freedom, at large, B 425; *at his large*, at large, B 1430.

Lauriol, spurge-laurel, *Daphne laureola*, C 143.

Leve, dear (voc. case), B 278. See **Leef.**

Londe; *faren in londe*, gone into the country, lit. land, C 59.

Lye, lie, falsehood, B 2157.

Mister, trade, craft, handicraft, occupation; lit. ministry; O. F. *mester*, from Lat. *ministerium*. *A good mister*, a good occupation or trade, A 613. *What mister men*, men of what craft, i. e. what sort of men, B 852; see note above, p. 259.

Oon, one; *a servant was I oon,* I was one (who was) a servant or devoted lover, B 956.

Paramours, *s. pl.* lovers, mistresses. C 47.

Parlement, deliberation, final decision, B 448. Lit. 'speech.'

Pinched (closely) pleated, (neatly) pressed into folds, A 151.

Poynt, particular object, aim, B 643.

Routhe, ruth, pity, B 1534.

Sarge, serge (coarse stuff), B 1710.

Seyn, seen, B 807, C 461.

Seyn, to say, A 284; *pr. pl.* say, C 157.

Stokkes, stocks, cut logs, B 2076,

Suyte, suit, set of clothing, B 2015.

Up, fully, completely, B 994.

Wele, happiness; *in hir wele,* in their (complete) happiness, B 1815.

Wormes, *s. pl.* worms, C 142.

Y-don, put; *of y-don,* put off, taken off, doffed, B 1818.

Yve; *erbe yve,* herb ive, ground ivy, *Ajuga chamaepitys,* C 146.

INDEX OF PROPER NAMES.

Many of the proper names are further explained in the Notes.

The references *in this Index* are to the Six-text Edition. Throughout the Knight's Tale and Nonne Prestes Tale, the numbers suitable to that edition are given *within marks of parenthesis*. Throughout the Prologue, the numbering is the same as in the text.

Saturne, Saturn, A 1088, 1328, 2450, 2685; **Saturnus**, 2443.

Scariot, Judas Iscariot, B 4417.

Scithia, Scythia, A 867, 882.

See, Grete, Great Sea, the Levant, A 59.

Serapion, an Arabian physician, A 432.

Sinon, B 4418.

Sonday, Sunday, A 455, 2188, 2209.

Southwerk, Southwark, A 20, 718.

Spayne, Spain, A 409.

Stace, Statius, A 2294.

Stratford atte Bowe, Stratford at Bow, A 125.

Tabard, an inn, A 20, 719.

Talbot, a dog, B 4573.

Tars, Tartary (?), A 2160.

Taurus, B 4384.

Thebane, *adj.* Theban, A 2515, 2526; **Thebanes**, *pl.* 2570; **Thebans**, 1877.

Thebes, A 933, 939, 967, 983, 986, 1002, 1019, &c.

Theseus, A 860, 878, 907, 963, 998, 1001, &c.

Thomas, saint Thomas, A 826.

Trace, Thrace, A 1638, 1972, 2129.

Tramissene, Tremessen, A 62.

Troye, Troy, A 2833, B 4419.

Turkeys, Turkish, A 2895.

Turkye, Turkey, A 66.

Turnus, A 1945.

Venus, A 1102, 1104, 1332, 1536, B 4532; oratory of, 1904, 1918; statue of, 1955; prayer to, 2221.

Vulcanus, Vulcan, A 2222.

Ware, in Hertfordshire, A 692.

Watte, Wat, for Walter, A 643.

William, William I., A 324.

Ydelnesse, Idleness, porter to Venus, A 1940.

Ypocras, Hippocrates, A 431.

Ypres, in West Flanders, A 448.

Zephirus, Zephyr, west wind, A 5.

THE END.

PRINTED IN GREAT BRITAIN AT THE UNIVERSITY PRESS, OXFORD
BY CHARLES BATEY, PRINTER TO THE UNIVERSITY